QUANTITATIVE
CHEMISTRY

Jürg Waser

PROFESSOR OF CHEMISTRY
CALIFORNIA INSTITUTE OF TECHNOLOGY

QUANTITATIVE CHEMISTRY

a laboratory text

W. A. BENJAMIN, INC.   *New York Amsterdam 1964*

QUANTITATIVE CHEMISTRY
A laboratory text

Library of Congress Catalog Card Number 61–15331
Manufactured in the United States of America

The publisher is pleased to acknowledge the assistance of Felix Cooper, who produced the illustrations, and of Galen Fleck, who copyedited the manuscript.

The manuscript was put into production on June 13, 1963; this volume was published on March 13, 1964

W. A. BENJAMIN, INC., New York, New York

to LINUS PAULING

in appreciation

*Much of the value of laboratory work
is lost unless such work
is based upon thorough comprehension
of the principle of the experiment
before the student enters the laboratory.*

L. W. TAYLOR

PREFACE

This is the laboratory text used at the California Institute of Technology for a course in general and quantitative chemistry. It describes the laboratory work for the first two of the three terms of the year; the third term is devoted to qualitative and semiquantitative analysis.

This laboratory text is suitable for any first course in quantitative chemistry, at the freshman or at a more advanced level. When it is used at the freshman level, a student has an initial advantage if he has successfully completed a good high-school chemistry course. This is not required, however, and a number of our students who have done well in the course have had poor or no high-school preparation in chemistry. Any modern general chemistry book may be used in conjunction with this laboratory text.

Some explanation of the course for general and quantitative chemistry at the California Institute of Technology and of the general philosophy underlying this text may be helpful. The course consists of two lectures, one recitation, and two 3-hour laboratory periods per week. Lectures, recitations, and laboratory work are closely coordinated. The student groups in recitation and laboratory are small, and there is close supervision of the laboratory work. Principles and their application are stressed throughout the course, and memorizing is kept to a minimum.

Although all the experiments described are, with one exception, in quantitative analysis, the teaching emphasis is always on precise measurements and quantitative thinking rather than on analytical methodology. Our experience at the California Institute of Technology indicates that experiments of this type lead to better laboratory techniques and incite the students to more competitive enthusiasm than do experiments with results that can be found in handbooks, such as molecular-weight measurements and the determination of the formulas of compounds. We further believe it important that students develop as early as possible a feeling for quantities and for the variables and sources of error involved in precise measurements. This, and the desire for good laboratory technique from the start, is why we place the quantitative work first.

In our experience the maximum benefit from laboratory work is achieved when the student understands each step in a procedure, and does not blindly follow a set of prescriptions. Since careful laboratory technique is one of our major concerns, a detailed introduction to elementary operations is provided at the beginning of the text. Sufficient theory for an understanding of the chemical and instrumental principles involved in each experiment is provided. Much of this material is admittedly advanced, but we do not expect mastery of each detail.

The experiments have been chosen to present a variety of different types of measurements and reactions. The one experiment outside the framework of quantitative analysis is the determination of the formula of a compound by the method of continuous variation. It has been chosen as an application of colorimetry and because of its appealing ingenuity.

In the laboratory, there is careful instruction on the use of the balance before the students are permitted to weigh. This requires a thorough orientation of the laboratory assistants. At the beginning of each new experiment, appropriate demonstrations of laboratory techniques are given by the teaching assistants. All the equipment used in these experiments can be purchased from commercial sources or easily made from commonly available materials.

We use the chainomatic, undamped balance in preference to the fully automatic one-pan balance because the former provides an excellent opportunity for an elementary discussion of a precision instrument. This type of balance also points up to the student the factors that determine and limit the precision of any measurement. The chainomatic balance requires careful handling, which, we believe, induces good laboratory technique. For rapid weighing the single-pan balance has, of course, advantages, and the workings of this instrument are described in one of the appendices.

The number of 3-hour periods allotted to and indicated with each assignment has been chosen so that the average student can do the work without feeling "rushed." There are no extra laboratory periods for slow students, and with few exceptions the work is completed by all. Students who have finished their work may repeat a determination if they are not satisfied with their results. It is not unusual for our students to do this, but it is possible only if the total load is not too heavy. Other students who have time ask for, and are assigned, special problems such as the titration of a polyprotic acid, a potentiometric titration, or exploratory work on new class experiments.

A brief outline of the lecture topics of the course as given at the California Institute may be helpful. The first term begins with a summary of stoichiometry, followed by a discussion of gas laws and colligative properties. More than half the term is taken up with a thorough treatment of the mass-action law, including solubility products, acids and bases, and the formation of complexes. At appropriate times lectures on gravimetric and volumetric techniques are presented.

The topics taken up at the beginning of the second term are electronic structure of atoms, ionic and covalent bonds, oxidation and reduction, and balancing of equations by oxidation numbers or by half-cell reactions. A discussion of electrochemistry follows, including electrode potentials, the Nernst equation, and electrolysis, all in time to provide background for the assignments on redox titration and coulometry. Beer's law and spectra are discussed prior to the colorimetric experiment. The time that remains is used to expand the earlier discussion of molecular structure, including material on the hydrogen bond and molecular geometry.

ACKNOWLEDGMENTS: I wish to thank William P. Schaefer for his contribution to the development and improvement of experiments described in this text. His detailed review of the manuscript and his many helpful suggestions are also acknowledged with appreciation. Many of the experiments were originally conceived and worked out by Ernest H. Swift, and I am grateful to him for this material as well as for his continued interest and encouragement. I have received many valuable comments from a number of colleagues who used the preliminary version of this text; in particular, I thank Alvin L. Beilby, Quintus Fernando, James J. Hogan, R. Ramette, R. Nelson Smith, and Kenneth N. Trueblood. I am indebted to Fred C. Anson, Dwight M. Smith, and David H. Klein for their help in the development of the course. I am greatly obliged to the publisher, William A. Benjamin and his staff, in particular Nancy Orban, for the great care that went into the production of this book, and to Felix Cooper, the illustrator, for the handsome artwork.

This book has profited from many discussions I have had with students and colleagues too numerous to be acknowledged individually. My debt of gratitude finally extends to my wife for constructive general criticism, continued help with the manuscript, and, most important of all, unfailing moral support.

JÜRG WASER

Pasadena, California
July 1963

CONTENTS

xi

Contents

QUANTITATIVE
CHEMISTRY

INTRODUCTION

The laboratory work described in this text has several objectives. They are:

1. To present chemical facts and experimental techniques, both appropriate aims for a course in chemistry

2. To develop a feeling for quantities, important for any good scientist or engineer

3. To provide training in the application of principles and thus to strengthen the power of logical reasoning

4. To induce neat and precise working habits, indispensable in any good research

In elaboration of these four points:

1

Personal experience with experiments. Chemistry cannot be learned from books alone. Many important facts can be appreciated in the laboratory only. Others are remembered because of particular experiences that have affected the visual, the olfactory, the auditory, or other senses and have left sometimes pleasant, sometimes unpleasant memories.

Quite generally, laboratory experiments are essential to a realistic understanding of science. Furthermore, experience in the laboratory is of great value in furnishing background for the critical judgment needed in reading the work of others, which is one of the important sources of information for the practicing experimental and theoretical scientist.

Appreciation of quantities. Chemistry is a quantitative science. A good chemist develops a quantitative feeling for the variables he deals with, be it the volumes or weights of substances he uses in the laboratory, the energies involved in breaking different types of bonds, the degree of completeness to which a given reaction proceeds, or any other quantities.

A quantitative feeling for the variables that may have a bearing on a given phenomenon is important for any scientist. The experimentalist has to make decisions as to what variables need be controlled in a certain experiment and what other variables need no such control because their effects can be neglected. Again, he may have to decide whether or not an effect that he is looking for will be distinguishable from other effects which appear similar. The theoretical scientist searching for the explanation of a phenomenon has to have the same kind of instinctive feeling in order to separate, from the many ideas that present themselves, those with merit and those that show no promise; in the mathematical development of these ideas, which is usually too cumbersome to be done precisely, he has to guess correctly what approximations are safe, again using his sense for quantities.

To develop such a feeling for the quantitative takes a great deal of practice. It should become second nature to ask the question: "What is the order of magnitude of this or that effect?"

Mastery of basic principles. In performing an experiment it is essential to understand the underlying principles, regardless of whether the experiment is original or follows established procedures. In particular, a knowledge of principles is needed to understand the factors affecting the accuracy of a given method of quantitative determination, to judge the range of variations that may be tolerated by that method, and to foresee its inherent limitations as well as its possible generalizations.

The ability to apply basic principles to specific cases is an important criterion of the understanding of the basic theory.

Precision of working habits.   An important trait of a good scientist is the ability to plan and perform neat, elegant, and precise experiments. This ability can be acquired even by persons who believe themselves to be clumsy and not mechanically minded. To attain it calls for patience, perseverance, and, above all, intelligence; its attainment can be cause for considerable pride.

General advice.   It is not likely that all the more difficult concepts presented in this text will be mastered on first reading. It should thus not be cause for serious concern if some points are not clear immediately. Such material should be marked and reserved for later study. A reading of Appendix III on how to study and how to solve problems is highly recommended.

*Safety rules and laboratory regulations
are followed by observations on laboratory
conduct in general, a discussion of
laboratory notebooks, and a description
of the grades of purity of chemicals.*

one

LABORATORY SAFETY AND GENERAL PRACTICE

SAFETY RULES

Safety rules will work only if you believe in them and encourage other students to believe in them also. Such rules are necessary for the protection of your surroundings as well as of yourself.

Your conduct is expected to be that of a mature person in surroundings where injury to persons or property may result from careless behavior.

*The following safety rules are to be followed strictly.
There is no halfway ground.*

1. No experiments with rocket fuels or explosives are tolerated.

2. Extra nonassigned work is permitted and, in fact, encouraged under appropriate circumstances. However, all such experiments should be discussed first with the instructor, and his permission must be obtained. Unauthorized experiments must not be performed.

3. Chemicals and equipment available in the laboratories are intended for course work and research only. They may not be taken away for outside use. No chemicals may be bought at the stockroom for personal use unless the instructor authorizes the purchase.

4. Safety glasses or prescription glasses must be worn in the laboratory at all times.

5. All injuries must be reported to the instructor.

SAFETY PROCEDURES FOR DEALING WITH CHEMICALS AND EQUIPMENT

Personal safety. Locate fire extinguishers, safety showers, and first-aid kits so that you will not have to search for them when you really need them.

Wear a laboratory apron or a laboratory coat. During hot weather an apron is more comfortable. Long trousers, shirts, and shoes (not sandals) are mandatory.

Corrosive substances on skin or clothes must be washed off promptly with large volumes of water. *Acid* burns may be treated afterward with a solution or paste of sodium bicarbonate. The washing off of *alkali* may be followed by treatment with very dilute acetic acid and further washing. The most important factor in all cases, however, is *plenty of water*.

Never suck directly on a pipet; always use a pipet bulb.

Do not aim test tubes at your neighbor or yourself, *especially when heating substances in them*.

Do not reach across lighted burners or place them under the shelves on your laboratory benches. If the desks are provided with hoods, do any heating under the hoods. This tends to keep the air in the laboratory cooler and fresher.

The *dilution of concentrated acid* is often accompanied by the evolution of heat due to the hydration of acid anions as well as of hydrogen ions. This effect is particularly pronounced for *sulfuric acid*, and if water is added to it, explosive boiling may occur locally and cause dangerous spattering of this highly corrosive liquid. However, when the same acid is added to a large excess of stirred, cold water,

5

the amount of heat evolved is not large enough to cause boiling. Thus, to dilute a concentrated acid, pour it slowly and carefully into distilled water while constantly stirring. In particular, never pour water into concentrated sulfuric acid. External cooling may be needed when the ratio of sulfuric acid to the water into which it is poured is large.

The vapors of *mercury* are very poisonous. Handle liquid mercury with care, and completely clean up any loose droplets. A silver coin is helpful, because even minute droplets of mercury stick to a silver surface that is clean or that is wetted with mercury (formation of silver amalgam). The mercury may be driven from the coin by heating it in a well-ventilated hood.

Laboratory environment. Any spilled material must be cleaned up promptly. Large areas contaminated with *spilled acid* should be neutralized with sodium bicarbonate and then sponged off with water. This applies, of course, to the areas under the hoods also. *Alkaline materials* may be neutralized with dilute acetic acid before being washed off.

Some laboratory desk tops consist of a plastic that is vulnerable to staining by silver nitrate solutions. Avoid spilling silver nitrate solutions on such desk tops, and promptly wash off any silver nitrate spilled despite your caution.

Flush liquid waste down the sink. Dilute corrosive liquids first, pour down the sink while a good stream of water is running, and continue the water stream for $\frac{1}{2}$ to 1 min. Do not run the water continuously or excessively at other times. Keep solid wastes out of sinks and drains, and dispose of such wastes in jars provided for the purpose. Inform your instructor of any floods or of stoppages of sinks.

Keep your desk clean and orderly. At the end of the period wash it, dry it, and put all your equipment back into the locker. You are also responsible for the condition of your floor space and for the portion of the reagent shelf opposite you. Be considerate in your treatment of equipment used by others, such as laboratory scales and centrifuges. Special rules concerning delicate equipment, such as analytical balances and pH meters, are given in the instructions explaining the use of these instruments. Do not use such equipment before you receive the permission of the instructor, regardless of whether or not you have previous experience. In general you are held responsible for any damage to such equipment.

GENERAL OBSERVATIONS

The laboratory instructions. The laboratory instructions that go with every assignment are very detailed. Such careful instructions are essential for achieving accurate results. Accurate results build up your self-confidence; they have no substitute. The instructions become less detailed as the year proceeds, because you yourself should think more and more of possible pitfalls in advance and should thus avoid them. However, think for yourself at all times. You may discover shortcuts that will not affect the accuracy of the results, and you may devise improvements, particularly after you have completed the recommended procedure and think over what you have done. But consult your instructor before deviating from a recommended procedure.

The cookbook method. Since the procedures are fairly detailed, there is danger that you may use them without comprehending the underlying reasons, in the way a cook uses recipes. Extensive discussions are given so that all the steps in a procedure have their explanation. Read these discussions carefully *before* undertaking the laboratory assignment. It is important that you *understand them* and that you remember them while doing the experiments. Ask questions about points that appear unclear or unexplained.

You should understand as much as possible of the background material provided. Less important material is printed in smaller type.

Make an outline of the work you intend to perform in a given laboratory period. This will help you conserve precious laboratory time and will assist you in retaining the background material. There are inevitable waiting periods in the laboratory, as there are in other experimental work. Use these periods for the preparation of later work or for study. Dry samples or precipitates, and let them cool in your desiccator ahead of time. Plan your trips to the stockroom. Make notes on what you will need, and procure everything you require at the same time.

The laboratory is a working place. Do not waste your time or that of your fellow students.

LABORATORY NOTEBOOKS

It is of great importance for a scientist or engineer to acquire the habit of keeping a detailed and accurate notebook on his experiments as well as on his ideas and theories. As part of the laboratory practice you are to record *all* your laboratory procedures and results.

7

To be of any value a laboratory notebook must conform to the following requirements:

A laboratory notebook must be permanent.   A permanently bound notebook with pages numbered in advance must be used. Loose scraps of paper are not tolerated and may be confiscated by the instructor. Entries are to be made promptly and in permanent ink (pen or ball point). Notes in pencil are not permanent; they can be erased or altered. Their presence may arouse doubt about the integrity of the work. Never tear pages from a notebook.

A laboratory notebook must be intelligible.   For each experiment the following items should be listed:

The procedure.   Entries must be in sufficient detail that the existing situation can be completely reconstructed at any time. Date each entry. This may be important in interpreting subsequently observed effects and in determining the sequence of experiments. It may even be a good idea to note the time of day. Enter all the conditions that could possibly affect the results described in sufficient detail that any other reasonably skilled person could repeat the experiment and duplicate your results. Record chemicals used, amounts, concentrations, temperature, pressure, etc. Sometimes humidity, weather, brand of chemicals, and other conditions prove to be important.

Observe carefully, and report what is happening rather than what you think *ought* to have happened. This may be invaluable in any later interpretation of anomalous results.

Show all your analytical weighings by explicitly noting each weight rather than the total sum only. Sometimes the results of an analysis are in error because some weights were not correctly summed, and checking is possible only if the original numbers are available.

The results.   Although all your observations must be entered at the time they are made, you may do numerical work and interpret your data outside the laboratory. However, show all the numerical computations in the notebook itself. Faulty analyses are often due to erroneous calculations and may be retrieved by checking the calculations in the notebook. Briefly label the computations for easier checking.

The conclusions.   Interpret your data, and show your conclusions. Include balanced equations for all reactions. Write down ideas and questions that occur to you.

Table of contents.   Keep an up-to-date table of contents at the beginning or end of your notebook.

A laboratory notebook must be complete.   Entries must be made promptly and habitually. The record must include poor results, faulty experiments, and unsuccessful ideas, not just the experiments that worked. Faulty experiments should be so labeled, and possible reasons should be given for their failure. Such a complete record produces confidence in the notebook.

Clearly label as such work performed by others.

General suggestions.   A good size for the notebook is 8 by 10 in. Such a notebook, when opened, will still fit under the analytical balance case. Square ruling is preferable to lines or to unruled pages. Do not crowd your notebook, but rather leave ample space; this makes for easier reading. Start a fresh page for each new experiment, and head it with a descriptive title. Reserve left-hand pages for computations. Identify all entries, even calculations.

Many experimental results are best recorded in the form of a table. You can save valuable laboratory time by thinking about and setting up in advance suitable tables in which to enter data.

Make your notebook as clear and as legible as possible, without, however, transcribing it. The notebook is to be a working tool; an honest ink line through some numbers or words does not harm it. It must become second nature to you to keep a good notebook. Transcribing it every few days would be fatal to this. It would also decrease the value of a notebook, particularly as a legal record.

GRADES OF PURITY OF CHEMICALS

Commercially available chemicals usually fall into one of the following classes.

Commercial, or technical, grade.   This grade is largely for industrial use and is, in general, unsuitable for laboratory reagents, because there may be many impurities.

USP grade.   The letters stand for United States Pharmacopoeia, the government standard for medicinal preparations (*pharmakon* = medicine; *poiein* = to make). Substances labeled in this way are pure enough to pass certain tests prescribed in the U.S. Pharmacopoeia and are therefore acceptable for drug use. There may, however, be appreciable impurities not tested for. In general, the USP grade is of lesser purity than the CP grade, described next. USP-grade chemicals are adequate for many laboratory purposes.

CP grade.   The letters stand for chemically pure, but the term is misleading, because purity is a relative concept that depends on the intended use of the substance. Often, CP-grade chemicals are nearly as pure as those of the reagent grade described next. However, there can be no reliance on this, and the designation is thus ambiguous and should not be used.

Reagent, or analyzed, grade. These chemicals are certified to contain impurities below the levels specified by the Committee on Analytical Reagents of the American Chemical Society (ACS). The labels of reagent-grade chemicals usually give the analysis of the batch of which the bottle is part. In chemical analysis, only reagent-grade chemicals should be used, and even so it should be realized that the analysis on the label may not be reliable. Not only may some impurities not have been tested for, but the manufacturer's analysis may have been faulty. Also, the reagent may have been contaminated on previous use.

Primary standard. Primary standards are substances of high enough purity that they can serve as reference substances in analytical work. Standard solutions are prepared from them either directly, by dissolving a known quantity and diluting to a known volume, or indirectly, by having a solution to be standardized react with a known amount of primary standard. To qualify as a primary standard, a substance has to satisfy requirements other than high purity, which will be discussed in connection with volumetric work. Primary standards can be prepared by high purification of reagent-grade chemicals; they may be obtained directly from the U.S. Bureau of Standards or other sources. Typical primary standards contain less than 0.05 per cent impurities.

The requirements of solid-state physics, manufacture of transistors, etc., are such that even higher degrees of purity are needed. Only a few parts per million of impurities can be tolerated, and similar requirements exist for critical materials in nuclear engineering, such as graphite. Even so, in one formula weight of substance, pure to 1 ppm, there are still of the order of 10^{17} particles of the wrong kind!

The following operations are described:
heating of materials, cleaning of glassware,
handling of liquid and solid chemicals,
filtering of solutions, working of glass,
and preparation of a desiccator. Even if
you are familiar with these operations,
it is to your advantage to check for points
you are not acquainted with.
A laboratory assignment concerns
checking into the laboratory
and the construction of simple glass equipment.

two

ELEMENTARY
LABORATORY
EQUIPMENT AND
OPERATIONS

HEATING MATERIALS

Gas burners.   Materials are customarily heated in the laboratory either by the use of a gas burner or by electrical means. The first method is less expensive and is commonly used unless highly combustible materials are heated, when electrical heating is preferred because of the greatly reduced fire hazard.

11

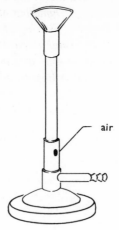

Figure 2-1   Bunsen burner with flame spreader.

In a gas burner, the combustible gas (usually natural gas) is mixed with an adjustable amount of air before being fed to the flame. Two common types are the *Bunsen burner* and the *Tirrill burner*.

In the Bunsen burner (Fig. 2-1), the air supply is regulated near the bottom of the burner by rotating a sleeve that has holes in it. In the usual version there is no stopcock on the burner, so that the flow of gas must be regulated by the valve in the gas line.

The Tirrill burner (Fig. 2-2) has at its bottom a needle valve that controls the gas flow. The valve in the gas line should always be opened completely when this type of burner is in use. The air flow may be regulated by rotating the tubular mixing chamber, thus increasing or decreasing the open space at the bottom of the burner.

Natural gas consists mainly of methane (CH_4) and, to a small extent, of ethane (C_2H_6) and other hydrocarbons; it may also contain a small amount of inert gases such as nitrogen and helium. When natural gas is lit without previous mixing with air, it burns with a luminous, yellow flame caused by glowing carbon particles. These particles are the result of a partial dissociation, at the elevated temperatures inside the flame, of the methane and other hydrocarbons in the natural gas. Such a flame deposits water and particles of soot onto a cool surface. It has reducing properties due to the hot, unburned gas inside it. It is called a *diffusion* flame because gas and air mix in the burning zone by diffusion. Because combustion takes place mainly in the surface zone of this flame, the surface and thus the flame are relatively large. For several reasons this flame is also relatively cool: the combustion is incomplete; the large flame surface implies a relatively large energy loss to the surroundings; and further energy loss is caused by the radiation of the glowing carbon particles.

By suitable manipulation of the air intake of the burner, sufficient air may be admitted to increase the degree of combustion of the gas. The flame becomes almost colorless; its size is diminished; and its temperature is increased. It is called a *premixed* flame, because the gas and air are mixed in advance, before burning. Maximum heat is reached when the flame shows two distinct zones, the inner zone being pale blue and cone-shaped (Fig. 2-2). This cone consists of unburned hot gas mixed with air and is reducing, and the pale-violet outer envelope has oxidizing properties. The reaction between gas and air occurs chiefly in the thin luminous region between the two zones, and the hottest part of the flame is just above the inner cone. Maximum heating of an object is obtained by placing it just above this hottest part of the flame, which will spread about it. Objects placed within the inner cone are not heated effectively. In heating glass tubes for the purpose of bending them, as will be discussed later, it is useful to widen the flame by using a wing top, or flame spreader (Fig. 2-1), on the burner.

When a cold burner is lit, its air-supply ports should be closed or be open less than normal. Next, the gas is turned on, the flame is lit,

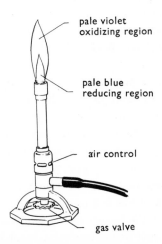

pale violet
oxidizing region

pale blue
reducing region

air control

gas valve

Figure 2-2   Tirrill burner with reducing flame.

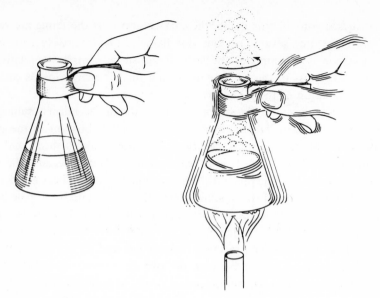

Figure 2-3 Heating and boiling of solution in flask.

and the air-supply ports are opened so that a short, pale-blue cone appears inside the flame. This flame emits a rustling sound, which should not be too noisy, however. If there is too much air, the flame may separate from the top of the burner and may even go out. If so, the ratio of air to gas should be diminished by increasing the amount of gas or decreasing that of air. A hot burner tolerates a larger ratio of air to gas. Sometimes when the air supply is too large, the unstable flame eventually strikes back through the central tube of the burner and continues to burn at the narrow opening of the gas jet inside this tube. This flame makes a hissing noise, is yellowish, and may change later to green because of the copper in the brass tubing of the burner. The burner heats rapidly and may become hot enough to melt the hose supplying the gas. Such a burner must be turned off immediately at the valve in the gas line. After it has cooled somewhat, it may be relit, with a diminished ratio of air to gas.

When heating an object like a flask, a beaker, or a crucible, choose a flame adequate in size but not larger than needed. If your desk space has a hood, place the burner inside it and do all your heating under it, whether or not corrosive vapors are involved. This reduces heating of the laboratory and decreases atmospheric contamination.

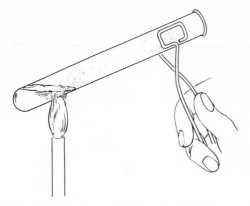

Figure 2-4 Heating and boiling of solution in test tube.

When finished with the burner, turn the gas off at the valve in the line, not at the burner, because gas hoses may leak.

Heating of solutions.   Conical flasks and test tubes containing solutions may be held directly over the flame, provided that they are continuously swirled or shaken. The neck of either container may be held with a test-tube clamp or with a tight loop made of a strong paper strip obtained by folding a sheet of paper into a strip of about 1 by 15 cm (Fig. 2-3). Holding the neck with the fingers invites either pain or loss of solution. Crucible tongs are equally unsuitable because of the chance of breakage by dropping or by crushing the neck.

For safe boiling and rapid evaporation of a solution fill a test tube to not more than about 20 per cent of capacity and a flask to not more than 40 per cent. To heat a solution in a *test tube*, incline it, shake it rapidly, and apply the flame just underneath the top surface of the solution (Fig. 2-4) rather than to the bottom of the tube, because the latter may cause bumping (an unsteady, explosive kind of boiling), with loss of solution. *Never point a test tube being heated toward another person, and never look directly into it.* Heat a *flask* only over a low flame and in such a way that the entire heated part of the glass wall is always covered with solution. If the flask is shaken rapidly, it is safe to evaporate solution until only a few milliliters are left.

There is danger of bumping when solutions are boiled in flasks or beakers placed on a wire gauze. Reduce this danger by applying the flame directly underneath the end of a stirring rod that has been placed in the vessel. The contact between the end of the rod and the bottom

15

of the vessel facilitates the formation of steam bubbles. Boiling solutions in a flask is safer than in a beaker because of the constricted neck. However, a beaker is preferable if a precipitate is to be formed in it and transferred to a filter or to another vessel. In this case the danger of solution loss by bumping or spattering may be reduced by covering the beaker with a watch glass that is separated from the rim by three small (2 to 3 cm long), U-shaped pieces of glass rod, as shown in Figure 4-4.

Do not place a hot beaker or flask directly on the laboratory desk, because the hot glass may become covered by a coat of paint or other material. It should cool first on wire gauze or asbestos.

CLEANING GLASSWARE

All glassware used should be clean. Aside from being visibly clean, wetted surfaces should drain without the formation of streaks or droplets. Usually, washing with soap or detergent solution is satisfactory. A suitable brush may also be helpful, but take care not to scratch the glass with any exposed wires. It pays to clean all glassware immediately after use.

Rinse with large amounts of tap water and then with a small amount of distilled water. Use the contents of your wash bottle; *do not go to the distilled water tap*. In general, glassware should be left to dry in the air. Drying with a towel or tissue may leave lint, paper fragments, or a film of grease. The use of compressed air is not recommended, because the air usually contains oil residues.

Do not use the conventional sulfuric acid–chromic acid "cleaning solution" unless so advised by the instructor. It produces bad burns on skin and clothes and therefore must be handled with great care. Also, the last traces of this solution are difficult to remove from a glass surface. Inorganic stains such as oxides of metals often yield more readily to concentrated hydrochloric acid.

DISPENSING AND WEIGHING SOLID CHEMICALS

Most solid chemicals are supplied in wide-mouth, screw-cap bottles. The *first* step in obtaining a certain amount of a chemical is to look for the correct bottle. Check the label carefully, both as to compound and as to degree of purity. Do not confuse chemicals having similar formulas, such as $NaNO_3$ and $NaNO_2$. If the compound in the bottle is the one wanted except for a difference in water of hydration, appropriate correction in the quantity taken is usually all that is necessary.

Second, if the contents of the bottle are caked, shake or roll the bottle in your hands, tap it gently, or roll it on the table top. It may be necessary to loosen the bottle contents with a rod or spatula. Ask the instructor to do this, so as to reduce the hazard of contamination.

Third, remove the screw cap, tilt the bottle, and tap or roll the quantity required into the cap. Closely estimate the amount you need, and take out just that much. Make it a habit to use small quantities of substances. This is not just a matter of expense: small amounts of reagents lead to neat working habits, which are a great asset in any experimental work, chemical or otherwise. Do not take reagent bottles to your desk. Rather, take your own container, such as a beaker, a watch glass, or a piece of paper, to the reagent shelf and transfer to it the amount of chemical needed. Excess substance on the bottle cap may be returned to the bottle if there has been no contamination. However, substance from paper or other containers should not be returned to the bottle. Possibly your neighbor has use for any excess substance you may have.

If the bottle has a hollow glass stopper, a procedure similar to that just described may be followed to remove substance from it. If the stopper is solid, tilt the bottle and operate it in such a way that the approximate amount of substance needed moves to its uppermost part. With one hand incline the bottle further, and gently shake or roll it. With the other hand partly withdraw the stopper to check the flow of the substance from bottle to watch glass or paper until the desired amount has come out.

Fourth, return the tightly closed bottle to the correct place on the shelf. Clean up any chemicals spilled on table, shelf, or laboratory scales.

Small amounts of solids may be transferred by using a stainless-steel or a porcelain spatula. It is poor practice and unacceptable to put a spatula directly into a reagent bottle. Rather, pour a very small amount of the substance on a small watch glass, and then use the spatula. With some practice, it is possible to estimate the quantity of substance thus transferred by considering the area of the spatula it covers or the extent to which it fills a porcelain spoon.

The approximate weights of substances may be determined by a *platform balance* (or "Harvard trip scale") (Fig. 2-5) or, more accurately, by a *triple-beam balance* (Fig. 2-6). A good platform balance permits weighing, within 0.1 g, of amounts not exceeding about 2 kg. If the object weighs less than about 200 g, the sliding weights on the levers

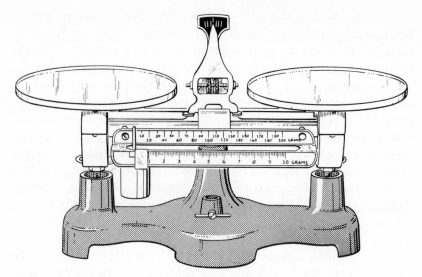

Figure 2-5   Platform balance.

suffice; otherwise, supplementary weights have to be used. The triple-beam balance is about ten times more sensitive than the platform balance and may be used to weigh, within 0.01 g, amounts not exceeding about 100 g. Somewhat more precise work can be done by means of a *pulp balance*, which in appearance resembles an analytical balance but which is much more crudely constructed. For exacting work an analytical balance is needed. This balance will be described in a later chapter.

To develop a sense for quantities, you are urged, whenever weighing, to take conscious notice of the bulk volumes of solids. With some practice you will soon be able to estimate different quantities of solids visually. This has the advantage of speeding up the weighing out of chemicals.

HANDLING AND MEASURING LIQUID CHEMICALS

When dispensing a liquid, proceed as follows. *First*, check the label for correct formula and concentration. If necessary, clean the outside of the bottle of accumulated dust, ammonium chloride, or other contaminant, rinse neck and stopper with distilled water, and wipe dry before removing the stopper.

Second, dispense the desired amount. Avoid spilling or getting the liquid on the bottle or your hands, and wash or wipe off any spilled amounts as soon as feasible. One helpful practice in pouring liquid from a glass-stoppered bottle is the following: Before removing the stopper, wet its lower part with the liquid in the bottle. Withdraw the stopper, and use the liquid adhering to it to wet a path across the neck and the side of the lip of the bottle; this wet path favors a more even flow of the liquid (Fig. 2-7). Hold the lip of the vessel from which you pour against the inside of the vessel receiving the liquid.

Be careful to prevent any contamination of the stopper. Its ground surface must not come into contact with the desk, your hands, or any other surface. The best procedure is to hold the stopper with your fingers; it may be held with the hand that holds the bottle or that holding the receiving vessel (Fig. 2-8). Replace the stopper as soon as you are finished.

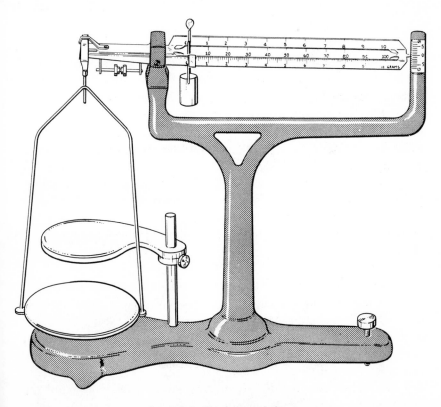

Figure 2-6   Triple-beam balance.

Third, replace the bottle on the shelf. If corrosive material has got on the outside of a reagent bottle, rinse it off and wipe the bottle dry afterward. Label your container unless the liquid is to be used immediately. Conserve reagents and solutions as much as possible. Many reagents are expensive, and the preparation of solutions represents a considerable amount of work.

In transferring liquid from a vessel other than a reagent bottle, hold a stirring rod against the lip of the pouring vessel and with its bottom end sticking into the vessel receiving the liquid. This is very helpful in avoiding spillage, because the rod guides the liquid being transferred (Fig. 2-9). However, to prevent any possible contamination, a stirring rod must not be used in this way in pouring from a common supply bottle.

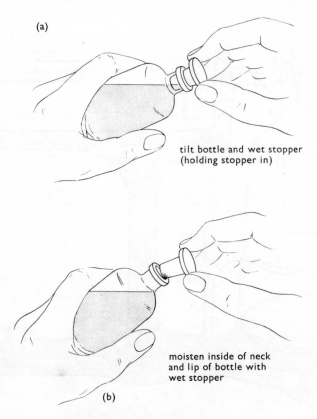

(a)

tilt bottle and wet stopper
(holding stopper in)

moisten inside of neck
and lip of bottle with
wet stopper

(b)

Figure 2-7 Removal of liquid from bottles.

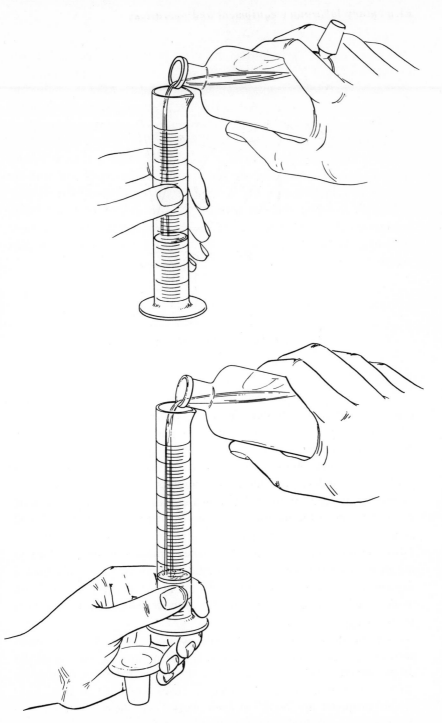

Figure 2-8 Two ways of handling a glass stopper.

Figure 2-9   Use of stirring rod to guide liquid.

Some of the reagent bottles are provided with dispensing pipets (glass tubes used to transfer liquids) or droppers, which must not be allowed to touch the sides of, or the liquid in, the receiving vessel. Never use your own dropper or pipet with common supply bottles.

Amounts of solutions and of pure liquids may be estimated by graduated cylinders and, for small amounts, by calibrated droppers. In determining the volume of liquid in a graduated cylinder, the position of the bottom of the meniscus (the curved upper surface) of the liquid is read. To avoid parallax errors, bring the meniscus to eye level (Fig. 2-10). At the proper eye level the etched graduation mark nearest to the meniscus must appear as a straight, horizontal line rather than a segment of an ellipse. On most graduated cylinders every fifth or tenth mark is etched completely around the cylinder, which is very helpful in avoiding parallax errors.

Droppers may be provided with scratch marks at the meniscus positions corresponding to 0.5 and to 1 ml. In addition, the size of the drops, which depends on the size of the tip of the dropper, may be calibrated by counting the number of drops contained in 1 ml. Calibrated droppers are useful in later work, and their construction is described more fully in a later section.

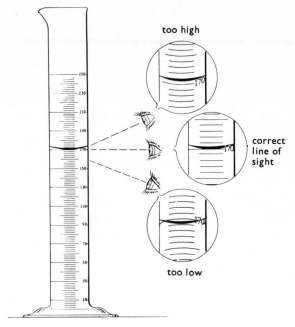

too high

correct
line of
sight

too low

Figure 2-10   Avoiding parallax error in reading meniscus.

To measure amounts of liquids more precisely, volumetric flasks, burets, and pipets are used. They will be discussed in a later chapter.

FILTERING SOLUTIONS

This discussion is limited to filtering with filter paper, which is usually employed to separate a precipitate from the supernatant prior to subjecting the precipitate to further chemical treatment, or simply to get rid of it. When the amount of precipitate is to be determined by drying and weighing it, a special grade of filter paper (discussed below), a sintered-glass crucible, or a filter mat prepared with asbestos fibers is often used. Sintered-glass crucibles will be described in connection with gravimetric work.

There are filter papers of various degrees of porosity. The larger the pore size of the paper, the more rapid the filtration and any subsequent washing of the precipitate, but also the larger the size of the particles that will pass the filter. Another important distinction between different

23

filter papers is implied by the terms *qualitative* and *quantitative*. If a precipitate is to be weighed, the filter paper must be burned off, because it is not possible to dry it to constant weight. Quantitative paper has been specially treated, during its manufacture, with hydrochloric and hydrofluoric acids to reduce to a very low value the amount of ash it leaves after burning. Such paper is much more expensive than untreated qualitative paper. Obviously, the quantitative paper should be used only when really necessary.

To provide a conical funnel with a filter insert, take a circular piece of filter paper of the proper grade and of such size so that the final insert is somewhat smaller than the funnel. Fold the paper exactly in half, and in half again. Tear a small irregular piece off one corner as shown in Figure 2-11. Open the fold with the intact corners, insert the resulting cone into the funnel, wet the paper with distilled water, and press the top of it to the glass so that a tight seal is formed. Next, add sufficient water to fill the stem of the funnel after passing through the

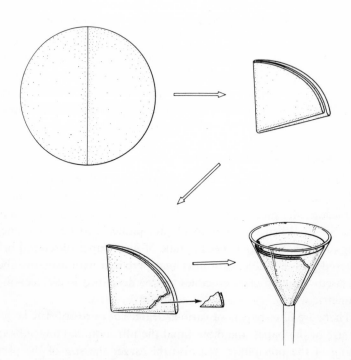

Figure 2-11   Preparation of filter-paper insert for funnel.

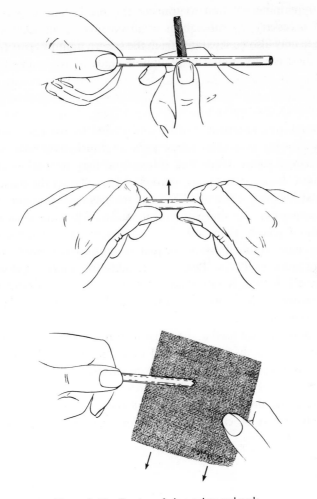

Figure 2-12 Cutting of glass tubes and rods.

paper. The stem will remain filled if the seal is tight. Begin the filtration. The liquid column in the stem will exert a hydrostatic pull on the liquid being filtered and considerably speed the process.

In filtering large amounts of solution let the precipitate settle first, and decant as much liquid as possible from it through the filter while guiding the liquid with a glass rod. This keeps the pores of the filter relatively unclogged, so that the liquid passes rapidly through. Finally, use the remaining solution to transfer the precipitate onto the filter, aided, if necessary, by subsequent small portions of distilled water. A precipitate may also be separated from the supernatant by centrifugation. This method is very useful in qualitative analysis, for example. It will not be further discussed here.

WORKING GLASS

Laboratory equipment is often constructed by working and sometimes by blowing into glass tubes, parts of which have been softened by high temperatures. Glass that softens and may be worked at about 600 to 800°C is called soft glass; hard class (e.g., Pyrex) softens and may be worked between 750 and 1100°C. Pyrex has high strength and low thermal expansion, so that equipment made of it withstands thermal shocks more readily than soft-glass equipment. Any internal stresses that may have resulted from unequal cooling after construction are greatly reduced in Pyrex. Pyrex is, in addition, more impervious to attack by alkali than is soft glass. Almost all glass equipment used in the laboratory, such as flasks, beakers, and burets, is made of Pyrex or a similar type of glass.

Soft glass is often used in the construction of such items as droppers, glass rods, and the bent tubing used in assembling wash bottles. The flame of a Bunsen or a Tirrill burner is hot enough to soften it, whereas an oxygen torch is needed to soften Pyrex.

Cutting and fire-polishing tubing and rods. A desired length of rod or tubing may be cut as follows: Hold the piece firmly in the left

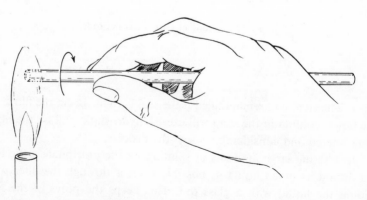

Figure 2-13 Fire-polishing (note rotation of the work).

hand, and with one resolute stroke of the edge of a sharp file held in the right hand draw a scratch perpendicularly across it (Fig. 2-12). Do not saw back and forth or use an old, dull file. Next, hold the rod or tubing with both hands, with the two thumbs opposite the scratch. Gently pull and bend against the thumbs. The glass should break cleanly without the use of undue force. If the break is not clean, the jagged edges may be trimmed by stroking a piece of wire screen against them. Tubing or rods larger than 10 to 12 mm in diameter require more elaborate techniques to be cut properly.

Any cut glass rod or tubing must be *fire-polished* to round the sharp edges. Hold the rod or tube horizontally with one hand and continually rotate it. Place the cut end in a blue, hot flame (Fig. 2-13). A short time after the flame has been colored yellow by the traces of sodium that evaporate from the glass, the sharp edges will begin to soften and become rounded. Remove the piece from the flame before it begins to thicken or the walls of tubing begin to collapse.

Arrange to support hot glass so that it will cool without touching and burning the desk. Remember that glass may still be hot even when it no longer glows.

Rotation of the work and annealing. Continuous rotation of tubes or rods is of great importance in the art of glassworking and -blowing. It promotes uniform heating and minimizes any sagging caused by gravity. Rotation should be continued as long as the glass is soft, even after removing the piece from the flame. Practice rotating a piece of glass tubing with each hand, until you have achieved smooth- ness of motion. The palm of the supporting hand should face down, and the tubing is rotated by the thumb and the index and middle fingers while it rests on the ring and little fingers (Fig. 2-14).

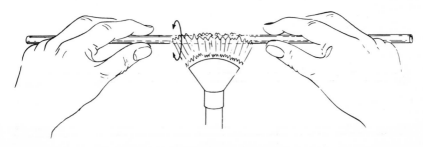

Figure 2-14　Rotation of the work.

27

Any worked piece of glass has better mechanical strength and resistance to thermal shock if it has been heated to and kept for a while at a temperature at which it is no longer soft but at which there is enough internal flow to relieve any strains. This process is called *annealing*. It is performed for soft glass by uniformly heating the worked portion with the relatively cool, yellow flame obtained by cutting off the air supply to the burner. The heating is continued until the glass is coated with soot. By that time the strains have been relieved; and the layer of soot slows subsequent cooling and makes it more uniform, reducing the development of further internal strain. It is particularly important to anneal any thickened glass, but even fire-polished ends of rods and tubes should be so treated.

In making more ambitious pieces, such as bent or constricted tubing and shaped rods, two factors are important. The glass must be *hot enough* to be quite soft before being worked, and the bending or other operation is generally executed *after* removing the piece from the flame.

Shaped glass rods. Glass rods with plain, fire-polished ends are used for stirring and for guiding liquids. Rods with shaped ends are useful in the following operations: A rod whose end has been shaped into a disk perpendicular to the axis of the rod may be used for breaking up lumps of material, and a paddle-shaped end is convenient to stir solutions in test tubes by rapid rotation of the rod (Fig. 2-15). A disk-shaped end is made by heating the end of a glass rod until it is very soft and has thickened by about one-third to one-half its original diameter. While heating the rod, briefly heat a flat, clean piece of metal or Transite. Remove the rod from the flame, and push the hot end perpendicularly against the hot metal or Transite surface with a quick rotary motion. Smooth any irregularities by reheating the glass. Carefully anneal the thickened part of this rod. To make a paddle-shaped end, proceed as before, but flatten the hot, thickened end of the rod

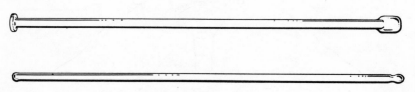

Figure 2-15 Stirring rods.

parallel to its axis by squeezing it with the preheated tips of a pair of crucible tongs or by pressing it between two preheated flat pieces of metal or Transite. Smooth any irregularities, and anneal carefully.

Tapers.   To make a taper or a tip, heat the middle portion of a piece of tubing until it is very soft. Do not pull the tubing while it is in the flame, because that would tend to make the walls thin and weak. Let the walls thicken by action of the surface tension of the glass and possibly by slight pushing. Synchronized, even rotation of both tube halves is very important. Remove the tubing from the flame, rotate it for a few seconds while orienting it vertically, and steadily pull the ends until the constriction desired has been reached. The more the walls were thickened, the thicker will be the walls of the final product. (The narrowing caused by the pulling affects the walls to about the same extent as the total diameter.) If only a short section of the tube has been heated, a short and abrupt taper will result. For longer tapers a longer section of tubing is heated by moving the tube along its own axis through the flame during heating or by using a flame spreader on the burner. For the tips used in droppers and wash bottles a suitably drawn-out tube is scratched with the file at its narrowest part and broken; a clean break is essential for proper functioning of the tips. The sharp tip edges are then fire-polished. Further constriction by letting the glass get too soft must be avoided.

Flared ends.   The rubber bulb of a dropper is held more securely if the glass tube to which it is attached is flared. To produce a flare, rotate the tube and heat the end until it is soft but has not started to sag. Withdraw the tube from the flame and rotate it against the pre-heated handle end of a file held inclined to the tube axis (Fig. 2-16). The size of the flare should be no larger than is needed to hold the rubber bulb tightly. Anneal the flared portion of the tube.

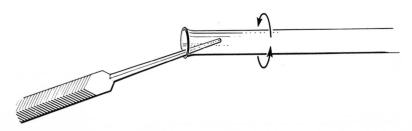

Figure 2-16   Flaring a tube end.

29

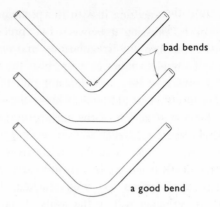

bad bends

a good bend

Figure 2-17   Bending of glass tubes.

Bending tubes.   To bend a tube, place the flame spreader on the burner before lighting the gas. Rotate the tubing, and place the part to be bent in the symmetrical, fan-shaped flame so that about 5 to 8 cm is heated uniformly. When the glass is sufficiently soft, remove the tube from the flame, continue its rotation for a few seconds, and bend the

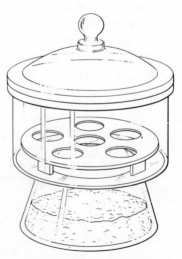

Figure 2-18   Desiccator.

ends upward until the desired angle between them has been achieved. Bend in a vertical plane with the bent part pointing down, because sagging caused by gravity tends to keep the cross section of the bent portion round. If the glass was not hot enough at the time of bending, the bent part is likely to be constricted and even buckled (Fig. 2-17). Be sure that the entire bend is in one plane. Anneal the bent tube.

Working glass is an art. Be patient in your efforts, and take pride in the appearance of your equipment.

DESICCATOR

A desiccator (Fig. 2-18) provides a dry atmosphere in which objects such as weighing bottles and crucibles may be allowed to cool and where they may be stored and protected from dust and laboratory fumes and gases. The bottom is filled with a drying agent, and the objects placed inside are supported by a porcelain plate with holes of a size to accommodate crucibles. The top of the desiccator and the lid are ground flat, and a thin layer of grease between them serves to form an airtight seal.

Commonly used desiccants, in sequence of increasing effectiveness, are anhydrous calcium chloride, silica gel, anhydrous calcium sulfate (sold commercially as Drierite), concentrated sulfuric acid, and phosphorus pentoxide. Anhydrous calcium chloride reduces the partial pressure of water to about 0.2 mm Hg, which is satisfactory for most purposes.

Instructions for cleaning and charging a desiccator with fresh drying agent are given in Procedure 2-5 below.

*The equipment in the laboratory lockers
is to be checked,
and wash bottles, calibrated droppers,
and other items are to be constructed.
The desiccator is to be charged with
fresh desiccant and its cover provided
with a new film of grease.*

Laboratory assignment 2*
(1 period)

CHECKING INTO THE LABORATORY;

CONSTRUCTION OF SIMPLE

GLASS EQUIPMENT

DISCUSSION

Most of the common equipment needed in the laboratory is in the lockers assigned to you. Some of the laboratory assignments require special equipment, which can be checked out of the stockroom for one laboratory period at a time. Such apparatus must be returned clean, dry, and in good condition. Return it as soon as possible, and never later than at the end of the laboratory period.

* Since there is no laboratory assignment in Chapter 1, we begin the assignments with number 2, corresponding to Chapter 2.

You will be assigned an analytical balance, which you must keep in good condition. A set of analytical weights for each balance is kept in the stockroom. This set is to be checked out whenever needed and returned at the end of the period. Items such as filter paper and stoppers, for which you may sign in the stockroom, are nonreturnable.

The chemicals needed in the regular laboratory assignments are kept in the laboratories. Chemicals for special purposes can be obtained in the stockroom, but only if authorized by the instructor.

PROCEDURES

2-1 Checking in. Take your registration card to the stockroom and exchange it for a desk key. Find the equipment list in your desk and check off the articles in the locker. If anything is missing or damaged, check with the instructor and obtain a replacement from the stockroom. When all your equipment is in order, sign the equipment list and turn it in. Laboratory work must not be started before this is done.

After you sign the equipment list, the contents of your locker are your responsibility. You may obtain replacements from the stockroom during the year by signing charge slips. At the end of the year you are expected to have your equipment complete and in working condition.

2-2 Glass rods. Using 4-mm-diameter soft-glass rod, construct (1) at least four plain 15-cm glass rods; (2) one or two glass rods with one end paddle-shaped, the other end flat and disk-shaped; (3) several small, U-shaped pieces, each 2 to 3 cm long, to support watch glasses on top of beakers when evaporating solutions (see Fig. 4-4, page 81).

2-3 Droppers. Construct two medicine droppers of about 15 cm length from soft-glass tubing of 6 mm outside diameter. Start with a tube about 30 cm long, and draw it out in the middle to provide the tips for both droppers. This tube diameter is chosen to make the rubber bulbs fit snugly, and this tube length should be sufficient to prevent the solution from being sucked inadvertently into the bulb of the finished dropper. Contact between rubber bulb and solution may result in contamination. Do not hold a dropper that contains solution upside down.

Calibrate both droppers by using distilled water and a 10-ml graduated cylinder. First, use a dropper to adjust the water level in the graduate so that the bottom of the meniscus is level with one of the milliliter marks etched around the entire circumference of the cylinder (avoid parallax errors). Empty the dropper, and draw exactly 0.5 ml into it. The level positions in the graduate must be read with the dropper removed, of course. Mark the position of the meniscus in the dropper with a light file scratch. Expel the liquid from the dropper, and repeat the foregoing procedure for 1 ml of liquid.

Finally, calibrate the drop size for each dropper by counting the drops delivered when the dropper contains 1 ml and is held vertically during delivery. The number of drops should be 25 to 30 and should be reproducible to within 1 to 2 drops. Change the size of the tip if your results fall outside this range. Convince yourself that the size of drops depends on the angle of tilt by repeating the count at 45° inclination. Always hold the dropper vertically when counting drops.

2-4　Construction of wash bottles.　　Wash bottles provide distilled water for rinsing equipment, diluting solutions, transferring precipitates by washing, and washing precipitates. To assemble the 1-liter wash bottle shown in Figure 2-19a, obtain 2 ft of soft-glass tubing of 6 mm outside diameter, a 1000-ml flat-bottomed round flask (a Florence flask), a new 4-cm piece of rubber tubing, and a new two-hole rubber stopper. Construct the inlet and outlet tubes by following the instructions given earlier. The length of the outlet tube depends on the size of the flask

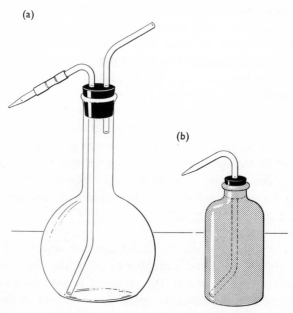

(a)

(b)

Figure 2-19　(a) 1000-ml glass wash bottle; (b) 250-ml polyethylene squeeze bottle.

lubricate with
water

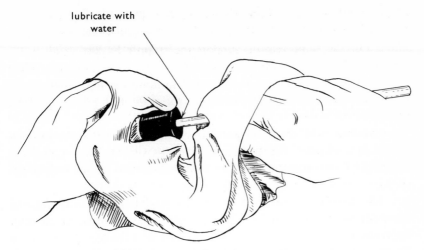

Figure 2-20   Insertion of glass tube into rubber stopper.

and should be measured to suit the flask. The bend near the bottom end of the tube should be as shown in Figure 2-19a. If only solid-rubber stoppers are available, a sharp cork borer well lubricated with glycerin may be used to cut the holes. Cut perpendicularly to the end surfaces

Figure 2-21   Removing desiccator cover.

of the stopper with a slow, rotary motion. Do not press too hard, because cutting through distorted rubber produces uneven, tapered holes. For the same reason, support the stopper by boring against a flat piece of wood (*not* the desk top). If glycerin is not available, dilute sodium hydroxide solution may be used to lubricate, but avoid getting it on your hands or the desk, and wash the stopper and borer carefully when you are done.

Lubricate with plenty of water when pushing a glass tube through a hole in a stopper, and protect both hands with a towel. Grasp the tube close to the point of insertion, and push it through the hole in the stopper with a rotary motion (Fig. 2-20).

The tip of the wash bottle is attached flexibly to the outlet tube by the short piece of rubber hose. It is possible to manipulate this tip with the index finger of the hand holding the flask so as to direct a stream of liquid in any way desired. Test for delivery of an even, undivided stream of water.

Construct a 250-ml polyethylene squeeze bottle, such as the one shown in Figure 2-19b.

2-5 Cleaning and charging of desiccator.   Remove the desiccator cover by sliding it sideways (Fig. 2-21), take out the porcelain plate, and remove the old desiccant; consult your instructor about its disposal.

Figure 2-22 Filling desiccator with fresh desiccant.

Use a paper towel to wipe off the old grease on the rim and cover. Apply a thin film of fresh petroleum jelly (Vaseline) to the ground top surface of the rim, put the cover back, and slide and rotate it until the film becomes transparent. Do not use too much jelly; excess amounts will be squeezed out and are likely to be messy.

Slide off the cover, and use a paper funnel to fill the bottom compartment of the desiccator with fresh calcium chloride desiccant (Fig. 2-22). Replace the porcelain plate and desiccator cover. The upper compartment of a desiccator must be kept scrupulously clean, because any foreign matter is likely to contaminate objects placed in it.

*An explanation of the principles of
construction and the details of operation
of an analytical balance
is followed by a discussion of sources
of weighing errors and the calibration of weights
and by suggestions on the proper care
of a balance. A laboratory assignment
consists of balance manipulations,
weight calibrations, and the weighing of an object.*

three

THE ANALYTICAL

BALANCE

PRINCIPLES OF CONSTRUCTION

A balance is an instrument that permits measurement of the *weight* of an object, the force by which it is attracted by the earth. This force is compared either with another force, like the retracting force of an extended spring (spring balance) or of a twisted quartz fiber (torsion balance), or, by the use of a lever, with the force of attraction by the earth of a collection of standard objects called weights (lever balance). Usually the purpose of weighing is to establish the *mass* of the object being weighed. If weighing is performed with a lever balance and in a vacuum, the force comparison is equivalent to comparing the masses

38

of object and weights. In the presence of air the buoyancy of objects and weights has to be taken into account, as will be discussed in detail later. If the weight of the object is compared with a nongravitational force as in a spring or a torsion balance, the balance calibration in terms of object mass depends on the geographical location. The acceleration of gravity g may vary as much as several parts per thousand with a change in latitude and altitude. In any given location, g is constant and the mass of an object is proportional to the weight. Indeed, the mass of an object is often referred to as its weight; this is permissible as long as it is understood that the term "weight" used in this context is an inaccurate synonym for mass.

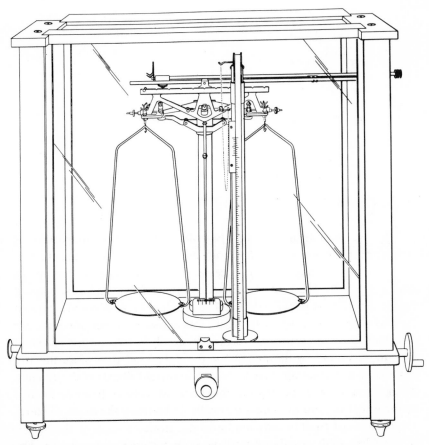

Figure 3-1   Analytical balance.

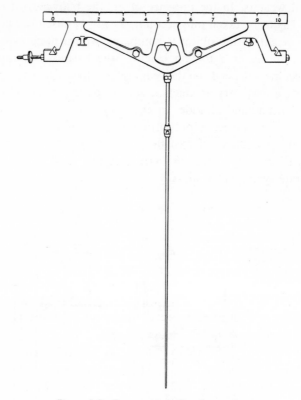

Figure 3-2   Beam with knife-edges and pointer.

In the analytical balance (Fig. 3-1) the weight comparison is performed by means of a beam acting as a lever with two arms of equal length. It has a knife-edge at its center and a knife-edge at each of its ends (Fig. 3-2). The central knife-edge points down and is supported by the center post of the balance. The terminal knife-edges are pointed up and support bearing plates set in stirrups, from which the pans are suspended. The object to be weighed is usually placed on the left-hand pan and balanced by the weights on the right-hand pan. Since the arm lengths of the beam are equal, the condition of balance is the equality of the gravity forces pulling on object and weights. A pointer attached to the center of, and extending vertically down from, the beam indicates the position of equilibrium on a horizontal scale.

To be useful, a balance must be both accurate and sensitive. The principal condition for *accuracy* is equality of the arm lengths of the beam, a test for which will be discussed later. If the knife-edges are not sharp or the surfaces bearing against them not plane, the effective arm lengths depend on the angle of inclination of the beam and change while the beam swings or oscillates around the equilibrium position, which is a source of inaccuracy. In addition, dull knife-edges cause friction, which hampers the free swinging of the beam necessary for the weighing procedures to be described later. Friction may also cause the oscillating beam to come to rest in a position other than that of true equilibrium. Good knife-edges and surfaces bearing against them are thus of great importance. Both are usually made of a special grade of agate that has a high degree of hardness, durability, and corrosion resistance.

The *sensitivity s* of a balance is usually defined as the change in the position of equilibrium of the pointer position caused by a weight change of unit weight. Thus, if the addition of a weight w causes a change p in the equilibrium position of the pointer,

$$s = p/w \qquad (3\text{-}1)$$

The usual units of s are scale units per milligram. Some of the factors affecting the sensitivity will be considered next.

Figure 3-3 is a simplified drawing of the beam in the equilibrium positions corresponding (1) to equal loads (unprimed letters) and (2) to a small excess load on the left pan (primed letters). The forces acting on the beam are shown by

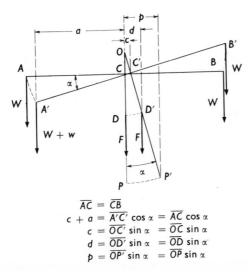

$$\overline{AC} = \overline{CB}$$
$$c + a = \overline{A'C'} \cos \alpha = \overline{AC} \cos \alpha$$
$$c = \overline{OC'} \sin \alpha = \overline{OC} \sin \alpha$$
$$d = \overline{OD'} \sin \alpha = \overline{OD} \sin \alpha$$
$$p = \overline{OP'} \sin \alpha = \overline{OP} \sin \alpha$$

Figure 3-3 Beam in two different equilibrium positions.

arrows. The central knife-edge of the beam is supported at O. The terminal knife-edges carrying the pans are at A and B when the loads in both pans are equal and at A' and B' when a small weight increment w has been added to the pan on the left. The end of the pointer is at P or P', respectively. The weights of the pans and the equal loads on the two sides are represented by W. The weight of beam and pointer is shown by the arrows F, acting at the center of mass of beam and pointer, situated at D or D', respectively. When the loads on both sides are equal, the equilibrium position of the pointer is vertical. In the equilibrium position corresponding to the small weight increment w on the left pan the following forces must be considered: The two forces W may be combined to $2W$ acting at C' midway between A' and B', whereas w acts at A' and F at D'. Thus, there exists the following torque balance:

$$wa = 2Wc + Fd$$

Using the relations given at the bottom of Figure 3-3,

$$w(\overline{AC} \cos \alpha - \overline{OC} \sin \alpha) = (2\overline{OC} \cdot W + \overline{OD} \cdot F) \sin \alpha$$

so that

$$\tan \alpha = w \cdot \overline{AC}/[\overline{OC}(2W + w) + \overline{OD} \cdot F] \qquad (3-2)$$

The angle α is observed in terms of the pointer deflection p,

$$p = \overline{OP} \sin \alpha \qquad (3-3)$$

For small angles α, $\sin \alpha$ and $\tan \alpha$ are almost equal to each other. In the same approximation w in the denominator of (3-2) is negligible compared with $2W$. For the sensitivity s the following relation is obtained:

$$s = p/w \approx (\overline{OP} \cdot \overline{AC})/(2\overline{OC} \cdot W + \overline{OD} \cdot F) \qquad (3-4)$$

This formula corresponds to the situation when the point O, at which the beam is suspended, is above the line AB connecting the terminal knife-edges, as shown in Figure 3-3. If O is below the line AB, the term $2\overline{OC} \cdot W$ in the denominator of (3-4) has to be given a negative sign. The sensitivity s thus decreases with the load W when $\overline{OC}$ is positive and increases when $\overline{OC}$ is negative. It is possible to make the denominator of (3-4) zero by a suitable choice of $\overline{OC}$ and W, when s becomes infinite. Any advantage that might be thought to accrue from such an arrangement is illusory, however, because the balance is in neutral equilibrium at this point. Indeed, the denominator can be made negative when s is negative and the equilibrium is labile.

It is of advantage to have the sensitivity independent of the load, which is the case when $\overline{OC} = 0$, so that all three knife-edges are in the same plane and the torque exerted by the force $2W$ is zero. Since even a beam of rigid construction bends under a load, it is best to have the central knife-edge slightly below the other two, so that all three knife-edges are coplanar at an *average* load. Under these conditions the dependence of the sensitivity on the load is small and

$$s \approx (\overline{OP} \cdot \overline{AC})/(\overline{OD} \cdot F) \qquad (3-5)$$

The three knife-edges must also be parallel to each other and perpendicular to the long axis of the beam.

Inspection of (3-5) shows that the sensitivity of the balance is the larger the longer the pointer and the balance arms, the lighter the beam, and (within limits) the higher the center of mass of beam and pointer. A slight decrease in sensitivity at higher loads also results from the increased friction in the bearings. It is usually possible to shift the center of mass of beam and pointers by means of an adjustment screw on the pointer (Fig. 3-2). The other factors just enumerated depend on the details of construction. It is not practical to increase the sensitivity of a balance by indiscriminate lengthening of the arms or by indiscriminate raising of the center of mass of beam and pointer, since both these changes also increase the period of oscillation of the beam. Such an increase lengthens the time it takes to make weighings and augments the erratic influence of friction on the motion of the balance. Another limitation to an increase in beam length is the difficulty in constructing a rigid beam without increase in weight, which would counteract and might even overcome any gains in sensitivity. The pointer length has its physical limitations also, and so do refinements in detecting changes in the pointer position that use a lens or other optical means. Many designs have been developed to effect a favorable compromise among the conditions just stated. Lightweight alloys and construction principles that combine rigidity with lightness are used for the beam, which is usually given an arm length in the neighborhood of 10 cm. Such "short-arm" balances are fast, with a period of oscillation of about 5 to 10 sec. The sensitivity is usually about three to five scale units per milligram, which is a good range for analytical work. A substantially larger sensitivity would be impractical, not only because of the increased period of oscillation that goes with it but also because of the greater dependence of a large sensitivity on the load and because of the erratic balance behavior that is encountered when the sensitivity is increased beyond a certain point.

The performance characteristics of an analytical balance are impressive. Weighings of objects up to the capacity of the balance, which usually is at 100 to 200 g, can be made with a precision of 0.05 to 0.1 mg; this is better than 1 ppm. There are available microanalytical balances that permit weighing of 10 to 25 g with a precision of 0.001 to 0.01 mg and quartz-fiber torsion balances with a capacity of 25 mg and a precision of 0.01 μg (1 μg $= 10^{-6}$ g).

Obviously, an analytical balance requires very careful handling if it is to retain its quality. In particular, any damage to the knife-edges and the surfaces bearing against them must be avoided.

   Analytical balances are enclosed in glass cases and provided with
a beam-arresting mechanism that permits lifting the central knife-edge
off the agate surface supporting it, as well as simultaneously separating
the terminal knife-edges on the beam from the agate surfaces mounted
in the stirrups that support the pans. A separate mechanism, the pan
arrest, stops lateral oscillations of the pans. Both mechanisms are
operated by knobs at the base of the balance. In some models they are
governed by the same knob, but separate controls are desirable. Both
mechanisms must be operated very carefully, as described later. A
balance must always be left with beam and pans arrested and with the
balance case closed.

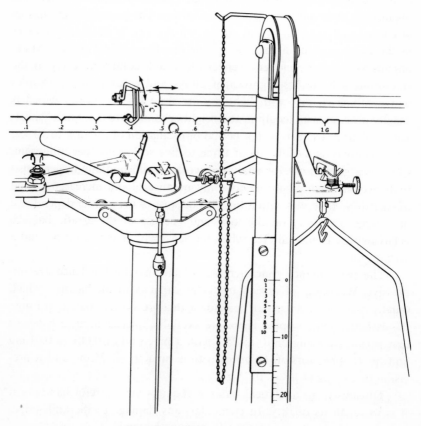

Figure 3-4   Chain and mechanism.

The weights used to weigh an object are usually made of brass or bronze and have a surface coating made of a material that is highly resistant to corrosion, such as gold, platinum, or nickel. Cheaper weights are coated with lacquer, which is less desirable. Weights below 1 g are usually made of aluminum, platinum, or tantalum. Often a weight set contains several weights of the same denomination. These are marked in some way to identify them and have to be calibrated individually. Weights must be treated with great care to avoid any change in mass. It is of interest that the brass removed in making a scratch 1 cm long, 0.1 mm wide, and 0.1 mm deep weighs 0.1 mg, the tolerance of analytical weights.

On the older type of analytical balance a 10-mg rider placed in the appropriate position on top of the beam by manipulating a system of levers is used to apply weights of 10 mg or less. In the more modern chain balances weights up to 100 mg are added by means of a fine gold chain (Fig. 3-4), one end of which is suspended from the right side of the beam and the other from a support that can be raised or lowered by a special mechanism, thus shortening or lengthening the part of the chain whose weight is carried by the beam. A scale with a vernier shows the effective weight thus applied. In some chain balances the chain is suspended from a vertical column or a vertical steel tape as shown in Figure 3-4, in others from a horizontal drum. A chain balance usually has V-shaped notches at equal intervals, ground with high accuracy, in the upper side of the beam. A system of levers permits placing a cylindrically shaped rider in any one of these notches. The notch spacings and the rider weight are carefully matched for each individual balance so that the notch spacing corresponds to multiples of 100 mg. Thus, all weights below 1 g are supplied in this type of balance by means of rider and chain.

DETAILS OF OPERATION

Determination of the point of rest.   The scale on which pointer deflections from the vertical position are measured usually has 10 or 12 divisions on either side of the center mark. It is useful to number these divisions mentally so the center mark is at 10 rather than 0 (starting with 0 or −2 on the left). This avoids mixing negative and positive scale divisions in the numerical computations described below and thus eliminates a source of error and confusion.

The *rest point* of the balance is the position of the pointer that indicates equilibrium between object and weights. It could be determined

45

by letting the balance swing until it stopped; but it is more convenient and more accurate to find the rest point from observations of the freely swinging balance, because influences of friction are minimized. The rest point of the empty balance is called the *zero point*. It need not coincide with scale division 10, and it may change from time to time. If the zero point differs much from the scale division 10, it may be made to coincide with that division by adjusting the zero position of the vernier of the chain weight scale. Descriptions of two methods of determining the rest point follow.

The long-swing method. It is assumed that when the balance swings freely, the amplitude of the swing decreases by the same amount Δ (the *decrement*) during each swing. If the rest point of the balance is r and the amplitude of the first swing h, then five consecutive extrema of swing are located as shown beneath Figure 3-5.

Consider the average of all extrema on the right, e_R, and the average of all extrema on the left, e_L.

$$e_L = (e_1 + e_3 + e_5)/3 = r - (h - \Delta)$$
$$e_R = (e_2 + e_4)/2 = r + (h - \Delta)$$

The average of e_R and e_L is just r.

$$(e_L + e_R)/2 = r$$

This cancellation of the effect of a *constant* decrement always occurs when an *odd* number of consecutive extrema of a swinging balance is averaged by the method just used. The extrema on the left are averaged

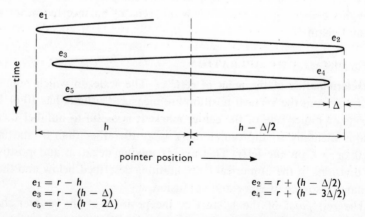

$$e_1 = r - h$$
$$e_3 = r - (h - \Delta)$$
$$e_5 = r - (h - 2\Delta)$$

$$e_2 = r + (h - \Delta/2)$$
$$e_4 = r + (h - 3\Delta/2)$$

Figure 3-5 Oscillations of balance pointer.

separately from those on the right, and the averages are averaged again. The assumption of constancy of the decrement is good if the amplitude of the swing is about 5 scale units (the total swing extending over about 10 scale units) and the number of swings is not too large. The prescribed method of releasing pan and beam will be discussed presently.

The short-swing method. If the amplitude of the swing is less than about two scale units, the decrement can be neglected for a few consecutive swings and the rest point is closely equal to the average between two extrema:

$$r \approx (e_1 + e_2)/2$$

With some practice it is possible to determine the average mentally, while the swinging pointer is under observation, and to *check this average visually.* The short-swing method saves time and computation, and its precision is usually well within the limits needed. It also produces less wear on the knife-edges than the long-swing method. The beam never swings rapidly, and it can be arrested easily without shock when the pointer position is near the center.

Methods of weighing. Three methods of weighing are described. Two of them do not require much practice and are recommended for beginners; the third takes more experience but affords a saving in time for routine work.

The first two methods require a determination of the zero point of the balance (its rest point when not loaded). This point must be redetermined each time a series of weighings is undertaken, and it is wise to check its value after the last weighing or even during a prolonged series of weighings. Note, however, that when an amount of substance is weighed by difference, the location of the zero point is immaterial and may be assumed to be at any convenient point on the scale. The error that an incorrect choice introduces is canceled when the difference between the two successive weighings is taken.

The *first method* is to *weigh by exact balancing.* The weights on the right-hand pan, the rider, and the chain length are adjusted until the rest point of the balance coincides with its zero point. Once the state of imbalance is less than a few milligrams, the final adjustment required for exact balancing may be estimated from the balance sensitivity and the difference between rest point and zero point.

In the *second method,* called *weighing by sensitivity,* the weights, the rider, and the chain length are adjusted approximately only, so that their total weight is within 1 or 2 mg of the required amount. The rest point is then determined, and a weight correction is computed from the difference between this rest point and the zero point by using the sensitivity *s* of the balance. Note that this weight correction has to be *added to* or *subtracted from* the total of weights, rider, and chain, depending on whether the rest point is to the right or left of the zero point. This method is called *weighing by sensitivity*. The sensitivity *s* may be determined at the time of weighing by adding or subtracting 1 mg on the right side, or it may have been determined once and for all as function of the load.

The *third method* is called the *single-deflection* method. At the beginning of a series of weighings the chain length is so adjusted that 1 mg is applied to the left side of the otherwise unloaded balance. The vernier of the chain weight scale is then readjusted to this new "zero," and the beam arrest is lowered. Finally, the pan arrests are released smartly without transferring any impulse to the beam, and the maximum excursion of the pointer during the first swing is determined. When weighing an object, the weights are adjusted until the pointer deflection is the same as observed originally. Care must be taken that the pans do not swing by themselves when finally released. This condition is attained by releasing and arresting the pans several times, with the beam arrested, until they are centered.

The maximum excursion of the pointer depends on the ratio of the torque exerted on the beam system, around its axis of suspension, to the moment of inertia of the system. (The effect of air damping is very minor.) We assume first that the moment of inertia is not changed by the presence of object and weights; in that case equality of the maximum pointer excursion implies equality of the torques. The torque for the loaded balance thus corresponds exactly to the torque of the original milligram, and therefore the weights added just balance the object if the balance sensitivity has not changed.

To consider the effect of the actual change of the moment of inertia, we assume that the presence of object and weights increase it by *p* per cent. The torque causing the pointer deflection when weighing must also be larger by *p* per cent, and the effective imbalance is thus not the original milligram but (with unchanged sensitivity) that milligram increased by the same percentage *p*. If *p* is less than 10 per cent and if the sensitivity of the balance remains essentially unchanged, the weight of the object obtained by the single-deflection method may be expected to be correct within 10 per cent of 1 mg, or within 0.1 mg. It is important to note that the correction of *p* per cent applies to the milligram generating the torque and not to the entire weight and object. The assumptions underlying the single deflection method are well satisfied, particularly if weighings by difference, involving at most a few grams, are performed.

The single-deflection method requires that the controls for beam and pan arrests be separate and that the pan arrests be so adjusted that they do not stick to the pans or otherwise affect the movement of the beam. The method takes practice but saves time when a whole series of weighings is required.

The choice between the three weighing methods described is a matter of personal preference. Beginners should first get experience with one of the first two methods.

Manipulation of beam and pan arrests; adding and removing weights. No manipulation involving either of the two pans must ever be undertaken *unless beam and pans are arrested.* The rider must not be moved *unless the beam is arrested.* Before releasing the beam, close the balance case, disengage the pan arrests, and let any oscillations of the pans come to a halt. If necessary, gently use the pan arrests to dampen oscillations. Carefully start releasing the beam while watching constantly whether the pointer begins to swing freely or whether it continues to go in the same direction as far as the receding beam arrests permit. If the imbalance begins to exceed about three to five scale divisions, gently arrest the beam again, and make suitable changes in weights (after arresting the pans), rider position, or chain length. Always change first the largest weight units of which you are not certain.

When a condition of balance is close, operate the beam release so as to obtain the appropriate amplitude for the long-swing or short-swing method. If releasing the beam does not cause suitable oscillations, they may be induced by slightly shortening or lengthening the chain for a moment.

When weighing by the first method described above, in which the original rest point is restored, slowly change the portion of the chain supported by the beam, while the balance is swinging, until the rest point coincides with the zero point. Otherwise, determine the rest point without a change in chain length and use the sensitivity to compute the appropriate weight correction.

When finished, manipulate the beam arrest so as to decrease the amplitudes of the beam oscillations gently, and finally lift the beam when the pointer is in a central position. *Never arrest the pans before the beam.* Most of the wear on knife-edges occurs as a result of horizontal shear when the beam is arrested near the return points of long swings or when the pans are arrested before the beam; for this causes rapid oscillations of the beam. (When the arrests are adjusted to move in the proper arcs, no such shear is supposed to arise; but it is better not to rely on this.)

The sequence of pan and beam release and arrest prescribed earlier has the following advantages: (1) Wear on knife-edges is minimized, particularly when the short-swing method is used and final arresting of the beam is done with the pointer in the middle only. (2) The release mechanism of the beam provides much better control of the movements of the beam than the pan release provides. When the short-swing method is used for rest-point determinations, the amplitude of the beam oscillations can be readily restricted by the beam release. (3) By sensitive operation of the beam release and by observing, from the motions of the pointer, how quickly the beam follows this release, the degree of inequality of object and weights may be judged. This enables the operator to decide rapidly what weights need to be changed and by how much. The beam is fully released only after it is established that it will swing freely and not outside a chosen amplitude.

It is poor practice to release the beam before the pans, to follow this by adjusting the smaller weights on the pans, and to test the progress of this adjustment by the temporary release of the pans while the pointer is being observed. This method causes wear of the knife-edges. In particular, in rearresting the pans rapid oscillations of the beam are difficult to avoid, and such oscillations result in excessive wear. It is also likely that arresting of the beam will be forgotten before changing the *heavier* weights, and the resulting sudden motions may cause damage.

WEIGHING ERRORS

In the following, sources of error and means of correction are discussed.

Inequality of balance arms. Let the left and right arms of a balance have the respective lengths a_L and a_R, and let the weight W_R, placed on the right pan, balance a given object on the left pan, while the weight W_L placed on the left pan balances the same object on the right pan. Thus the following conditions of balance apply to the weight W of the object:

$$a_L W = a_R W_R \qquad a_L W_L = a_R W$$

Dividing left and right sides,

$$W/W_L = W_R/W$$

so that

$$W = \sqrt{W_L W_R} \approx \tfrac{1}{2}(W_L + W_R) \qquad (3\text{-}6)$$

where the approximation makes use of the relationship $\sqrt{(1 + \delta)} \approx 1 + \delta/2(\delta \ll 1)$ (see Appendix I) and is thus valid when $|W_R - W_L|/W_R \ll 1$. Inserting this result in either of the two original equations and solving for a_L/a_R,

$$a_L/a_R = \sqrt{W_R/W_L} \approx 1 + (W_R - W_L)/2W_L \qquad (3\text{-}7)$$

Again the approximation is valid when $|W_R - W_L|/W_L \ll 1$.

These relations are the basis of the *transposition*, or *double-weighing*, method devised by *Gauss*, in which the object is weighed first on one pan and then on the other. The results yield true weight and the ratio of the arm lengths.

Another method of weighing with a balance of unequal arm lengths is the *substitution method* due to *Borda*, in which the object is balanced against any suitable items, such as weights from an old set, commonly called the *tare*. The object is then removed and replaced on the same pan by precise weights until they balance the tare. The sum of these precise weights equals the weight of the object; the exact weight of the tare and the ratio of the arm lengths remain unknown. The Gauss method is preferable, because no extra set of tare weights is needed and more information is obtained with the same amount of work. In addition, the precision of the Gauss method is twice that of the Borda method.

Note that, if the required precision of a balance with a maximum load of 200 g (on each pan) is 0.2 mg, the ratio of the arm lengths must be within the limits

$$\left|\frac{a_L}{a_R} - 1\right| \leq \left|\frac{W_R - W_L}{2W_L}\right| = \frac{2 \times 10^{-4}}{400} = 5 \times 10^{-7}$$

Thus, if the arms are 10 cm long, the central knife-edge must be within 2.5×10^{-6} cm, or 25 mμ from the center. (The wavelength of blue light is 400 mμ.) It is not practical to manufacture beams with unit ratio of arm lengths at such a precision, nor would the equality of distances be maintained under conditions of different load. Nevertheless, whatever this ratio is at a certain load, the precision of the knife-edges and bearing plates is high enough for that ratio to be meaningful and maintained, for different positions of the beam, to better than 1 part in 10^6. If a precision of 1 part in 10^6 in determining the weight of an object is desired, the Gauss method of double weighing has to be used. In a good analytical balance the arm lengths seldom differ by more than 1 part in 25,000.

Buoyancy. The weight in air of an object is equal to the weight the object would have in the absence of air diminished by its buoyancy, or the weight of the air displaced by it. The weights used are buoyed up too, and since their face values are their weights *in vacuo* (or their masses, to be precise), any buoyancy correction has to be applied to them also. Let W_v be the *vacuum* weight of the object and d_{ob} its density. The buoyancy of the object equals its volume times the density d_{air} of air, or $d_{air} W_v/d_{ob}$. The *apparent* weight W_a of the object in air is equal to that of the weights balancing it, and their buoyancy is $d_{air} W_a/d_{wt}$, where d_{wt} is the (average) density of the weights. The condition of balance is

$$W_v - \frac{d_{air} W_v}{d_{ob}} = W_a - \frac{d_{air} W_a}{d_{wt}} \tag{3-8}$$

which may be rearranged to give

$$W_v = W_a + d_{air}\left(\frac{W_v}{d_{ob}} - \frac{W_a}{d_{wt}}\right)$$

Since the difference between W_v and W_a is small, W_v is usually replaced by W_a on the right side, so that

$$W_v \approx W_a + W_a\left(\frac{d_{air}}{d_{ob}} - \frac{d_{air}}{d_{wt}}\right) \tag{3-9}$$

A more precise approach is to solve (3-8) for W_v:

$$W_v = W_a(1 - d_{air}/d_{wt})(1 - d_{air}/d_{ob})^{-1} \tag{3-10}$$

When the object is a solid or liquid, d_{air}/d_{ob} is small compared with 1 and the approximation $(1 - \delta)^{-1} \approx 1 + \delta (\delta \ll 1)$ may be used (see Appendix I) so that

$$W_v \approx W_a(1 - d_{air}/d_{wt})(1 + d_{air}/d_{ob})$$

Multiplying the parentheses and neglecting $d_{air}^2/d_{wt}d_{ob}$ as small compared with 1 leads to (3-9), which is thus based on the assumptions just stated. If the object is a gas, the more precise equation (3-10) must be used.

The buoyancy correction is usually so small that it can be neglected except in the most exacting work. It is needed in calibrating volumetric equipment. Although the density of air depends on such factors as humidity, barometric pressure, and carbon dioxide content, an average value of 1.2 g/liter is usually satisfactory.

Moisture. Dried substances in open containers may absorb moisture if the atmosphere within the balance is humid. Hygroscopic substances must be weighed rapidly and in closed containers.

Temperature differences of object and balance. Temperature equality of the object to be weighed and the balance is obviously important. An object which is warmer than its surroundings will be found too light because air currents tend to lift the pan it is on; the object will appear to gain weight with successive weighings. For example, a 25-ml crucible which was 1 °C warmer than the air in the balance was found to be low by about 0.1 mg.

Electrification.   Glass vessels may acquire static electricity when wiped with a dry cloth. Such objects may show an erroneous weight and cause erratic swings because of the mutual attraction between the charged vessel and other parts of the balance. Avoid vigorous rubbing of glass objects prior to weighing.

Balance defects.   Occasionally a balance does not give reproducible zero points and shows a great decrease in sensitivity with load because of worn knife-edges or other defective parts. Any such behavior should be brought to the attention of the instructor.

Reproducibility of chain position.   It is important to check frequently to see that the chain is suspended properly, so that the reading taken actually corresponds to the chain weight. In some balances it has been observed that the weight pulling on the beam depends on whether a given position of the chain-operating mechanism is approached from above or below. This effect is very small and cancels if the scale and vernier positions are always approached from the same side before taking a reading. It is not important unless the accuracy sought is at least of the order of 0.1 mg.

Inaccurate weights; weight calibration.   Weights are easily damaged by dropping or by less than very careful handling. If at any time there is suspicion of inaccuracy, the weights must be calibrated.

It is good practice to check equipment upon which heavy reliance is placed, at least for internal consistency. For this reason the chain, the rider, and the smaller weights should be checked against each other and against a calibrated 1-g weight to be supplied by the instructor. It is less important to calibrate the weights above 5 g, and for two reasons: (1) The weight of an object heavier than 5 g rarely has to be known to an accuracy of better than 0.1 per cent, which is 5 mg. A weight in a good weight set is seldom off by more than 1 or 2 mg. (2) The weights of precipitates or samples encountered are rarely beyond 1 or 2 g, but the weight of the container usually is. If, however, the same larger-weight pieces are used in weighing full and empty containers, any errors in these weights cancel. The importance of recording in the laboratory notebook all the weight pieces used is evident.

THE PROPER CARE OF AN ANALYTICAL BALANCE

Some of the material given below has been discussed previously, but the importance of treating a balance properly demands its repetition. Study these rules carefully:

The analytical balance

1. *Whenever* using an analytical balance, check to see that it is level (a level indicator is usually provided), that the beam and pan arrests are operating smoothly, and that the rider and chain mechanism are working properly. Never attempt adjustments or repairs; rather, report improper conditions to the instructor.

Ascertain the rated capacity of the balance, and do not exceed it. Most analytical balances are designed for a maximum load of 200 g on each pan. At maximum load the sensitivity should be not less than 40 per cent of its value at zero load; this obviously does not apply to the rare case when the sensitivity keeps increasing with the load.

2. Keep the balance scrupulously clean. Any material spilled on the pans or in the case or corrosion on the pans should be reported immediately. Gently brush the pans off with a small, soft camel's-hair brush (provided for that purpose only) before each series of weighings.

3. Keep the balance case closed except when moving weights or objects on or off the pans.

4. Release the pans *before* the beam. Operate the beam release with great care. Sense the position at which the knife-edges make contact, and make this contact as gentle as possible.

Arrest the beam before the pans, and only when the pointer is near the center of the scale.

Always arrest beam and pans before changing weights or objects. If only the rider or chain is manipulated, the pans need not be arrested but the case must remain closed. Always arrest the beam and pans and close the case before leaving the balance.

5. Sit directly in front of the balance, and look straight at the pointer and scale to avoid parallax errors. The first swings of the balance may be erratic because of air currents in the balance case or oscillations of the pans. Wait until the extremes of the swings are showing an orderly decrement before recording scale readings.

6. Use only your own weights. Handle the weights with the ivory-tipped forceps provided for that purpose only; never use your hands. Objects to be weighed must not be touched with the fingers. Do not scratch or drop weights, and do not place them on the table supporting the balance.

7. Place weights and objects as near as possible to the center of the pan. Do not release the beam until the pans are free and no longer in motion.

8. Substances must not be placed directly on the pans. When

weighing a crucible, protect the pan with a small watch glass. Avoid getting any desiccating agent on the pans.

9. Before weighing them, allow hot objects to cool to balance-room temperature. Avoid generating electrostatic charges.

10. When making successive weighings, use the same larger weights whenever possible.

11. Triple-count the weights to avoid error. (*a*) Count the weights on the pan. (*b*) Count the spaces in the box. (*c*) Check the weights as they are removed from the pan. Carefully recheck rider position and chain length.

12. Record the separate weights individually in your notebook, rather than add them mentally. Do not carry scraps or loose sheets of paper into the balance room for this purpose.

13. When all weighings are completed, remove all glassware, etc., from the balance case and its surroundings, check whether or not the pans and beam are arrested, the brush is in the case, and the case is closed; and generally make certain that you are leaving the balance in satisfactory shape.

THE SINGLE-PAN BALANCE

For rapid weighing a so-called single-pan balance is advantageous. Its principles and operation are described in Appendix II.

*The operations of an analytical balance
are to be studied and practiced.
Weight pieces of 1 to 5 g
are to be calibrated
and an unknown object is to be weighed.*

*Laboratory assignment 3
(1 period)*

WEIGHING OPERATIONS

PROCEDURES

3-1 Examination of balance.   Examine the balance, and look for the knife-edges supporting the pans and the beam. Check the suspension of the chain. Familiarize yourself with the operations of the different knobs without jarring the beam or the pans. Practice moving the rider to different beam locations; this must always be done with the beam arrested, of course. Make certain that you understand how the vernier of the chain-weight dial works.

Write your name and section number and the name of your instructor on a card to be placed in the balance case. These cards are to contain the names of all students using the same balance. *Whenever starting to use the balance*, check to see that all the knife-edges and bearing plates are in appropriate positions and that rider and chain mechanisms are working properly before releasing beam and pans. After checking the balance and before using it, place your card on top of the others in the balance case.

3-2 Determination of the rest point of the balance. 1. Determine the rest point of the balance by the *long-swing method*, as follows: With the balance case closed, *gently* lower the pan arrests and lock them. Carefully turn the beam release, and determine whether or not the mass inequality between the two pans is small enough that the pointer will not move off scale. When this condition has been satisfied, set the beam in motion by *carefully* turning the beam release so that a total swing of about 8 to 10 divisions is obtained. Before taking any pointer readings, let the balance swing a few times without disturbance. Note the position of the pointer for five consecutive extrema, and determine the rest point as suggested in the general discussion. Repeat once or twice.

2. Determine the rest point of the balance by the *short-swing method*. Practice finding the point of rest by visually estimating the central point of the short swings (one or two scale units). Record this value of the rest point, and, without arresting the beam, repeat the determination by recording extremes of a swing and taking the mean.

3-3 Determination of the sensitivity of the balance. Determine and plot the sensitivity *s* of the balance (scale units per milligram) for the following loads on each pan: 0 g, 10 g, 50 g. Place the weights near the center of the pans. Note that the rest point with weights of equal face value on the two pans need not coincide with the zero point, because the weights may not be exactly equal (equality of the arm lengths is usually much more precise). However, this is immaterial for the determination of the sensitivity, unless the pointer is significantly off the center position. In that case the chain should be so adjusted that the pointer is close to scale division 10.

3-4 Weighing an object. (Procedures 3-4 and 3-5 may be preceded by Procedure 3-6.) Obtain an object of unknown weight from your instructor and weigh it by the two methods described earlier, as follows:

1. Determine the zero point of the balance by the short-swing method.

2. Place the object near the center of the left pan and the largest weight estimated to be still below the weight of the object near the center of the right pan. Release the pan arrests, and wait until the

pans no longer swing, or dampen their motions by the gentle use of the pan arrests. Carefully begin lowering the beam until the knife-edge is in contact with its support. Continue the lowering by a small amount to see whether weights should be added or taken away. Arrest beam and pans, adjust the weight, and repeat the procedure just described. Time is saved by proceeding from larger weight adjustments to smaller ones, rather than the other way around. Once the weight difference between weights and object is below 1 g, close the case and begin adjusting the rider position and finally the chain, always with the beam arrested, until you are within a few milligrams of the correct weight. Never let the balance swing freely until you have convinced yourself by partly releasing the beam, as just described, that the pointer will not leave the scale during a swing. When that point has been reached, the chain may be adjusted without rearresting the beam, so as to bring the rest point within a few scale units of the zero point. Determine the position of this rest point.

3. Add or subtract 1 mg from the right side to determine the sensitivity. (This step is not necessary if the sensitivity is already known for this load.) Establish the weight of the object, accurate to 0.1 mg, by appropriate computation.

4. Let the beam oscillate for a total of about 2 scale divisions, and slowly adjust the chain length until the midpoint of the oscillations has shifted to the zero point. Note that, if a precision of 0.1 mg is required and the sensitivity of the balance is 3 scale units/mg, an agreement between the rest point and zero point of 0.3 scale unit is satisfactory. Compare the weights obtained by methods 3 and 4.

Pay attention to the proper use of *significant figures*. By convention the digits are extended to, but not beyond, one digit whose value is doubtful. An extended discussion of this topic may be found in Appendix I.

3-5 Checking of the arm lengths of the balance. Redetermine the weight of the object by placing it on the right pan and the weights on the left. Note that the weights of rider and chain have to be subtracted. Compute

$$\sqrt{W_L W_R}, \quad (W_L + W_R)/2, \quad \sqrt{W_R/W_L}, \quad \text{and} \quad 1 + (W_R - W_L)/2W_L.$$

3-6 Calibration of weights. Prepare in your notebook a table similar to Table 3-1. Assume that the accuracy of the spacing of the beam notches, the uniformity and the weight of the chain, and the graduations of the scale and vernier that measure the chain length are commensurate with the over-all accuracy of the balance, of the order of 0.1 mg. The equality of the beam lengths has been tested in Procedure 3-5.

To calibrate the rider, obtain a standard 1-g weight from the instructor. Return the standard weight immediately after using it. If none is available for the moment, skip the rider calibration and return to it later.

Place the rider in the 1-g notch and the 1-g standard weight on the left pan, and compare the two. Note that the vernier may have to be used to extend the scale of chain lengths to the negative side. Calculate the weight r that corresponds to the rider in the 1-g notch. It should be correct within 0.1 mg.

Begin with the calibration of the weight set. Place the 1-g weight on the left pan, and compare its weight with that of the rider. Continue by placing the weight marked 2 on the left pan and compare it with the combined weights of the rider in the 1-g notch and the 1-g piece on the right pan. Proceed as suggested by Table 3-1. (Some weight sets contain up to three 1-g pieces marked 1, 1*, and 1**. They are all calibrated directly by comparison with the rider.)

TABLE 3-1   *Example of a Weight Calibration*

Calibration of rider

standard 1-g weight on left pan	rider in 1-g notch	weighing result
Actual weight 1.0002 g (given by instructor)	r	+0.2 mg
Actual rider weight r = 1.0002 g − 0.2 mg = 1.0000 g		

Calibration of weight set

face value of weight on left pan	weight combination on right side	actual weight on right side	weighing result	true weight on left side	weight correction
1	Rider r	1 g	−0.1 mg	1 g − 0.1 mg	−0.1 mg
2	r + 1	2 g − 0.1 mg	+0.3 mg	2 g + 0.2 mg	+0.2 mg
2*	r + 1	2 g − 0.1 mg	−0.5 mg	2 g − 0.6 mg	−0.6 mg
5	r + 2 + 2*	5 g − 0.4 mg	+0.7 mg	5 g + 0.7 mg	+0.3 mg

In all this work correctness of the chain is assumed. To check the consistency between chain and rider, place the 1-g weight on the left pan and the rider in the 0.9-g notch, and move the chain to the 100-mg position. The equilibrium position of the balance should agree within 0.1 mg with that when the chain is at the 0-mg position and the rider is in the 1-g notch. A more detailed check on the quality of the chain mechanism and the positions of the beam notches would require standard weights that are multiples of 10 mg.

PROBLEMS

3-1 Gauss double-weighing method.   Derive or prove the approximate relationships given in equations (3-6) and (3-7).

3-2 Weighing by sensitivity.   The total of the weights on the right-hand pan of a balance, including rider and chain, is 23.5910 g. The zero point is at 9.3, the rest point is at 6.7 scale units, and the sensitivity is 3.6 scale units per milligram. What is the weight of the object on the left-hand pan, to 0.1 mg?

3-3 Buoyancy correction.   What is the buoyancy correction for 1.00000 g NaCl ($d = 2.1$ g/cm^3), as weighed in air by the use of brass weights ($d = 8.4$ g/cm^3)? What is the buoyancy correction for the water used for calibrating a 1-liter volumetric flask? Express both corrections in per cent as well as in weights. Assume an air density of 1.2 g/liter.

3-4 Balance geometry.   (a) The arm lengths of a balance are 10.00 cm, the pointer length is 20.00 cm, the weight of beam and pointer is 30 g, and the sensitivity is 4 mm/mg. Compute the distance from the plane of the three knife-edges (assumed to be coplanar) to the center of mass of beam and pointer (OD in Figure 3-3). (b) In a good balance the arm lengths are equal to within 1 part in 10^5. What is the maximum distance between the center knife-edge and the mid-point between the terminal knife-edges? Express this in terms of the wavelength of blue-green light, 500 mμ.

3-5 Gauss transposition method.   Two 1-g weights, one marked 1 and the other 1*, were compared with a balance of a sensitivity of 3.7 scale units per milligram at a load of 1 g. The zero point was at 10.3, the rest point with the weight 1 on the left and the weight 1* on the right was at 10.5, and the rest point with the location of the weights reversed was at 9.6. Draw what conclusions ·you can about the weights and the arm lengths of the beam.

3-6 Weight dependence on location.   The earth's acceleration is reported to be about 9.79 m/sec^2 in Florida and 9.81 m/sec^2 in New York. What is the percentage difference of the weights of a 1-g mass at these two locations? What is the difference in weight milligrams?

3-7 Buoyancy correction.   An object is to be weighed with an accuracy of 2 parts in 10^4, using brass weights. What are the requirements for the density of the object so that no buoyancy correction need be made? Repeat for an accuracy requirement of 1 part in 10^4 (Density of brass: 8.4 g/cm^3; of air: 1.2 g/liter.)

REVIEW QUESTIONS

3-1. What is the difference between mass and weight?

3-2. Define the sensitivity of a balance.

3-3. What theoretical requirements have to be met so that the balance sensitivity is independent of the load?

3-4. What is the Gauss double-weighing method?

3-5. Name several sources of weighing errors.

*Definitions and brief explanations
of the mole and the formula weight
are followed by an examination
of the principles of gravimetric analysis.
The discussion of the chemical and physical
nature of the precipitate includes concepts
such as the solubility product, coprecipitation,
adsorption, relative supersaturation,
and aging and digestion of precipitates.
A section on general techniques and considerations,
and another on gravimetric techniques follow.
In a laboratory assignment
chloride is determined gravimetrically
by precipitation as silver chloride.*

four

GRAVIMETRIC ANALYSIS

Analytical work depends on stoichiometry (Greek: *stoicheion* = elementary constituent; *metrein* = to measure), which deals with the elementary composition of substances, and the relationship between the quantities of substances that are involved in chemical reactions with each other. The discussion of gravimetric principles is preceded by a section in which stoichiometric concepts are reviewed briefly. If needed, details may be found in a general-chemistry text or in the short monograph *The Mole Concept in Chemistry*, by William F. Kiefer (Reinhold, New York, 1962).

THE MOLE AND THE GRAM FORMULA WEIGHT

The *atomic mass* of an element is the average mass of one of its atoms in atomic mass units. The *average* is to be taken over the different *nuclides* (atomic species of definite atomic number Z and mass number

M) in their natural abundances. The *atomic mass unit* (a.m.u.) has been defined by both chemists and physicists in international agreements (1961) as exactly one-twelfth the mass of one C^{12} atom. (This unit had previously been defined by chemists as one-sixteenth the mass of the average O atom and by physicists as one-sixteenth the mass of the O^{16} atom. This led to two separate atomic mass scales that are now unified.) The atomic mass of an element is usually referred to as its *atomic weight*, following the widespread use of "weight" as a synonym for "mass" referred to in the preceding chapter. This usage is adopted here also.

The accuracy to which the atomic weight of a given element is known reflects not only the accuracies of the methods used to determine its value but also the fact that the natural abundances of the different nuclides vary slightly, depending on the source of the element considered. If one is interested in macroscopic amounts of elements and compounds, without knowing or wishing to define their precise nuclidic composition, the minor imprecision in the concept of atomic weight is, of course, unavoidable. It is fortunate that the natural abundances for most nuclides do not vary enough to affect usual stoichiometric considerations.

The *nuclidic mass* of a given nuclide, defined as the mass of one of its atoms in a.m.u., is, of course, not affected by the abundance of the nuclide and is thus inherently a more precise quantity than the atomic mass.

The *molecular weight* of a substance is the average weight (or more precisely, mass) of its molecules in atomic mass units. By its definition this term is restricted to substances that consist of definite molecular species.

Although chemists are greatly interested in the properties of individual atoms, molecules, and ions, many of their experiments involve macroscopic amounts of these particles. It is thus extremely useful to agree on a macroscopic unit that always contains the same number N of the microscopic units like atoms, molecules, or ions. This unit is the mole. The number N, called *Avogadro's number*, is *defined* as the number of atoms contained in exactly 12 g of C^{12}. One *mole* of a given chemical species (atoms, molecules, ions) is the amount that contains Avogadro's number of the particles. The *value* of N is 0.6022 × 10^{24}.

By definition, Avogadro's number of C^{12} atoms weighs exactly 12 g and one C^{12} atom weighs exactly 12 a.m.u. Avogadro's number N may thus be considered to be the *scale factor* from a.m.u. to gram:

$$N \text{ a.m.u.} = 1 \text{ g} \qquad 1 \text{ a.m.u.} = (1/N)\text{g}$$

As a consequence, the weight in grams of one mole of a given chemical species is numerically equal to the molecular weight of the species. For example, the molecular weight of CH_4 (methane) is $12.00 + 4 \times 1.008 = 16.03$, and N molecules of CH_4 weigh 16.03 g. This is the reason the mole is sometimes called *gram-mole* and is defined as that quantity of substance whose weight in grams is numerically equal to the molecular weight of the substance. However, it is more useful to tie the mole to Avogadro's number than to the gram and to drop the prefix "gram." The mole concept may then be applied to entities other than atoms and molecules. For example, one mole of electrons contains a quantity of electric charge, one *faraday*, that is fundamental in electrochemistry. Similarly, one mole of photons is a fundamental unit in photochemistry and has the name *einstein*.

It is useful not to use the term "mole" for substances that contain several ionic or molecular species. For example, the sum of the atomic weights of Na and Cl is $22.99 + 35.45 = 58.44$, but 58.44 g of NaCl crystals does not represent 1 mole of sodium chloride, because the crystals consist of Na^+ and Cl^- ions; there are no NaCl molecules in solid or molten sodium chloride or in aqueous sodium chloride solutions. However, 58.44 g of solid NaCl does contain Avogadro's number, or 1 mole, of Na^+ ions and 1 mole of Cl^- ions.

When it is *either immaterial or not known* what molecular or ionic species a given substance contains, the gram formula weight, to be defined shortly, will be used as a practical stoichiometric unit in which to express quantities of this substance. This unit is based on the *formula weight* of a substance, which is the sum of the weights of the atoms in the formula of the substance. It thus depends on the particular way in which it is customary or convenient to write the formula.

For example, phosphorus pentoxide is usually given the formula P_2O_5, for which the formula weight is $2 \times 30.97 + 5 \times 16.00 = 141.94$. It is known, however, that phosphorus pentoxide consists of P_4O_{10} molecules, and if P_4O_{10} is chosen as the formula of phosphorus pentoxide, then the formula weight has twice the value just given, or 283.88. This value, of course, is also the molecular weight of phosphorus pentoxide. To give another example, calcium sulfate may be available as $CaSO_4$ of formula weight 136.14, as $CaSO_4 \cdot \frac{1}{2}H_2O$ of formula weight 145.15, or as $CaSO_4 \cdot 2H_2O$ of formula weight 172.18. Finally, the number 58.44 that appeared earlier in connection with sodium chloride is the formula weight of NaCl in this terminology. It is its molecular weight only when definite NaCl molecules are under discussion, as they are known to exist in the vapor under certain conditions.

The *gram formula weight* of a substance is the quantity whose weight in grams is numerically equal to the formula weight. The gram formula weight and the mole are thus parallel stoichiometric units. Usually the *gram* in *gram formula weight* is dropped unless the correct meaning of *formula weight* cannot be discerned from the context.

Thus, one formula weight (1 gfw) of P_2O_5 is 141.88 g of this substance. Similarly, 1 gfw of $CaSO_4$ is 136.14 g of $CaSO_4$, 1 gfw of $CaSO_4 \cdot \frac{1}{2}H_2O$ is 145.15 g of $CaSO_4 \cdot \frac{1}{2}H_2O$, and 1 gfw of $CaSO_4 \cdot H_2O$ is 172.18 g of $CaSO_4 \cdot 2H_2O$. The amounts of these last three substances contain 1 mole each of Ca^{++} ions and 1 mole each of $SO_4^=$ ions.

Frequently the units *millimole* (mmole) and *milliformula weight* (mfw) are useful. They are a thousand times smaller than the units discussed. A number of formula weights are given on page 397.

Concentrations of solutions are often expressed by giving the number of gram formula weights contained in a liter of solution and following this number by the letter *F*. Thus 1 liter of 2.5 *F* HNO_3 contains 2.5 gfw of HNO_3. In referring to specific molecular or ionic particles, their concentrations may be given in moles per liter of solution. This *molar* concentration of a certain species is indicated by placing brackets around the chemical symbol of the species. Thus $[Ba^{++}]$ stands for the concentration of Ba^{++} ions in moles per liter of solution. Concentration units will be discussed in greater detail in Chapter 5.

PRINCIPLES OF GRAVIMETRIC ANALYSIS

In gravimetric analysis the substance to be determined is usually converted from the dissolved state into a precipitate of small solubility and of definite and known composition, which is then separated from the aqueous phase, dried, and weighed. From the weight and the composition of the precipitate the quantity of the substance being determined can be computed and related to the weight or volume of the original sample.

For example, the quantity of sulfate in a solution may be determined by adding a reagent containing Ba^{++} ions in excess, so that the sulfate is precipitated as $BaSO_4$, which is only slightly soluble. This precipitate is filtered off, washed, dried, and weighed.

In a variant of the usual gravimetric procedure, the substance being determined is volatilized and its quantity either determined directly or found indirectly by measuring the weight loss of the original sample. This indirect method is often used in the determination of water.

For a successful gravimetric analysis both the chemical and the physical nature of the precipitate are important. The first bears on the composition of the precipitate, the second on the filtrability. The chemical nature of precipitates will be discussed first, and an account of their physical nature will follow.

The chemical nature of the precipitate

The following conditions are required of a gravimetric precipitate and of the reaction responsible for its formation:

1. The quantity of substance that remains unprecipitated must be negligible in terms of the precision required. This is stated briefly by saying that the precipitation must be *quantitative*. In gravimetric work this usually corresponds to losing not more than 0.1 mg, corresponding to the sensitivity of the analytical balance.

2. The precipitate must be pure and its composition definite, or it must be convertible into a compound of definite composition. It must be stable at elevated temperatures so that it may be dried to the point where it contains either no water or a definite stoichiometric quantity.

3. The particles of the precipitate must be large enough to be separable from the supernatant by filtration.

4. It is of advantage for the precision of an analysis to have a relatively large weight of precipitate correspond to a relatively small quantity of substance being determined.

The first two items are treated in detail below, and the third is discussed in the section on *The physical nature of the precipitate.*

Solubility of the precipitate; the solubility product.   Consider the determination of sulfate by the precipitation of $BaSO_4(s)$ (the letter s in the parentheses stands for *solid*). The precipitation reaction is

$$Ba^{++} + SO_4^{=} \rightarrow BaSO_4(s) \qquad (4\text{-}1)$$

When solid barium sulfate is shaken with water, the minute amount that dissolves exists primarily in the form of Ba^{++} and $SO_4^{=}$ ions, so that the reverse of reaction (4-1),

$$BaSO_4(s) \rightarrow Ba^{++} + SO_4^{=} \qquad (4\text{-}2)$$

is the solution of $BaSO_4(s)$ in water. When $BaSO_4(s)$ is precipitated according to (4-1), the precipitate formed will react according to (4-2). At equilibrium a balance exists between these two reactions; it is indicated by writing

$$Ba^{++} + SO_4^{=} \rightleftharpoons BaSO_4(s) \qquad (4\text{-}3)$$

The same equilibrium is established when $BaSO_4(s)$ is being shaken with water, even though the equilibrium equation when starting with $BaSO_4(s)$ is written inversely to the above,

$$BaSO_4(s) \rightleftharpoons Ba^{++} + SO_4^{=}$$

For typographical reasons the double arrows $\rightleftharpoons$ are often replaced by an equals sign, $=$.

When there is equilibrium between Ba^{++} ions, $SO_4^{=}$ ions, and the $BaSO_4(s)$ precipitate, the product of the concentrations $[Ba^{++}]$ and $[SO_4^{=}]$ is, at least approximately, constant:

$$[Ba^{++}][SO_4^{=}] = K_{SP} = 1 \times 10^{-10} \qquad (4\text{-}4)$$

The expression on the left of this equation is called the *solubility product*, and its approximate constancy is a consequence of the *mass-action law* to be discussed in Chapter 7. The value of the solubility product constant K_{SP} for $BaSO_4(s)$ is experimentally found to be 1×10^{-10}. Solubility product constants depend on the temperature, and the value stated applies to 25°C.

To understand the bearing of the solubility product principle (4-4) on the solubility of a barium sulfate precipitate under different conditions, consider first the equilibrium obtained by shaking an excess of $BaSO_4(s)$ with 1 liter of distilled water. Let the gram formula weights of $BaSO_4(s)$ going into solution be x, so that $[Ba^{++}] = [SO_4^{=}] = x$ moles/liter. (The concentration of any dissolved $BaSO_4$ *molecules* is negligible.) Applying (4-4) leads to $x^2 = 1 \times 10^{-10}$, whence $x = 1 \times 10^{-5}$ gfw/liter.* Consider next the result of shaking an excess of $BaSO_4(s)$ with 1 liter of a solution already containing 0.1 gfw of $BaCl_2$, so that $[Ba^{++}] = 0.1$ to start with. If y gfw of $BaSO_4(s)$ goes into solution, the following concentrations result: $[SO_4^{=}] = y$ and $[Ba^{++}] = 0.1 + y$. Applying (4-4) shows that $y(0.1 + y) = 1 \times 10^{-10}$. This quadratic equation is solved quickly and with sufficient accuracy by neglecting y in the parentheses on the assumption that y will prove to be small compared with 0.1. Thus, $y = 1 \times 10^{-10}/0.1 = 1 \times 10^{-9}$ gfw/liter, which is indeed small compared with 0.1. It is seen that the original presence of Ba^{++} ions decreases the solubility of $BaSO_4$, and closer examination of (4-4) shows that, the higher the original Ba^{++} concentration, the

---

* It is useful even if not strictly logical to use the units formula weight per liter and mole per liter interchangeably when there is numerical equality between the corresponding quantities.

lower the solubility of the $BaSO_4(s)$. Similarly, if $BaSO_4(s)$ is shaken with a solution already containing $SO_4^=$ ions, the solubility will be the lower, the higher the original concentration of $SO_4^=$ ions. This is called the *common-ion effect*. Accordingly, it may be desirable to use an excess of Ba^{++} ions in precipitating $BaSO_4(s)$, to wash the precipitate with a solution containing small amounts of Ba^{++} ions, and to use distilled water only for the last one or two washings.

The situation is, however, often more complicated, as will be shown next by discussing the example of $AgCl(s)$, a substance formed by reacting Ag^+ and Cl^- ions. The equilibrium is expressed by

$$AgCl(s) = Ag^+ + Cl^- \qquad (4\text{-}5)$$

and the solubility product, at 25°C, has the experimental value

$$[Ag^+][Cl^-] = 1.8 \times 10^{-10} \qquad (4\text{-}6)$$

However, the concentration of AgCl *molecules* in solution at equilibrium with $AgCl(s)$, even though small, is not always negligible as was the case for the concentration of $BaSO_4$ molecules. Its value is $[AgCl] = 3.6 \times 10^{-7}$ mole/liter at room temperature. Upon solution of $AgCl(s)$ in distilled water, 3.6×10^{-7} mole/liter of AgCl molecules is formed, as well as Ag^+ and Cl^- ions in equal concentrations that satisfy Eq. (4-6). The solubility of $AgCl(s)$ in distilled water is the sum of the solubilities as molecules and as ions, or $(1.8 \times 10^{-10})^{1/2} + 3.6 \times 10^{-7} = 1.3 \times 10^{-5} + 3.6 \times 10^{-7} \approx 1.3 \times 10^{-5}$ gfw/liter. The concentration of AgCl molecules is thus negligible under these circumstances. However, in dissolving $AgCl(s)$ in 1 liter of a solution containing 0.1 gfw of $AgNO_3$, the concentration of AgCl molecules is no longer negligible. Let the concentration of Cl^- ions be y; thus $[Cl^-] = y$, and $[Ag^+] = 0.1 + y$. Inserting these quantities into (4-2) and solving yields $y = 1.8 \times 10^{-9}$. To obtain the solubility of $AgCl(s)$, the equilibrium concentration of AgCl molecules has again to be added; the solubility is thus $3.6 \times 10^{-7} + 1.8 \times 10^{-9}$ gfw/liter. It is seen that now the solubility of $AgCl(s)$ is due almost entirely to molecular species AgCl, and indeed that this solubility cannot be reduced by the common-ion effect below the value of 3.6×10^{-7}.

Thus, the common-ion effect reduces the solubility of $AgCl(s)$ below its value in distilled water, 1.3×10^{-5} gfw/liter, but not below the value of 3.6×10^{-7} gfw/liter. Yet another important effect enters in when the Cl^- concentration begins to exceed 10^{-3} mole/liter. This is the formation of the complex ion $AgCl_2^-$ and of others containing still more chloride, which substantially increases the solubility of $AgCl(s)$,

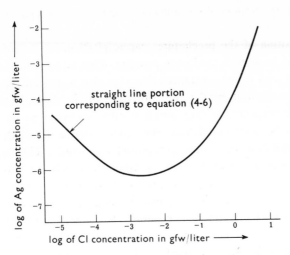

Figure 4-1   The solubility of AgCl as a function of the chloride concentration.

as is evident from Figure 4-1. For example, in a solution in which $[Cl^-]$ = 5.0 moles/liter the solubility of AgCl(s) is 6.0×10^{-3} gfw/liter. Thus, when the Ag^+ ions are precipitated in a solution by adding a reagent containing Cl^- ions, the solubility of the resulting AgCl(s) will be decreased by a small excess of Cl^- ions, but will be increased substantially by a large excess.

Other factors affecting the solubility of a precipitate may have to be considered also. Thus, the addition of an organic solvent such as ethyl alcohol to an aqueous medium may decrease the solubility of relatively soluble compounds like $CaSO_4$ and $SrCrO_4$ to the point where precipitation becomes quantitative. At times, quantitative precipitation must be carried out in an entirely organic medium. This is the case with nickel chloride, which is very soluble in water but which can be precipitated quantitatively by passing HCl gas through an ether solution containing nickel.

Another factor that is of importance for some precipitations is the *acidity of the medium*. For example, the silver salt of carbonic acid is only slightly soluble in a neutral medium but dissolves in dilute nitric acid with the formation of CO_2. Silver salts of many other weak acids show a similar behavior. The solubility of AgCl(s) is not substantially changed, however, by making the solution acid. In a dilute nitric acid solution silver and chloride ions thus quantitatively form a silver chloride precipitate even in the presence of anions of weak acids.

A final factor that may need consideration is the *temperature*, an increase in which usually increases the solubility of a salt. Thus, precipitates of $PbSO_4$(s) and $SrSO_4$(s) should be filtered at room temperature to avoid appreciable losses. In general, however, filtration of hot solutions is permissible and even desirable, as will be discussed later.

Composition of the precipitate; coprecipitation. A precipitating agent should be specific as far as possible. That is, it should not form a precipitate with other substances that may also be present, nor should such other substances hinder the formation of the desired precipitate. Such specific reagents are rare, and it is often necessary to separate the substance to be determined from the other constituents of the sample before precipitation of a pure compound is possible. This separation may at times be achieved by *reprecipitation*, in which the impure solid formed by the original precipitation is dissolved again. Since the resulting concentrations of impurities are usually smaller than in the original solution, renewed precipitation generally leads to a purer precipitate. If necessary, the process may be repeated several times. Other methods of separation may also be used, such as prior precipitation of the interfering substances with other reagents.

The situation is often complicated by the phenomenon of *coprecipitation*, the contamination of the precipitate by substances that are actually soluble under the conditions of the precipitation. The phenomena mainly responsible for coprecipitation are adsorption, formation of solid solutions, and mechanical inclusion, which will be discussed in turn.

Adsorption. The most important of the mechanisms responsible for coprecipitation is probably *adsorption* (Latin: *ad* = to or toward; *sorbere* = to suck in). This is a general phenomenon that is often observed. It may be defined as a concentration increase of a gas, a liquid, or a dissolved substance in the region between two phases, known as the *interface*. Coprecipitation can be caused by the adsorption of dissolved substances on the surface of the precipitate.

To understand how such adsorption may come about, consider, for example, a crystallite of AgCl containing in its interior Ag^+ ions that are tied to the Cl^- ions surrounding them by electrostatic forces, as well as by forces of the kind that hold two H atoms together in an H_2 molecule and that are called covalent bonds; similarly, the Cl^- ions are tied to the Ag^+ ions closest to them. In the interior of the crystallite an Ag^+ ion, for example, is surrounded by Cl^- as well as by other Ag^+ ions. An Ag^+ ion at the surface is no longer completely surrounded, and thus it exerts attractive forces on negatively charged ions in the solution. A Cl^- ion in the solution that reaches an appropriate site next to Ag^+ ions at the surface will be held by them (at least for a period of time; ions, of course, continually leave the surface, while others become attached to it). These forces exerted on ions in the solution by Ag^+ ions at the surface and similar forces exerted by surface Cl^- ions on positive ions in the solution are responsible for the growth of the crystallite. Although charged particles other than Ag^+ and Cl^- ions are also attracted by the ions at the surface, Ag^+ and Cl^- ions are favored, because they fit precisely into the corresponding sites.

Suppose now that the Ag^+ ions in the solution have been depleted but that Cl^- ions still remain. These Cl^- ions continue, for a while, to fill the sites available to them. This process is termed *primary adsorption* (Fig. 4-2). However, the surface acquires a negative charge by this process, which in turn attracts a layer of foreign positive ions. This is called *secondary adsorption*. If there is an excess of Ag^+ ions rather than of Cl^- ions in the solution, there is primary adsorption of Ag^+ ions and secondary adsorption of negative foreign ions. Experiments have shown that, if there is competition between the ions held by secondary adsorption, those that form the least soluble precipitate with the primary

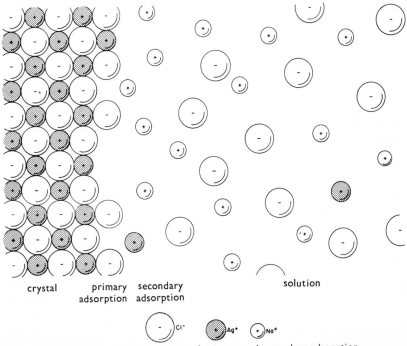

Figure 4-2   Schematic view of primary and secondary adsorption.

adsorbed ions have the strongest tendency to be adsorbed, even though any such precipitate would be soluble in the absence of the AgCl crystal-lite, as has been stated earlier.

This mechanism of adsorption applies to other ionic precipitates also, and the sequence of preference for secondary adsorption of foreign ions just discussed is general. Molecules rather than ions may also be adsorbed, particularly if the forces holding the crystallites together are mainly covalent in nature. (Covalent forces cannot be discussed here, beyond stating that electron pairs are largely responsible for them and recalling that they hold together the atoms in an H_2 molecule.)

Other mechanisms of adsorption may, of course, be involved in the adsorption of molecules on surfaces of nonionic character, as, for example, in the adsorption of gas molecules at a solid-gas interface. Adsorption is a very important phenomenon that is receiving attention from both the experimental and the theoretical side. As an example of practical application, adsorption plays a significant part in speeding up reactions in liquids and gases by solid catalysts.

The adsorption mechanism discussed earlier applies not only to crystalline particles, in which the ions are arranged in a regular pattern, but also to *amorphous* particles (Greek: *a-* = not; *morphe* = form), in which the arrangement of the ions is random except that positive ions are surrounded by negative ions, and vice versa. The particles of amorphous precipitates usually have highly irregular and therefore large surfaces, so that adsorption is large. Examples of amorphous or near-amorphous precipitates are the hydrous oxides of many metals such as aluminum and trivalent iron. The AgCl precipitate obtained by the reaction of, e.g., 0.1 F Ag^+ and Cl^- solutions consists of extremely fine crystalline particles that are clumped together and thus have certain amorphous aspects. Often the *crystalline* particles of gravimetric precipi-tates are *imperfect*, particularly if they have been formed rapidly; although the arrangement of the ions follows, in the main, a regular pattern, there are many irregularities. The sites of such irregularities are particularly favorable to adsorption, and ions at such sites are less strongly bound to the crystallite than are ions in normal sites.

Solid solution. Although coprecipitation often occurs by surface adsorption, foreign ions may also be built into the lattice of the crystal-lites of the precipitate. For example, when $BaSO_4$ is precipitated, foreign ions of either charge may be trapped during the growth of the crystallites on the sites normally occupied by Ba^{++} and $So_4^=$ ions, particularly if the precipitation takes place rapidly. However, even when the precipi-tation occurs slowly, so that there is equilibrium at all times between the ions in the solution and the surfaces of the growing crystallites, foreign ions may be built into the lattice. The resulting crystallites have these foreign ions distributed uniformly throughout their lattices. Such intimate mixtures on the molecular level are called *solid solutions* in analogy to liquid solutions. The quantity of foreign ions thus coprecipitated will be the larger, the larger their concentration in the aqueous solution; but even at high concentrations the solubility of foreign substance in the host crystal is, in general, limited. The exception to this situation is provided by the case in which the foreign ions fit almost precisely into the sites of the ions whose places they take and exert similar forces on the other ions. This usually implies that the two substances have the same crystal structure; i.e., the spatial arrangement of corresponding particles in crystals of the two substances is practically the same. Such substances are called *isomorphous* (Greek: *iso-* = same; *morphe* = form).

For example, $KMnO_4$ and $KClO_4$ are isomorphous; the MnO_4^- and ClO_4^- ions have similar dimensions and charge distributions. These two substances form solid solutions in all proportions, and if $KClO_4$ is precipitated from a solution also containing $KMnO_4$, even at very low concentrations, the resulting crystals contain a uniform distribution of MnO_4^- ions, shown by their pink color. $BaSO_4$, $BaCrO_4$, $PbSO_4$, and an unstable form of $PbCrO_4$ are isomorphous, and, indeed, $PbSO_4$ and $BaCrO_4$ readily form solid solutions with $BaSO_4$.

Mechanical inclusion. A final mechanism of coprecipitation is *mechanical inclusion* of small amounts of solution, which may be enhanced by rapid precipitation. This is probably the least important cause of coprecipitation, because its extent can usually be controlled by proper choice of conditions and of the precipitation method.

Precautions to minimize coprecipitation. The following measures are recommended as a matter of practical experience; they can, in part, be understood from the foregoing exposition. Situations specifically known to be afflicted by large coprecipitation should be avoided. To minimize adsorption, the conditions of precipitation should be so chosen that the *total surface area of the precipitate* is *small*, implying relatively large particles. These conditions will be discussed in a later section on physical characteristics of precipitates. The concentrations of foreign substances that may be adsorbed must be kept low, but it should be realized that the amount of substance adsorbed is not proportional to its concentration. Rather, the percentage adsorption is greater at small concentrations, and there is a tendency for saturation and thus leveling off of adsorption once the entire surface available is covered. The sequence of addition of reagents may also be important, because it may matter which ions have relatively large concentration during the precipitation.

Washing a precipitate removes only small amounts of adsorbed substances and none that are inside the particles. More effective may be the operation called *digestion*, the heating of the precipitate with the supernatant solution to near boiling for a period of time. During this digestion, very fine particles tend to dissolve and reprecipitate on larger particles, as will be explained later. This general increase in particle size is paralleled by a decrease in total surface area and a general perfection of the crystallites; these changes tend to reduce coprecipitation.

It is also often possible to arrange that the adsorbed compound be volatile and removable later by heating the precipitate.

For example, if AgCl(s) is formed by adding a neutral solution of $AgNO_3$ to one of KCl, there may be secondary adsorption of K^+ ions that remain after washing and drying. However, if the precipitation is carried out in the presence of HNO_3 and the precipitate is washed with dilute HNO_3, the K^+ ions are largely replaced by H^+ ions. Upon heating the filtered and dried precipitate, any acid adsorbed is readily removed.

As another example, ions of aluminum may be precipitated by a base in the form of their hydrous oxides. If, however, Cu^{++}, Zn^{++}, Mg^{++}, or other foreign ions are present, they are strongly adsorbed by the huge surfaces of these gelatinous, amorphous precipitates. If the precipitation is carried out in the presence of large quantities of NH_4^+ ions and washed with a solution of NH_4Cl, these foreign metal ions are largely replaced by NH_4^+ ions that may later be removed as NH_3 by heating the dried precipitate.

If all other means fail, removal of coprecipitated substances may be effected by one or several reprecipitations, except when isomorphous substances are involved. In that case, changing the precipitating agent may lead to substances that are not isomorphous, or other methods of separation may be used.

Stability of the precipitate. A precipitate may satisfy all conditions of purity and stoichiometric composition, but it may not be stable at the elevated temperatures that are needed to remove either all of the water or at least enough for the quantity remaining to be in stoichiometric relation to the whole. Such a precipitate cannot be used for gravimetric purposes unless heating to a high or a moderately high temperature changes it into another compound of definite and known composition, whose weight thus has a definite relationship to the quantity of substance to be determined. This process is called *ignition*.

For example, Mg^{++} ions may be precipitated as magnesium ammonium phosphate ($MgNH_4PO_4 \cdot 6H_2O$), the composition of which does not, however, necessarily correspond precisely to this formula. Ignition at 1100°C converts the precipitate to magnesium pyrophosphate ($Mg_2P_2O_7$), of stoichiometric composition

$$2MgNH_4PO_4 \cdot 6H_2O \rightarrow Mg_2P_2O_7 + 2NH_3 + 13H_2O$$

so that the weight in this form is stoichiometrically meaningful.

The physical nature of the precipitate

A gravimetric precipitate should consist of relatively large particles so that it may be readily separated from the supernatant by filtration and so that the total surface area is small and adsorption is minimized.

Particle size. It is useful to classify particles according to their size. *Individual ions* have a diameter of the order of 1 to 3 A ($1 A = 0.1 m\mu = 10^{-8}$ cm). *Colloidal particles* are defined as having a diameter between 10^{-7} and 10^{-5} cm, or 1 and 100 $m\mu$. They are very hard to separate from a liquid containing them, requiring an ultracentrifuge with a gravity field corresponding to as much as 250,000 times that of the earth or an ultrafilter with very small pores, such as can be made of collodion or parchment. We shall call *fine particles* those of diameter in the range of 10^{-5} to 10^{-3} cm, or 100 $m\mu$ to 10 μ, and *coarse particles* those of diameter larger than 10^{-3} cm, or 10 μ. Although fine particles are retained by special filter paper or can be centrifuged with a simple centrifuge (gravity field of the order of 1000 to 2000 g), it is coarse particles that are desirable in gravimetric work, because they are retained by regular filter paper or filter crucibles.

Dependence of solubility on particle size. The solubility of a solid depends on the particle size, that of colloidal particles often being greater than that of larger particles. The reason lies in the greater surface area per gram of substance of colloidal particles compared with larger particles, as well as in the larger total length of particle edges and the total number of particle corners. Ions on the surface exert uncompensated electrostatic and other forces toward the outside of the particle, as described earlier, and are thus inherently less tightly bound than ions in the interior. This is true to a yet greater extent of ions located in particle edges, and even more so for ions in corners. Thus, the less the total number of corners, the total edge length, and the total surface area of the particles of a given quantity of substance, the higher the stability of these particles and the lower their solubility. A rough measure of the stability with which the ions on the outside of a crystallite are held, relative to those on the inside, appears to be the hardness of the crystal; the harder the crystal, the larger, usually, the difference, found experimentally, between the solubility of colloidal particles and that of coarser particles. Thus, the solubility of relatively hard $BaSO_4$ particles of diameter 0.2 μ has been found to be some 80 per cent greater than that of coarse particles, and that for relatively soft PbI_2 particles of diameter 0.4 μ is found to be only 2 per cent greater than that of coarse particles.

Mechanism of precipitation. The first step in the formation of a precipitate is agglomeration of a sufficient number of ions so that the resulting particle is more likely to grow than to fall apart again and thus is not all corners, edges, and surface. This process is called *nucleation*, and the smallest particles that are stable and that serve as growing centers for larger particles are called *nuclei*. Before incipient precipitation takes place, the solution thus has to be supersaturated, i.e., has to contain more substance than corresponds to the equilibrium between solution and precipitate actually present. Often foreign material such as dust, the walls of the vessel, and particularly scratches and other roughnesses on the walls serve as centers of nucleation.

Once initial nuclei have been formed, there may be competition between their growth into larger particles and the formation of further nuclei, depending on the quantity of ions still in the solution and the relative stability of the nuclei. As the particles grow, their solubility may decrease to a greater or lesser extent, depending on the relative tightness with which ions in exposed positions are held to the particles. If the solubility decrease is reasonably large, the larger particles will grow at the expense of the smaller ones. This growth of larger particles and simultaneous solution of smaller ones is thus a specific effect whose magnitude depends on the surface stability of the substance involved.

Relative supersaturation. This effect to be described, which also governs the particle size of the precipitate, is general, since it depends on the conditions of precipitation rather than on the nature of the substances concerned. For a given quantity of final precipitate, the larger the total number of nuclei, the smaller the resulting particles, because there is competition between the nuclei for the ions in the solution that have not yet been precipitated or that have resulted from the dissolving of unstable colloidal particles. It has been found that the number of nuclei depends on the *relative supersaturation*, which is defined as follows: Let Q be the actual concentration of substance being precipitated and S the equilibrium solubility. For supersaturated solutions Q is larger than S, and the ratio $(Q - S)/S$ is a positive quantity, called the relative supersaturation. If the relative supersaturation is large at the beginning of precipitation, the number of nuclei formed is large and the final precipitate will be colloidal, or very fine. If the relative supersaturation is small when precipitation occurs, a correspondingly smaller number of nuclei are formed and then grow into relatively large particles.

The physical characteristics of the precipitate of a given substance may thus be changed by changing the relative supersaturation at which the precipitation starts. For example, $BaSO_4$ precipitates as a distinctly crystalline, though finely divided precipitate, when dilute aqueous solutions (e.g., 0.1 F) of Ba^{++} and $SO_4^{=}$ are mixed. However, from a solution containing 50 per cent alcohol it precipitates in colloidal form and upon coagulation resembles aluminum hydroxide; in alcoholic solution the solubility S of $BaSO_4$ is smaller than in water, and the relative supersaturation achieved is thus larger. Similarly, an increase in relative supersaturation may be achieved by rapidly mixing highly concentrated solutions containing, respectively, $SO_4^{=}$ and Ba^{++} ions. The result is a highly viscous, gelatinous precipitate. Finally, relatively large crystals of $BaSO_4$ are obtained by precipitating it from strong hydrochloric acid solution, in which S is larger than in a neutral solution.

A further example of the principles just discussed concerns the difference between precipitates of $BaSO_4$ and $AgCl$, as obtained by mixing dilute aqueous solutions of the respective ions. The solubility products of both substances are about the same; yet $BaSO_4$ forms a fine-grained crystalline precipitate, whereas that of $AgCl$ is a curdy, flocculated colloid (see below). Although the solubility products of the two substances are almost the same, however, the solubility of the relatively hard $BaSO_4$ particles is markedly increased as their size is decreased, whereas that of the relatively soft $AgCl$ particles depends only little on the particle size. Thus, at incipient precipitation, the degree of supersaturation is much smaller for $BaSO_4$ than it is for $AgCl$; the number of nuclei formed is thus smaller for $BaSO_4$, and they grow into larger particles. Furthermore, owing to the dependence of the solubility on size, the larger $BaSO_4$ particles tend to grow at the expense of the smaller ones, whereas a similar effect is almost completely lacking in the case of $AgCl$.

For precipitates of *very low solubility* and for ordinary methods of mixing the reagents the relative supersaturation will always be large, so that colloidal or very fine grained precipitates result. In addition, any growth of large particles at the expense of smaller ones will be slow, because the concentration of ions in the saturated solution will be very small.

It is sometimes possible to avoid colloidal or very fine grained precipitates by a method called *homogeneous precipitation*, in which the concentration of the precipitating species is raised so gradually that the relative supersaturation always remains small.

Nickel sulfide provides a good example. It is very hard to cause NiS to be precipitated in other than colloidal suspensions when H_2S gas is bubbled through a solution containing Ni^{++} ions. There exist, however, substances like thioacetamide (CH_3CSNH_2) that slowly evolve H_2S upon heating of a solution containing them, particularly in the presence of H^+ or OH^-

$$CH_3SCNH_2 \xrightarrow{H^+ \text{ or } OH^-} CH_3CONH_2 + H_2S + \text{other products}$$

When a solution containing thioacetamide and Ni^{++} ions is heated slowly, relatively large crystals of shiny brown NiS can be grown readily.

Flocculation of colloidal suspensions. As previously discussed, the surfaces of particles tend to acquire electrical charges of equal sign by primary adsorption. Although secondary adsorption of foreign ions tends to compensate these charges, the compensation is only partial. If the particles are of colloidal size, the electrostatic repulsion between the particles may prevent their coagulation and keep them in suspension. If now the concentration of foreign ions in the solution is increased, the particle charge is decreased by further secondary adsorption. It may be possible to decrease the charge to a level at which the particles coalesce and precipitate. This precipitation of colloidal particles is called *flocculation.* Multiply-charged ions are particularly effective in flocculating colloidal precipitates. Flocculated precipitates are contaminated by the adsorbed foreign ions, and the flocculating agent should be so chosen that these ions will not cause difficulties later in the analysis.

If a flocculated precipitate is washed with distilled water, enough of the secondary adsorbed ions could be lost so that the flocculated particles could again become a colloidal suspension. This process, called *peptization,* may be very troublesome, because it may cause a carefully filtered precipitate to begin passing through the filter upon washing. It may be prevented by adding suitable ionic substances to the wash water, substances that may be removed later by volatilization.

A good example of the flocculation of a colloidal suspension is provided by the precipitation of AgCl, as formed upon the slow addition of a solution containing Ag^+ ions to one containing Cl^- ions. There is an excess of Cl^- ions in the supernatant during most of the precipitation, and the negative charge acquired by the primary adsorption of Cl^- ions by the colloidal particles of AgCl keeps many of these particles in suspension. The point at which the amount of silver added exactly corresponds to the chloride in the solution is termed the *equivalence point.* In the vicinity of this point the excess chloride ions become sufficiently depleted so that there is a strong tendency for sudden flocculation of a major portion of the precipitate. This sudden flocculation is quite noticeable, and the point at which it occurs has been called the *clear point,* even though there is *no complete clearing* of the solution. If a large excess of Ag^+ ions beyond the clear point is added, the precipitate is peptized because of primary adsorption of Ag^+ ions. Such an excess is thus to be avoided. Similarly, the precipitate is at least partly peptized when washed with distilled water. For that reason the precipitate is usually washed with dilute nitric acid. The H^+ ions adsorbed are later volatilized as HCl (with a very small weight loss), and so is any HNO_3 still adhering to the precipitate.

Aging and digestion of precipitates. When a freshly formed precipitate is left in contact with the supernatant for a period of time, or *aged*, there are frequently changes in the surface, such as a decrease in the total surface area and removal of strained and imperfect regions. Both effects are due to recrystallization. Small particles tend to be more soluble than large ones, as already discussed, and ions located in imperfect and strained regions are less tightly held than normal and therefore tend to return to the solution, to be deposited again in more perfect fashion. These changes of the surface cause a beneficial decrease in adsorbed foreign ions and thus lead not only to a more filtrable but also to a purer precipitate. Increase of the temperature greatly enhances the speed of the recrystallization. This is the reason for the frequently beneficial influence on the precipitate of *digestion*, i.e., of maintaining it in contact with the supernatant at a temperature near boiling for a period of time, as mentioned earlier. Fortunately, it has been observed that flocculated colloids usually undergo rapid aging, particularly on digestion. In this way a major portion of the adsorbed contaminants may often be removed.

GENERAL TECHNIQUES AND CONSIDERATIONS

The following material pertains not only to gravimetric work but to analysis in general. Gravimetric techniques are considered separately in the next section.

Sample size and over-all precision

In any experiment, the desired accuracy of the results and the precision of the methods employed should be considered. Once the over-all precision has been determined, the precision of all steps involved should be chosen to be of the same order of magnitude. Consider, for example, a titration of inherent precision of 0.1 per cent in which a solution of known concentration of potassium dichromate is used One liter of this solution, containing a known quantity of $K_2Cr_2O_7$ in the neighborhood of 30 g, is to be prepared. It would be a waste of time to weigh the dichromate closer than to 10 mg.

79

The size of the samples chosen in a given determination generally depends on the accuracy of the determination. For example, in gravimetric work, where the possible accuracy is often 0.1 per cent, the samples usually are chosen of such size that the precipitate produced weighs about 0.5 g and the accuracy of the weighings is just above the over-all accuracy.

Weighing and drying the sample

A convenient sample container used for precise work is the weighing bottle (Fig. 4-3), a cylindrical glass bottle of some 10 to 100 ml capacity, whose neck is not constricted and whose glass cover fits tightly, by means of a ground seal, into or over the rim of the bottle.

Depending on the circumstances, it may be more convenient to weigh a sample directly or by difference. In *weighing directly*, the clean receiving vessel or a piece of glazed paper is weighed first, the desired quantity of substance is transferred to it, and the weighing is repeated. The quantity of substance *contained* in the vessel or on the paper is thus known. In *weighing by difference*, the weighing bottle or other vessel containing the substance is weighed before and after removing the sample. This establishes the quantity of substance *removed* from the vessel.

The direct weighing method is preferable when there is need for an exact quantity of substance, since finely powdered substance may be added or taken away with a narrow spatula until the precise weight has been reached. It is also more convenient when a large quantity of substance is being weighed. When several samples are needed, weighing by difference is faster than direct weighing. It is preferable when hygroscopic substances are involved.

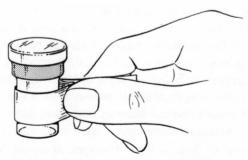

Figure 4-3 Weighing bottle and method of handling it.

Figure 4-4   Drying of sample.

When precise sample weights are required, both the empty and the filled weighing bottle must be dried at the elevated temperatures of an electric oven. The bottle is first placed inside a marked beaker that is covered with a small watch glass to prevent contamination. The watch glass is supported on the beaker by three short U-shaped pieces of glass rod (2 to 3 cm long) hanging from the rim as shown in Figure 4-4. This enables vapors to escape. For the same reason the top of the weighing bottle must be removed. If feasible, place the weighing bottle inside the inverted top (Fig. 4-4); otherwise, lean the top sideways across the mouth of the bottle. Once dried, weighing bottles must not be touched with the fingers. They are best held by a loop made of a strip of strong paper (Fig. 4-3), and the bottle top may be handled by using a piece of filter paper to prevent direct contact between fingers and glass. Beakers are conveniently handled by beaker tongs (Fig. 4-5).

Weighing bottles are left to cool in a desiccator, which provides a reasonably dry atmosphere and offers protection from dust and from the fumes common to a laboratory. The desiccator cover may be removed by sliding it sideways (see Fig. 2-21), but it should not be left off any longer or removed any more often than necessary. It takes a considerable period of time for the atmosphere inside a desiccator to become dry, since any water vapor present must reach the drying agent by diffusion before being removed. A desiccator thus serves not to dry objects, but rather to keep already dry objects in that state. Extreme

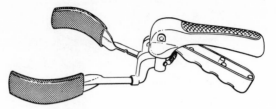

Figure 4-5 Beaker safety tongs.

dryness inside it is not essential unless the substance being weighed is hygroscopic. The minute amount of water that may be adsorbed by the surfaces of weighing bottles and sample even from a relatively humid atmosphere does not add noticeably to their weights.

No object hotter than about 100 to 150°C should be placed in a desiccator. One reason is that the partial vacuum created by the cooling of the air surrounding hot objects makes opening of the desiccator difficult, and any fast inrush of air may cause loss of sample. Before being weighed, a weighing bottle should be left to cool for 20 to 30 min. Any drying should be repeated until constant weight has been reached, within limits determined by the over-all precision of the procedure.

Because of its general applicability, a procedure for drying samples and weighing out by difference follows.

PROCEDURE FOR DRYING SAMPLES AND WEIGHING OUT BY DIFFERENCE

Put the sample in a weighing bottle and crush any lumps with a *clean* spatula or stirring rod. Material to be dried should be finely divided and free-flowing. Place the weighing bottle containing the sample in a beaker covered by a small watch glass as shown in Figure 4-4. Label the beaker with pencil on the ground space provided for this purpose. Paper labels must not be used in an oven because of the high temperatures. Place the weighing bottle inside the inverted top or lay the top of the weighing bottle across the mouth of the bottle. Once dried, transfer the weighing bottle to the desiccator, but not with the fingers (see Fig. 4-3).

When it is cool, weigh the weighing bottle and transfer the quantity of sample desired to a clean beaker or other receiving vessel marked with pencil. To prevent dust-sized sample particles from escaping, the top of the weighing bottle must be removed carefully. Hold the weighing bottle right above the beaker, and keep the top close to the bottle opening. Use filter paper to handle both weighing bottle and top. Replace the top of the weighing bottle while still holding both right above the beaker. Immediately cover the beaker with a watch glass. Use all the precautions you have learned concerning the balance and techniques of weighing. Record all individual weights, as well as all other pertinent information, in your notebook. Weigh the weighing bottle again. Repeat the procedure until three or four samples have thus been weighed out.

Treatment of data

It is very important to check all computations that lead from the laboratory data to the final results. The safest method is to repeat these computations on a different page, preferably on a different day.

The best estimate of the quantity sought is the *mean* or average m of the n individual results x_i ($i = 1, 2, ..., n$),

$$m = (x_1 + x_2 + \cdots + x_n)/n = \sum x_i/n \tag{4-7}$$

A measure of the quality of the individual results is the unbiased standard deviation s

$$s = \sqrt{\sum (m - x_i)^2/(n - 1)} \tag{4-8}$$

and the unbiased relative standard deviation s/m (see Appendix I). It is possible, as explained in Appendix I (Table I-2, page 370) to calculate so-called confidence limits from s and n; but with n only 3 or 4 the value of such limits is questionable, and it is further to be emphasized that such confidence limits do not take the possibility of systematic errors into account.

Sometimes one of the results looks suspicious because it deviates considerably more than the others from the mean. Check your notebook to see whether you made an error or whether the determination is suspect on experimental grounds. A value that is experimentally unsound should be discarded or given low weight when computing the mean, regardless of how close the value is to the mean.

If no error that would rule out the questioned value can be found, statistical criteria may be applied to find the probability that the deviation is due to a gross experimental error. Such a test is the *Q test*, in which the deviation d of the suspect value from its closest neighbor is compared with the range r of the values, the difference between the highest and the lowest value. There are 9 chances out of 10 that a gross error is involved if d/r exceeds 0.64 in the case of five, 0.76 for four, and 0.94 for three observations. Note that with this rejection rule a *valid* result would be rejected in 1 out of 10 cases. Furthermore, statistical rules become less reliable the lower the number of samples.

Another possibility is to report not the mean of the results, but their *median*, which is obtained as follows. Order the results by increasing magnitude. If their number is odd, the median is the value in the middle of the list; if it is even, it is the average of the two values closest to the middle. It has been suggested that the median is closer to the true value than the mean when one of the observations is questionable and there is insufficient reason to reject the observation. Particularly with only three results this appears to be a safer course than rejection of a value.

To repeat, however, the only *safe* procedure is to check for actual calculation errors or experimental misfortunes. If none can be found, additional analyses, which may strengthen the case against the questioned observation, should be performed.

For a more extensive discussion see the two references given at the end of Appendix I.

Important rules

The following important rules should always be in your mind:

1. *Do not rush. Haste makes waste.*
2. *Label all containers.*
3. *Be conservative about discarding any solution or material before you have finished an assignment.*

TECHNIQUES OF GRAVIMETRIC ANALYSIS

The precipitation

From the earlier discussion the following general rules emerge:

1. The precipitation should be from dilute solutions that are mixed slowly and with efficient stirring to avoid high local concentrations. Low concentrations further the growth of relatively large particles and minimize coprecipitation (unless solid solution is involved).

2. Only a small excess of precipitating reagent should be used in order to minimize adsorption and peptization of colloidal precipitates. The sequence of addition may influence the quantities of coprecipitated substances. Sometimes the addition of small amounts of foreign ions is helpful to flocculate a colloidal suspension. The choice should be restricted to substances that form volatilizable compounds.

3. A high temperature is generally beneficial, because the solubility of a precipitate is generally higher at elevated temperatures and the relative supersaturation smaller. The rate of recrystallization is also increased, furthering particle growth and perfection. A high temperature of precipitation, however, does not necessarily minimize adsorption effects.

4. Aging and digesting a precipitate are usually helpful in decreasing adsorption and increasing particle size. If the precipitate solubility is too large at high temperatures but is sufficiently small at room temperature, cooling just before filtration is indicated.

5. The concentration of substances known to lead to coprecipitation should be kept as low as possible. If the purity of the precipitate is not sufficiently high, it may usually be improved by reprecipitation.

6. The precipitation should be carried out in a beaker rather than in a conical flask, because this simplifies the transfer of the precipitate to the filter.

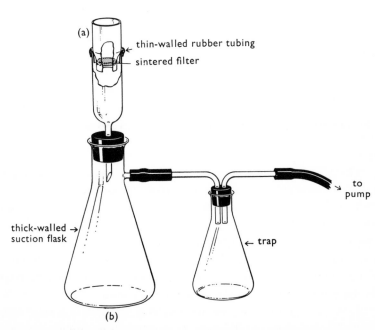

Figure 4-6 (a) Sintered-glass crucible; (b) Suction flask with crucible funnel, sintered-glass crucible, and trap.

Filtering and washing

The most convenient way to filter a gravimetric precipitate is by suction through a sintered-glass crucible. Such a crucible contains a filter element made of glass particles that have been sintered together to form a porous disk of relatively uniform porosity (Fig. 4-6*a*), Sintered-glass crucibles are available with various pore sizes, are easy to clean, come quickly to constant weight, and may be heated up to 500°C if heating or cooling is not too rapid. Crucibles are often numbered, and the number should be recorded. If there is no such number, the crucibles must be marked in some other permanent fashion. When in use, a sintered crucible is attached by a piece of thin-walled rubber tubing of large diameter to a crucible funnel (or filter-funnel) that is held by a rubber stopper seated in a suction flask (Fig. 4-6b). The suction flask is connected by heavy-walled rubber or plastic tubing to a vacuum pump, usually of the aspirator type. A trap between suction flask and pump is advisable to prevent backflow into the suction flask or loss of filtered solution into the vacuum pump. Suction flasks are heavy-walled to avoid implosions. For the same reason the trap should be either a conical flask not larger than 125 ml or another suction flask.

The following general rules apply to the filtering and washing of a precipitate:

1. Filtration is fastest when carried out at elevated temperatures, because the viscosity of a hot solution is much less than that of a cold one. Filtration at or below room temperature is recommended only when the precipitate is too soluble in the hot supernatant.

2. The first milliliters of the filtrate must be tested for completeness of precipitation. A test tube placed underneath the crucible funnel and inside the suction flask is convenient for catching the initial filtrate and testing it.

The last drops of wash solution that have passed the precipitate on the filter must be tested for completeness of washing.

3. The wash solution may be distilled water, unless the precipitate is relatively soluble or there is danger of peptization. If it is necessary to decrease the solubility of the precipitate, the initial portions of the wash solution should contain ions common with the precipitate. If the precipitate tends to be peptized, even the last portions of the wash solution must contain ions that prevent peptization.

4. A precipitate must be washed directly after filtering, before becoming a caked mass full of cracks and before becoming resistant to solvents. A total given volume of wash solution is more effectively used

in many small portions than in a few large portions, as can be seen by solving Problem 4-9.

5. Filtering and washing are best carried out by the decantation procedures that will be described in the following section and more fully in Procedure 4-3.

Filtering and washing by decantation. Because fine-grained and flocculated colloidal precipitates tend to clog the pores of a filter, time is saved by not transferring the precipitate to the filter with the main body of supernatant. Rather, the precipitate is let settle, and as much supernatant as possible is *decanted* through the filter. Similarly, the main body of the precipitate may be washed *before* being transferred to the filter. The wash solution is added in small portions to the beaker containing the precipitate. The mixture is agitated; the precipitate is permitted to settle; and the wash solution is decanted into the filter crucible. Finally, the main body of precipitate is transferred to the crucible with the aid of small amounts of wash solution.

Filtering and washing by decantation are particularly appropriate for very fine grained and for gelatinous precipitates, because most of the supernatant and wash solution is not required to pass through the main body of precipitate. Filtration and washing are thus rapid. When the solubility of the precipitate is relatively large, the method should not be used, because it requires more wash solution than is absolutely necessary. For a coarse-grained precipitate that filters well there is no advantage to filtering and washing by decantation.

Drying

Precipitate and crucible are dried in an electric oven at the temperature required to remove either all water or the amount necessary so that the remaining water is in stoichiometric relation to the remainder of the precipitate. The crucible with and without precipitate should be heated equally and to constant weight within the limits desired.

*The chloride content of a solid sample
is to be determined by dissolving
a weighed quantity and precipitating
the chloride as silver chloride.
The precipitate is filtered,
washed, dried, and weighed.*

Laboratory assignment 4
(5 periods)

GRAVIMETRIC DETERMINATION

OF CHLORIDE

DISCUSSION

The gravimetric determination of Cl as $AgCl(s)$ is a very accurate method that yields good results even in the hands of a beginner. Furthermore, it serves well to illustrate many of the principles and techniques of gravimetric analysis. Very little coprecipitation is involved, particularly after the precipitate has been digested. With special precautions the method is capable of exceedingly accurate results, and it has been used in atomic weight determinations.

The solubility of $AgCl(s)$ in pure water is 1.9 mg/liter at 25°C and 21 mg/liter at 100°C. The solubility can be reduced by a small excess of Ag^+ ions, and the precision to be expected with reasonable care is 1 or 2 parts per thousand. An excess of Ag^+ ions should amount to not more than 0.01 mole/liter, for reasons explained earlier. Because many weak acids, such as carbonic and phosphoric acid, form silver salts that are only slightly soluble, the precipitation of AgCl is usually carried out in an acid medium. Although this removes interference of the kind just mentioned, other anions that form silver salts insoluble in an acid medium must not be present. Examples are Br^-, I^-, and $S^=$ ions. Furthermore, ions that form stable, unionized molecules or complexes with Cl^- must be absent. An example is divalent mercury, because mercuric dichloride exists in solution almost exclusively as molecular $HgCl_2$. Any compounds capable of reducing silver salts to Ag must also be absent.

Light decomposes AgCl(s) into chlorine and metallic silver:

$$2AgCl + hv \rightarrow 2Ag + Cl_2$$

This may cause gain or loss of weight, depending on when it occurs. If it occurs after the filtration, there is a weight loss. If it occurs before filtration in a solution containing excess Ag^+ ions, the Cl_2 diffusing from the decomposed AgCl reacts as follows:

$$3Cl_2 + 5Ag^+ + 3H_2O = 5AgCl(s) + 6H^+ + ClO_3^-$$

while the metallic Ag remains. The weight of the precipitate is thus increased. These effects are negligible if prolonged exposure to bright daylight is avoided, even though the color of the precipitate may change from white to gray or purplish violet owing to the fine dispersion of colloidal silver in the surface of the AgCl particles.

The drying of AgCl(s) is efficient. At 100 to 120°C, from 0.03 to 0.04 per cent water remains; at 200°C, 0.01 per cent; and essentially none when the AgCl is fused at 455°C, which does not cause decomposition or significant volatilization. This last procedure is required only when the extreme precision of atomic weight determinations is required.

PROCEDURES

4-1 Preparation of the sample. Obtain a chloride sample from the instructor and record its number in your notebook. Dry the sample for 1 hr at about 110°C. (For details see procedure for drying sample and weighing out by difference, page 82.)

Clean three 400-ml beakers and mark them with pencil. They need not be dry, but they should have had a final rinse with a small amount of distilled water. Note that tap water may contain sufficient Cl⁻ to ruin the determination if used rather than distilled water to rinse equipment. Inquire from the instructor about the approximate chloride content of your sample so that you may compute the sample weight desired. This should be such as to produce an AgCl precipitate of at least 0.5 g, for reasons of weighing precision, but not more than about 1 g, because large amounts of precipitate are difficult to filter and wash.

Accurately weigh out by difference three samples, one into each of the 400-ml beakers.

Compute the approximate amount of $0.2\ F\ AgNO_3$ solution needed for each sample, and obtain the total amount needed from the supply bottle available. Use this solution sparingly, and be careful not to stain desk tops or hands with it, because Ag is readily deposited.

Dissolve each of the samples in 100 ml of water. Avoid any splashing. Add 1 ml of chloride-free $6\ F\ HNO_3$ to each sample. It is wise to test the $6\ F\ HNO_3$ for chloride by adding to 1 ml one drop of $0.2\ F\ AgNO_3$ solution.

4-2 Precipitation of the AgCl.   Transfer about 30 ml of the $0.2\ F\ AgNO_3$ solution to a 50-ml beaker. Heat one of the sample solutions to about 80 to 90°C, and keep it hot. The precise temperature is immaterial and no thermometer is needed. From a dropper add 1-ml portions of the $AgNO_3$ solution. Hold the dropper with the $AgNO_3$ solution close to the surface of the solution in the beaker to avoid splashing. Shake or stir vigorously after each addition of $AgNO_3$, but avoid loss of solution. Keep the beakers covered when not stirring or adding $AgNO_3$. Use a stirring rod that has been fire-polished carefully, and be sure not to scratch the inside walls of the beaker. Scratched and other rough surfaces promote the formation of precipitate that will adhere and resist transfer to the filter crucible later on.

The agitation and the elevated temperature promote at least partial flocculation of the precipitate, which facilitates observing the effect of each new portion of $AgNO_3$ added. As the rate of precipitation decreases, diminish these portions until they consist of single drops. In the vicinity of the equivalence point there is a strong tendency to sudden coagulation of most of the precipitate. Note, however, that the solution does *not* clear *entirely*. Add five more drops of $AgNO_3$ solution after reaching this point.

It is of advantage to establish completeness of precipitation before filtering, as follows: Continue stirring the hot solution, or let it stand for a few minutes, until the supernatant is clear enough that any turbidity produced by adding one further drop of 0.2 F AgNO$_3$ would be noticed. If a turbidity is produced, add five more drops of AgNO$_3$ and continue the heating, stirring, and testing described above until the test for chloride ions is negative. [An additional test of the completeness of the precipitation will be performed on the filtrate obtained in the next procedure (4-3). If this test is positive, all the chloride still contained in the filtrate must be precipitated and added to the original AgCl precipitate.]

Do not carry out the precipitation and the subsequent operations in sunlight or in intense artificial illumination. Even in diffuse light there will be discoloration of the precipitate, but any corresponding change of stoichiometric composition is well within the precision of the determination. Digest the precipitate by continued heating and stirring, until the entire solution is clear. This may take 1 to 2 hr. Alternatively, let the precipitate age and the solution clear by letting the mixture stand in the dark, preferably overnight.

4-3   Filtering, washing, and drying of the precipitate.   Carefully wash three sintered-glass crucibles, first by sucking concentrated ammonia water through them to remove any old AgCl precipitate that may still adhere. Follow this by distilled water, 6 F HNO$_3$, and finally distilled water again. Record in your notebook any numbers or other distinguishing marks of the crucibles, so that you can be sure you can tell them apart. Dry them at 170°C for 1 hr, protected by a marked beaker (no paper labels!) and a watch glass. Use beaker tongs to handle the beaker. Place the hot and dry crucibles in the desiccator, in the holes in the porcelain plate provided for this purpose. Use a piece of filter paper to pick up the crucibles, which must not be touched by the fingers before weighing. Let the crucibles cool in the desiccator for 20 to 30 min, and weigh them with a small watch glass between crucible and pan. Although this watch glass is not really needed at this point, it will protect the pan from the corrosive influence of any traces of HNO$_3$ at the later weighing of crucible and precipitate. The same watch glass is to be used in all weighings, but it is wise to determine its weight also, in case it is lost or there is a mix-up. Repeat the drying and weighing until constant weight within about 0.2 mg has been reached.

Also prepare a wash solution by mixing 5 ml of 6 F HNO$_3$ with 500 ml of water. Transfer this solution to a small wash bottle. Alternatively, the wash solution may be kept in a beaker and dispensed with a dropper.

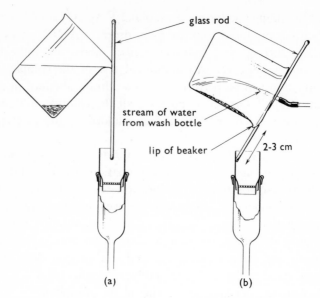

Figure 4-7   (a) Filtration by decantation; (b) Transfer of last portions of precipitate.

Filter and wash the precipitate at elevated temperature by the decantation method, as follows: Clamp the suction flask and the trap to a ring stand. Allow the precipitate to settle as much as possible. Next decant the hot supernatant into the sintered-glass crucible, with suction applied. Use a glass rod as guide, as shown in Figure 4-7a. Insert a test tube to catch the first milliliter of filtrate and test it with one drop of 0.2 F AgNO$_3$ solution. Take care not to disturb the precipitate and to avoid loss by splashing. To release the suction, loosen the stopper of the trap. Do not turn off the aspirator before releasing the suction. As the decantation proceeds, more and more particles of the precipitate will pass into the crucible. The main body, however, will remain in the beaker.

Examine the filtrate carefully for any particles that may have passed the filter. If such particles are found, the liquid containing them must be passed through the filter once more and the suction flask must be carefully washed so that none of the precipitate is lost. If passing of the precipitate through the filter persists, the precipitate should be digested for a longer time or a sintered-glass crucible with finer pores should be chosen.

The precipitate is ready for washing by decantation after as much supernatant has been poured off as is feasible without transferring a major portion of the precipitate into the crucible. It is wise first to pour the filtrate already passed into another vessel so that this solution need not be filtered a second time in case washing causes peptization of the precipitate. Next, any precipitate on the walls of the beaker is washed down by means of a wash bottle or a dropper containing the wash solution. Swirl gently or stir to establish equilibrium between contaminant of the precipitate and wash solution. Let the precipitate settle and decant the wash solution into the crucible. Repeat this process several times with small portions of wash solution. Always wait until all liquid has been sucked from the precipitate in the crucible before adding new wash solution. Finally, transfer the main portion of the precipitate to the crucible by a stream of wash solution, as shown in Figure 4-7b. The wash bottle must be full so that the stream of wash solution is even and not interrupted by air bubbles, which cause dangerous splashing.

A variant of the method just described for transferring the bulk of the precipitate to the crucible is to produce a slurry with the last portion of the wash solution, to transfer this to the crucible, and to use the method shown in Figure 4-7b only for the last remnants of precipitate.

Remove any particles still adhering to the walls of the beaker or the glass rod by gentle rubbing with a rubber "policeman" and transfer them to the crucible with the wash solution. Wash the glass rod and rubber policeman, directing the water into the crucible. Carefully examine the beaker, glass rod, and policeman for remaining particles. Test the filtrate for remaining Ag^+ ions by adding one drop of 6 F HCl to 1 ml of it.

Before drying in the oven, the precipitate must be sucked reasonably dry to avoid any violent boiling of water still adhering to it. The precipitates are dried for 1 hr at 170°C. This relatively high temperature is chosen to volatilize practically all adsorbed HCl and adhering HNO_3. Cool the crucibles for 30 min in the desiccator. A strip of blue litmus paper placed in the desiccator should not turn red.

4-4 Weighing of the precipitates.   It is very hard to remove all traces of acid from the crucibles. To prevent corrosion of the balance pans, the small watch glass mentioned earlier must be placed between crucible and pan. Repeat the drying and weighing until constant weight has been reached within 0.2 to 0.4 mg, depending on the weight of the precipitate. Discard the AgCl precipitate in one of the special bottles placed in the laboratory for this purpose.

4-5 Calculation of the results. Compute the weight percentages of chloride in the sample corresponding to your separate determinations. Double-check all calculations. Compute the mean m of the results, their unbiased standard deviation s, and their *relative* unbiased standard deviation s/m [Eqs. (4-7) and (4-8)]. If one of the results differs substantially from the mean, consider the alternatives presented on page 84.

PROBLEMS

4-1 Gram formula weight. A mixture of 50.00 ml of $0.2\,F$ HCl and 120 ml of $0.1\,F$ NaHCO$_3$ is evaporated to dryness.* How many formula weights of what substances are present in the residue?

4-2 Stoichiometry. Compute the following for Cu(NO$_3$)$_2$: (*a*) formula weight; (*b*) per cent oxygen by weight; (*c*) weight containing 1.000 g oxygen; (*d*) number of N atoms in 1.000 g of compound.

4-3 Analysis of silver. A piece of silver alloy weighing 160 mg was dissolved in nitric acid and the Ag precipitated by adding HCl. The resulting AgCl weighed 191 mg. What was the percentage of Ag in the alloy?

4-4 Composition of a salt hydrate. Nickel sulfate forms a hydrate of the formula NiSO$_4 \cdot n$H$_2$O. When heated sufficiently so that all water is lost, the weight decreases by 41.1 per cent. What is the value of n?

4-5 Empirical formula. Derive the simplest chemical formulas of the compounds with the following compositions, given as weight fractions: (*a*) Al 0.750, C 0.250; (*b*) Sn 0.528, Fe 0.124, C 0.160, N 0.188; (*c*) K 0.161, Pt 0.402, Cl 0.437; (*d*) Na 0.323, P 0.219, O 0.451, H 0.007; (*e*) Si 0.274, F 0.370, Cl 0.346, H 0.098.

4-6 Stoichiometry. A 0.5840-g piece of Ag foil had become tarnished because of formation of Ag$_2$S, with a weight increase of 1.0 mg. What fraction of the original Ag has been converted to Ag$_2$S?

4-7 Stoichiometry. A mixture of Zn and Mg was burned in oxygen to ZnO and MgO, with a weight increase of 40.9 per cent. What was the weight percentage of Zn in the original mixture?

4-8 Stoichiometry. A mixture of pure Fe$_2$O$_3$ and pure Fe$_3$O$_4$ contains 29.5 weight per cent oxygen. What is the weight fraction of Fe$_2$O$_3$ in the mixture?

4-9 Washing precipitates. Let V be the total amount of wash solution, v the volume of liquid remaining with a precipitate after draining, and c the concentration of substance that is to be essentially removed by washing. Suppose that at the start the precipitate is drained and that the wash solution is applied in n equal portions, each of volume V/n. (*a*) By what factor is the concentration c reduced after n such washings? (*b*) Assume that $v = 0.5$ ml, $V = 30$ ml, and $c = 1$ g/liter. Find the value of this factor for the cases $n = 1$ and $n = 3$.

---

* The concept of formality F has been defined on page 65 and will be further explained on page 97.

4-10 Analysis of chlorides. (*a*) How many milliliters of 0.2 *F* $AgNO_3$ solution correspond to 1 g of AgCl?* (*b*) The weight of a sample containing chloride was 0.3724 g. The AgCl precipitate produced from the sample weighed 0.7324 g. What is the weight per cent of chloride contained by the sample? (*c*) This sample was actually a mixture of KCl and NaCl. What percentage of it was NaCl? If the precision of the analysis is 1 part in 1000, what is the precision of this answer?

REVIEW QUESTIONS

4-1. Why is nitric acid added (*a*) to the chloride solution, before the precipitation of AgCl; (*b*) to the wash liquid?

4-2. How do you determine (*a*) when all of the chloride has been precipitated; (*b*) when the precipitate has been adequately washed?

4-3. Give brief reasons for the following operations or steps: (*a*) The chloride solution is heated before the silver nitrate is added. (*b*) The silver nitrate solution is added slowly, not rapidly. (*c*) The silver chloride suspension is allowed to stand overnight, or it is digested for an hour or two in contact with the solution from which it was precipitated. (*d*) A trap is placed between the suction flask and the aspirator pump. (*e*) Crucibles and weighing bottles are not placed in the oven directly.

4-4. Point out and, if possible, rectify the errors, inconsistencies, and sources of trouble in the following analysis. An air-dried sample weighing exactly 14.6237 g and containing about 5 weight per cent of Cl as well as impurities of KBr, NaH_2PO_4, and $NaHCO_3$ was dissolved in exactly 100.00 ml of distilled water. The chloride was precipitated as AgCl by rapidly adding 0.2 *F* $AgNO_3$ solution. Twice the volume needed was added to ensure complete precipitation of the chloride. The precipitate was filtered immediately, the suspension being kept in motion so as to transfer as much of the precipitate to the sintered-glass crucible as possible. The remaining precipitate was transferred to the crucible, and the precipitate was washed with distilled water to which a few drops of NH_3 had been added. After liberal final washing with distilled water, the precipitate was dried and weighed.

4-5. Briefly explain the following terms: primary and secondary adsorption, flocculation, relative supersaturation, coprecipitation, digestion of a precipitate, homogeneous precipitation, peptization, isomorphism.

REFERENCES

I. M. Kolthoff and E. B. Sandell, *Textbook of Quantitative Inorganic Analysis*, 3rd ed., Chaps. 3, 6 to 8, 17, Macmillan, New York, 1952.

H. A. Laitinen, *Chemical Analysis*, Chaps. 6 to 11, McGraw-Hill, New York, 1960.

E. H. Swift, *Introductory Quantitative Analysis*, Chaps. 11 to 13, Prentice-Hall, Englewood Cliffs, N.J., 1950.

* See footnote on page 94.

*Concentration units are defined,
and volumetric apparatus is discussed.
In a laboratory assignment
procedures for the calibration
of burets, pipets,
and volumetric flasks are given.*

five

VOLUMETRIC
EQUIPMENT

Before the discussion of volumetric equipment and its calibration, volume and concentration units are briefly reviewed. If needed, further details may be found in a general chemistry text or in the short monograph mentioned at the beginning of Chapter 4.

UNITS OF VOLUME AND OF CONCENTRATION

Units of volume.   Both the cubic meter and the liter are fundamental units in the metric system. Whereas the cubic meter is directly related to the metric unit of distance, the liter is related to the kilogram. The liter is defined as the volume of 1 kg of water at its maximum density (at 3.98 °C) under normal atmospheric pressure (water is slightly compressible). When the kilogram was defined as the mass of a certain platinum-iridium cylinder, the mass of the cylinder was made as nearly equal to that of 1000 cm^3 of water at its maximum density at 1 atm as possible. Equality was almost achieved, but later measurements showed that 1 liter equals 1000.028 cm^3. Thus, while the volumes of the milliliter and the cubic centimeter may be considered identical for many purposes, the two are different units of volume and must not be confused. Correspondingly, densities may be expressed in grams per cubic centimeter (*absolute density*) and in grams per milliliter (*relative density*—relative to water at 3.98 °C and under atmospheric pressure).

Concentration units. In describing the concentration of a solution the following units are used. The *formality* of a solution indicates the (gram) formula weights of *solute*, as the substance dissolved is called, in 1 liter of *solution*. The *molarity* of a certain species in a solution is its concentration in moles per liter of *solution*. The letters F and M are used to express the formality or molarity of a solution and are abbreviations for (gram) formula weights per liter and moles per liter. Thus a 2 F solution of NaCl contains 2 × 48.44 g of NaCl in 1 liter of solution. It is 2 M in Na$^+$ ions and 2 M in Cl$^-$ ions. A bracket enclosing the chemical symbol of a molecular or ionic species is used to denote the molarity of that species. Thus [Na$^+$] = 2 and [Cl$^-$] = 2 in the solution just described. Similarly, a 1 F solution of CaCl$_2$ is 1 M in Ca^{++} ions and 2 M in Cl$^-$ ions. Thus [Ca^{++}] = 1 and [Cl$^-$] = 2. A 0.001 F solution of CaSO$_4$ can be made by dissolving 136.1 mg of CaSO$_4$ and diluting to 1 liter or by doing the same thing with 145.2 mg of CaSO$_4 \cdot \frac{1}{2}$H$_2$O or with 172.2 mg of CaSO$_4 \cdot$ 2H$_2$O. A solution that is 0.1 F in HCl and 0.2 F in NaCl contains in the same liter of solution 0.1 gfw of HCl and 0.2 gfw of NaCl. Since HCl in aqueous solution is completely dissociated into H$^+$ ions and Cl$^-$ ions, [H$^+$] = 0.1, [Na$^+$] = 0.2, and [Cl$^-$] = 0.3 in this solution. (However, see also the last paragraph of this section.) It is seen that the formality concept permits a precise description of a solution in terms of its preparation, whereas the molarity permits a description of it in terms of the molecular and ionic species it contains.

A third concentration unit, the *normality*, is adapted to express conveniently the stoichiometric relationship between quantities of solutions that react with each other. It is related to the gram equivalent, which will be discussed first.

97

TABLE 5-1   *Examples of Gram Equivalents*

reaction		gram equivalents of reactants	
(1) $2HCl + Ba(OH)_2 = BaCl_2 + 2H_2O$		HCl	$Ba(OH)_2/2$
(2) $H_2SO_4 + NaOH = NaHSO_4 + H_2O$		H_2SO_4	NaOH
(3) $H_2SO_4 + 2NaOH = Na_2SO_4 + 2H_2O$		$H_2SO_4/2$	NaOH
(4) $Ag_2SO_4 + 2NaCl = 2AgCl(s) + Na_2SO_4$		$Ag_2SO_4/2$	NaCl
(5) $AgNO_3 + 2KCN = K(Ag(CN)_2) + KNO_3$		$AgNO_3$	2KCN

A *gram equivalent weight*, or simply *equivalent*, of a substance is the quantity that corresponds directly or indirectly, *in the reaction under consideration*, to one mole of hydrogen atoms. To express the relationship by an equation, let one gram formula weight of the substance considered be W_f, and let this quantity be equivalent to i mole of hydrogen atoms. One gram equivalent weight W_{eq} of the substance is then

$$W_{eq} = W_f/i$$

The number i, which usually is an integer but may also be a fraction, will be called the *equivalence index* of the substance. Note that both W_{eq} and i depend on the *reaction considered* and not just on the substance.

Examples of reactions and the gram equivalents of the reactants are shown in Table 5-1. In the reaction equations of Table 5-1 the formulas of the compounds are used, rather than just the reacting ions, since the emphasis is on stoichiometry. The chemical symbols in the column "gram equivalents of reactants" stand for the gram formula weights.

TABLE 5-2   *Normalities of 0.5 F Solutions*

substance	reaction	normality
HCl	(1)	0.5 N
H_2SO_4	(2)	0.5 N
H_2SO_4	(3)	1.0 N
$AgNO_3$	(4)	0.5 N
KCN	(5)	0.25 N

Note that the NaOH in reaction (2) reacts with H_2SO_4 to give the acid salt $NaHSO_4$, whereas in (3) the salt Na_2SO_4 is produced, so that the gram equivalent of H_2SO_4 is different in the two cases. No acid or base is directly involved in reactions (4) and (5), and in reaction (5) $i = \frac{1}{2}$ for KCN.

The *normality* of a solution is its concentration in gram equivalent weights per liter of solution. It is thus related to the formality by the equation

$$\text{normality} = i \times \text{formality}$$

Table 5-2 gives the normalities of $0.5\ F$ solutions participating in the reactions specified. The letter N stands for gram equivalents per liter. Often the *milli-equivalent* (meq) or one-thousandth of an equivalent is useful. The normality is also the concentration in meq/ml.

All examples given are of the type sometimes called metathetical reactions (double decompositions; Greek: *metatithenai* = to transpose). The concepts of gram equivalent and normality are also used for oxidation-reduction reactions, where i stands for the number of electrons involved in the reaction of one formula weight of substance, as will be explained in a later chapter.

The above concentration units express *volume concentrations* and are thus used in volumetric work. In measuring quantities of solutions by weighing, the following *weight concentrations* are used instead. The *weight formality* of a solution indicates the formula weights of solute per kilogram of *solvent*, whereas the *weight molarity* expresses the moles of solute species per kilogram of *solvent*. Note that volume concentrations are defined in terms of the *solution* volume; weight concentrations, in terms of the *solvent* weight. These definitions have the following background: The solution volume is directly accessible to measurement, whereas the solvent volume is not, and indeed it may not even be obtained exactly by subtracting the volume of the solute in the dry state from that of the solution, because there may be a change of volume in dissolving the solute and diluting the solution. On the other side, weights are additive, and the weights of solution and solvent are proportional to each other. To convert a volume concentration into the corresponding weight concentration, the density of the solution at the particular concentration has to be known.

In many texts the word *molal* is used to express weight molarity. There is no cause to introduce this usage into this text, since volume concentrations only will be used. Brackets always indicate volume molarity.

It should be mentioned that the restriction of the terms "mole" and "molar" to situations when only the species referred to is included is not, and indeed cannot be, carried through always with absolute consistency. For example, 1 liter of liquid water is said to be $1000/18 = 55.6\ M$ in H_2O at $3.98°C$ ($55.4\ M$ at $25°C$), even though it is known that there is considerable association of H_2O molecules in liquid water. However, this association is by relatively weak bonds (so-called hydrogen bonds) and changes constantly; at any given instant the individual H_2O molecules can still be recognized even though they may be tied weakly to others. Another example is the case of the H^+ ion, which does not exist in significant concentrations in aqueous solutions but is bonded to a water molecule to form the *hydronium ion* H_3O^+. Indeed, these hydronium ions are loosely associated with further H_2O molecules. It is nevertheless useful and customary to denote by the symbol $[H^+]$ the concentration, in moles per liter of solution, of the total of all H_3O^+ ions, including those associated with other H_2O molecules. It is thus to be understood that $[H^+]$ is a convenient shorthand symbol only. Similar conventions are used in many other cases. For example, in a solution of $CuCl_2$, the Cu^{++} exists mainly in the form of complexes with H_2O molecules like $Cu(H_2O)_4^{++}$, in which $4H_2O$ molecules are chemically bonded to a Cu^{++} ion; the symbol $[Cu^{++}]$ is used to denote the total concentration of actual Cu^{++} ions and all its complexes with H_2O molecules.

VOLUMETRIC EQUIPMENT

In volumetric analysis the quantity of a substance is determined by measuring the quantity of a solution of known concentration (a standard solution) that reacts with it. This kind of measurement is called a *titration*. Volumetric methods are used more widely than are gravimetric methods, since they can usually be carried out more rapidly once standard solutions have been prepared. The requirements that have to be met by a reaction to make it suitable for volumetric work will be discussed in Chapter seven. In the following sections, volumetric equipment and its use are described and information about its accuracy is given.

Types of equipment. Volumetric equipment exists in two types, (1) to contain, and (2) to deliver, a specified amount of liquid. *Volumetric flasks* are usually calibrated *to contain a fixed amount*, because it is difficult to empty a flask reproducibly. A volumetric flask is a glass-stoppered, pear-shaped vessel with a flat bottom and a long, narrow neck with the calibration mark (Fig. 5-1). The narrowness improves the precision with which the volume contained can be set by adjusting the liquid level to the calibration mark. Volumetric flasks are used to prepare standard solutions. A known amount of substance is dissolved in the flask and the solution is carefully diluted to the mark.

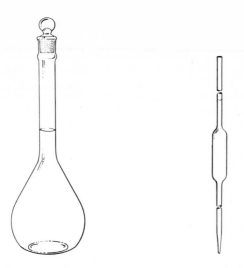

Figure 5-1 Volumetric flask.   Figure 5-2 Transfer pipet.

Transfer pipets are designed *to deliver a fixed volume* (Fig. 5-2). Again the calibration mark is on a narrow part of the equipment to assure good precision. A transfer pipet is used to measure out a fixed volume of solution, either to be titrated with another solution contained in a buret (see below) or for other purposes. There also exist *measuring pipets* with regularly spaced calibration marks that permit *delivery of variable volumes* (Fig. 5-3). Measuring pipets are not very precise and find little application in quantitative work.

Burets, finally, are long, cylindrical tubes of uniform bore that are graduated along most of their length for delivery of variable volumes. At the lower end there is a device for controlling the outflow of liquid. In the *Geissler* buret this is a stopcock (Fig. 5-4a). In the *Mohr* buret, in which a short piece of rubber tubing connects the tip with the calibrated part of the buret, it is a pinch or a screw clamp or a glass bead inside the rubber tube. The Mohr buret is less expensive but also less precise. It must not be used with iodine, permanganate, or other solutions that attack rubber. Alkaline solutions tend to cause sticking of the stopcock of a Geissler buret; in addition, the stopcock may become clogged with excess grease if not lubricated properly. Both difficulties are avoided by using burets provided with a self-lubricating *Teflon valve*. These come in both the regular style (Fig. 5-4a) and one that has a

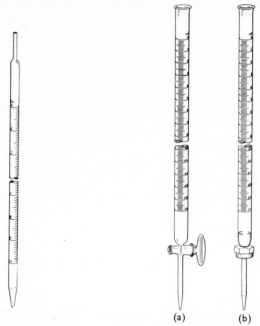

Figure 5-3   Measuring pipet.   Figure 5-4   (a) Buret with stopcock.
                                                    (b) Buret with Teflon valve.

valve operated by horizontal rotation (Fig. 5-4b). Burets are used mainly for titrations.

The top level of a liquid in a relatively narrow part of a vessel is usually a curved surface, called the *meniscus*, and it is important to establish which part of this level can be read most reproducibly or adjusted to a calibration mark. With a transparent liquid this part is generally the base of the meniscus, whereas for an opaque liquid, such as a permanganate solution, the upper surface is used. To help in avoiding parallax errors, the calibration marks in volumetric flasks or pipets cover the entire circumference of the neck or stem, respectively, and the calibration marks of burets extend at least halfway around the tube. Flasks, pipets, and burets must always be read with the eye level so adjusted that the front and rear parts of the graduation nearest the meniscus appear to be coincident.

Since the bore of a buret is relatively large, particular care must be taken in adjusting or reading the meniscus. The meniscus should always be shaded in the same manner, regardless of lighting and level height. This is best done by surrounding the buret just below the meniscus with a strip of black paper held there with a paper clip, as shown in Fig. 5-5, and placing a white card or filter paper behind the meniscus. The paper strip may be replaced by a piece of dark rubber hose slit open on the side. A white card whose lower half has been blackened may be used in place of this arrangement and may be just as satisfactory.

The most common type of buret has 50 ml capacity and is graduated into 0.1 ml. Such a buret is read to 0.01 ml by visually interpolating between the 0.1-ml marks. If the calibration mark appears to flatten the bottom of the meniscus, the reading should, as a rule, be 0.01 ml larger than the value of that mark. If the meniscus just shows below the mark, the reading should be 0.02 ml larger than that value. The precision of reading the position of a meniscus tangent to a calibration mark is, of course, higher than when the meniscus is between marks.

Precision of volumetric equipment. To give reproducible results, volumetric equipment must be scrupulously clean so that water will drain evenly from the surfaces rather than form streaks and droplets. For pipets and burets the volume delivered depends on the outflow time, because the main flow of the liquid is followed by the slower drainage of the liquid adhering to the walls. For example, when the contents of a 50-ml buret were delivered in 30 sec, the "after-drainages" of 0.01, 0.05, and 0.10 ml collected after 1, 5, and 10 min, respectively. When the delivery was slowed so that the buret emptied in 100 sec, the respective after-drainages were 0.00, 0.00, and 0.02 ml. The flow rate of

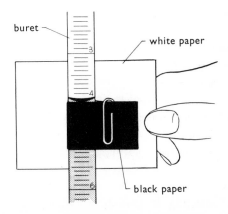

Figure 5-5 Aid in reading position of meniscus.

TABLE 5-3   *Minimum Outflow Time for Pipets*
(Maximum 1 min in all cases)

Capacity, ml, up to and including	5	10	50	100	200
Minimum outflow time, sec	15	20	30	40	50

TABLE 5-4   *Minimum Outflow Time for Burets*
(Maximum 3 min in all cases)

Length graduated, cm	70	60	50	40	30
Minimum outflow time, sec	160	120	90	70	50

a buret or pipet is governed by the size of the tip. Tables 5-3 and 5-4 show some of the specifications of the U.S. Bureau of Standards (1941) for minimum outflow times. All equipment data given in this chapter apply to so-called class A equipment, which is usually so marked.

The volume of liquid delivered by pipets also depends on the treatment given to the liquid remaining in the tip. This liquid may be left "as is," or it may be blown out, but experiments show that more reproducible results are obtained by touching the tip to the wet surface of the receiving vessel at a specified time after the delivery of the main volume of liquid, as is described in the procedures of the laboratory assignment. The marking T.D. ("to deliver") often found on pipets implies that the liquid collecting in the tip must *not* be blown out.

The drainage of organic solvents, and thus the amount delivered from pipets, may differ significantly from that of water, owing to considerable differences in surface tension. This also holds for concentrated solutions of acids, bases, and salts, but the differences are negligible for most volumetric work involving solutions of low to moderate concentrations, such as 1 *F*.

In Tables 5-5 to 5-7 are given some of the tolerances for volumetric equipment, as recommended by the U.S. Bureau of Standards.

Calibration of volumetric equipment.   Volumetric apparatus is usually bought already calibrated. It is useful and often important, however, to check the existing marks by recalibration, because the precision of the original calibration in manufacture may not have been as high as desired and may be outside the limits recommended by the Bureau of Standards. In particular, the volume of liquid delivered by pipets depends on the details of handling (as described above).

TABLE 5-5 *Tolerance for Volumetric Flask ("to Contain")*

capacity, ml, less than and including	limit of error, ml
25	0.03
50	0.05
100	0.08
300	0.12
500	0.30
1000	0.50

TABLE 5-6 *Tolerance for Transfer Pipets*

capacity, ml, less than and including	limit of error, ml
2	0.006
5	0.01
10	0.02
30	0.03

TABLE 5-7 *Tolerance for Burets*

capacity, ml, of total graduated portion, less than and including	limit of error, ml, of total or partial capacity
2	0.01
5	0.02
10	0.03
30	0.05
50	0.10

It is equally important that the calibration of burets and pipets provides practice in their manipulation and experience in the precision that may be expected.

The calibration of volumetric equipment may be performed either by weighing the water held by a volumetric flask or delivered by a pipet or buret or by measuring the volume of this water. The equipment needed for the second method has to be calibrated in turn, so that the second method is indirect, or secondary. The direct, or primary, method is preferred.

Since glass vessels change their volumes with temperature, it is important to settle on the temperature to which the calibration marks apply. In the United States the standard temperature for volumetric glassware has been set at 20°C by the Bureau of Standards. If the temperature at which the calibration is performed differs from this value, the density change of water as well as the volume expansion of glass must be taken into account. The volume V_t of glass of temperature t°C is related to that at 20°C, V_{20}, by the approximate formula

$$V_t \approx V_{20}[1 + \gamma(t - 20)] \tag{5-1}$$

where γ is the cubic expansion coefficient of glass. A satisfactory average value for this coefficient is 2.5×10^{-5} (°C)$^{-1}$. Within the range of 10 to 35°C the expansion of glass can thus usually be neglected in analytical work. The change with temperature of the density of water is considerably larger and must be taken into account. It is best to refer to a table giving this density at different temperatures, such as the one on page 398. It is, of course, the relative density, in grams per milliliter, that is needed here. In addition, the weight of the water should in general be corrected for air buoyancy.

The density of a solution and, therefore, its concentration depend on the temperature. For dilute solutions the ratio of the densities at two temperatures closely approximates the ratio for pure solvents. The temperature dependence of the concentration of a solution is approximately

$$c(t_2) \approx c(t_1)[d(t_1)/d(t_2)]_{\text{pure solvent}}$$

because the concentration is inversely proportional to the density.

To obtain an idea of the sizes of the various terms involved in checking a volumetric flask, consider the following example, in which the flask, filled to the mark, was found to hold 995.3 g water at 26°C, weighed in air. The vacuum weight (more precisely, mass) of this water is, by (3-9),

$$W_v = 995.3 + 0.0012(995.3/0.9968 - 995.3/8.4)$$

where the factor in front of the parentheses is the approximate density of air and the denominators are the densities of water at 26°C and of brass, respectively. Using the approximation $(1 - \delta)/(1 - \varepsilon) \approx (1 - \delta)(1 + \varepsilon) \approx 1 - \delta + \varepsilon(\delta, \varepsilon \ll 1)$, we obtain $995.3/0.9968 \approx 1000.0(1 - 0.0047 + 0.0032) = 998.5$. The buoyancy term thus becomes $0.0012(998.5 - 118) = 1.06$, and $W_v = 996.36$ g. (In intermediary computations it is wise to retain more figures than are significant.) The volume of the flask at 26°C is

$$V_{26} = 996.36/0.99681 \approx 1000(1 - 0.00364 + 0.00319) = 999.55 \text{ ml}$$

To obtain the volume at 20°C, the expansion formula for glass (5-1) is used, so that

$$V_{20} = 999.55(1 - 6 \times 2.5 \times 10^{-5}) = 999.55 - 0.15 = 999.4 \text{ ml}$$

*Laboratory assignment 5
(1 to 2 periods, in part optional*)*

CALIBRATION OF VOLUMETRIC

EQUIPMENT

PROCEDURES

5-1 Calibration of a buret.   Fill a 500-ml conical flask with distilled water, cover it with a watch glass, and let it stand until it has attained room temperature. In the meantime, clean your buret with soap solution or detergent until water drains evenly from it without leaving streaks or droplets. If a resistant film of grease is encountered, it may be necessary to use 6 F NaOH. Do not let this solution remain in the buret for more than 5 to 10 min, because it tends to etch glass.

---

* Essential calibrations are those of pipets and of the 30, 40, and 50 ml marks of burets. Other calibrations may be completed in free intervals during later periods, if desired.

"Cleaning solution" (available in the stockroom or prepared by dissolving 30 g of commercial sodium dichromate in 500 ml of commercial concentrated sulfuric acid), should be used as a last resort only, with the approval of the instructor. *Never pour cleaning solution at a level near that of your eyes.* In addition, wear safety glasses or your regular glasses, as always. Aside from the *danger* connected with the use of cleaning solution, it is also hard to remove the last traces of the solution from glass surfaces.

To use the cleaning solution, invert the buret and dip its upper end into a beaker containing about 100 ml of the solution. Open the buret valve and carefully apply suction to the tip with a hose connected through a trap to the suction pump until the acid level is above the calibrated portion of the buret (Fig. 5-6). Close the valve, and let the solution stand. Finally, let the cleaning solution drain back into the beaker, and draw up several portions of fresh water before continuing the rinsing of the buret in its normal orientation and letting any water drain through the valve.

After cleaning, the buret should be rinsed with large amounts of water, particularly if cleaning solution has been used. Let part of the wash water flow through the tip and the remainder through the top opening by inverting the buret. Finally, rinse thoroughly with distilled water, and check for satisfactory drainage.

Fill the buret with distilled water from a beaker; use a funnel, and avoid overflow. Do not fill the buret directly from your wash bottle, because the mouthpiece may not be clean, or it may get caught in the top of the buret and break.

Force any air bubbles from the tip by letting the liquid flow with the valve fully open while gently tapping the tip. Check the delivery time with the valve open all the way. (See Table 5-4 for recommended limits for the delivery time.)

Test the valve for leakage as follows: Fill the buret nearly to the zero mark with room-temperature water, wait $\frac{1}{2}$ min for drainage, and read the meniscus level as described earlier (Fig. 5-5). Check for constancy of the level after 10 min, and in the meantime weigh with a precision of 1 mg, a 50-ml conical flask covered by a small watch glass. The flask must be dry on the outside but not necessarily on the inside.

If the buret valve is a glass stopcock rather than a self-lubricated Teflon valve, it should be tested for leakage as follows: Clean plug and bore of all grease, wet the plug, and replace it firmly in the "closed" position. Test for leakage, turn the plug through 180°, and test again. Dry plug and bore, and lubricate by applying a thin film of petroleum jelly or stopcock grease to the plug, but only on either side of the hole in it; otherwise, the grease is likely to get into the hole and into the tip. Reinsert the plug and press firmly and rotate it until a transparent, uniform film of lubricant has formed. At times excess grease clogs the buret tip. To remove

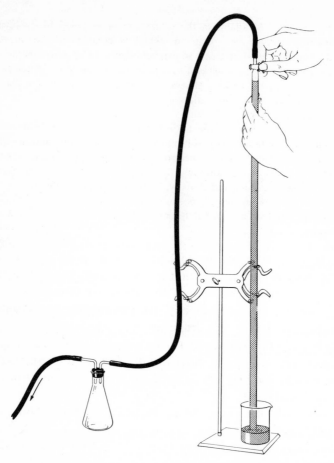

Figure 5-6   Cleaning buret with cleaning solution.

such grease, heat 100 ml of water to boiling in a 250-ml beaker. Fill the buret, open the valve, and lower the tip into the hot water. This is usually successful. The shortcut of heating the tip with a match has its hazards.

In using a buret with a glass stopcock it is important to acquire the habit of always pushing the valve plug into the bore when the plug is being rotated. A right-handed person should operate the buret with the left hand, with the hand around the buret so that the stopcock is operated from the opposite side and thus is pulled into the bore; the right hand should be used to hold and swirl the receiving flask.

Let the buret drain, and refill it with water of room (and known and recorded) temperature so that the level is above the calibrated portion. Remove the funnel, and open the valve slightly until the meniscus has moved to within about 0.02 ml of the zero line. Allow 30 sec for drainage; check to see that there are no air bubbles in the tip; and adjust the meniscus so that it is just tangent to the zero line. (Although not necessary, it is more precise to perform the calibration between fixed reference marks.) Touch the buret tip to a wet glass surface to remove any drops hanging from it.

Slowly deliver water into the weighed flask, while avoiding any splashing, until the meniscus is just above the 5-ml (or 10-ml) line. The rate of outflow should be such that delivery of 5 ml takes about 15 to 20 sec. Since the hydrostatic pressure is higher for a full than for a nearly empty buret, the valve should not be opened completely when solutions are being drained from the upper half of the buret. After 30 sec, to allow for drainage, adjust the meniscus to be just tangent to the etched mark. Touch the buret tip to the wet inside surface of the conical flask, and replace the watch-glass cover on the flask. Refill the buret to just above the zero level, so that there is ample time for drainage during weighing. Weigh the flask.

Repeat the above procedure, now delivering and weighing 10 ml (or 20 ml) of water. Repeat until the entire buret has been calibrated. Empty and reweigh the receiving vessel whenever the total weight exceeds about 100 g. It is preferable to refill the buret each time, since

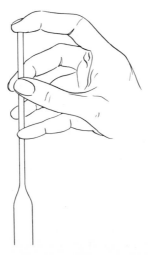

Figure 5-7   Operation of pipet.

in that way the drainage conditions in actual titrations are reproduced more closely. The calibration by continued withdrawal of 5-ml (or 10-ml) portions is slightly less accurate but faster.

Repeat the calibration until duplications within 0.02 ml have been reached. From the temperature and weights of the portions of water withdrawn compute the volumes of these portions. Apply a buoyancy correction unless this correction is less than 0.01 ml. Compute the buret corrections, and plot them against the volumes delivered.

Before putting the buret away, refill it with distilled water and close it with a clean stopper. Otherwise, the good drainage properties will be rapidly lost, probably because of the formation on the walls of a thin film of grease or other material. If this occurs, renewed cleaning is necessary.

5-2 Calibration of a pipet. Clean your pipets by the methods described at the beginning of Procedure 5-1.

If the use of cleaning solution appears necessary, consult first with your instructor. Use a pipet bulb to draw up cleaning solution to a level above the calibration mark but still at a safe distance from the bulb. Let stand, and eventually rinse with copious amounts of water. Finally, rinse with distilled water.

Check pipets for satisfactory drainage; determine the times required for the pipets to empty; and compare the results with Table 5-3.

Weigh a 50-ml flask, with a small watch-glass cover, to a precision of 1 mg. Only the outside of this vessel need be dry. Suck distilled water of room (and known) temperature into the pipet until it is slightly above the calibration mark. Make it a habit *always* to use a pipet bulb, not just for corrosive or poisonous liquids. Do not push the bulb completely over the stem of the pipet when applying suction; form a seal by holding it lightly against the pipet opening. Do not use too strong suction, because bubbles may form and may adhere to the pipet walls. Quickly remove the bulb, and place the index finger over the top opening of the pipet, so that an airtight seal is formed. *Do not use the thumb for this purpose.* A good way to hold the pipet steady is to have the middle and ring fingers on one side and the thumb and little finger on the other while using the index finger to control the outflow of liquid by checking the inflow of air (Fig. 5-7).

With a clean piece of tissue or towel remove any liquid adhering to the outside of tip and lower stem. Hold the pipet vertically, and operate the index finger so that the liquid slowly drains from the pipet until the meniscus is just tangent with the calibration mark. Avoid any violent movement of the pipet after this, so as not to lose liquid before being ready for delivery. Touch the tip to a wet glass surface to remove any hanging drops.

Move the tip well inside the weighed receiving vessel so that there will be no splashing and loss of liquid; do not, however, touch any glass or liquid surface. Hold the pipet vertically, and permit the liquid to drain completely from the pipet. After 15 sec lightly touch the pipet tip against the wet side of the flask. Do not blow out any liquid remaining in the tip, because the reproducible volume remaining there is included in the calibration.

Reweigh the flask and compute the volume of the water; apply a buoyancy correction when it amounts to or exceeds 0.01 ml. Calibrate each pipet twice or until agreement within 0.02 ml is reached. With every new calibration empty and reweigh the conical flask.

5-3 Calibration of volumetric flasks. Clean your volumetric flasks by the methods described at the beginning of Procedure 5-1. Pay particular attention to the inside of the neck near the calibration mark.

Consult with your instructor if the use of cleaning solution appears to be indicated. Use only a few milliliters, and so manipulate the flask that the solution eventually comes into contact with all the surface of the wide part of the flask. Finally, let the cleaning solution drain slowly through the neck while rotating the flask so that the solution reaches all parts of the neck.

Rinse thoroughly, first with tap water and finally with distilled water. Dry the flask by clamping it and letting it remain in an inverted position; the drying may be hastened by inserting a tube which reaches nearly to the bottom and by *drawing* air through this tube. Do not use compressed air, because it contains oil and other undesirable vapors. Drying with tissue or a towel is also undesirable, because both leave small fragments.

Place the stoppered bottle on one of the two pans of a pulp balance having a capacity above 1 kg and a precision of 0.01 g or better. In addition, place on the same pan weights of a total face value equal to the capacity of the flask in milliliters. Unless the calibration mark of the flask is grossly in error, these weights will be slightly heavier than the water the flask has been calibrated to contain. Place tare weights—weights from an old set, lead shot, or other suitable material—on the other pan until the rest point of the balance is near the center of the scale. Remove the weights after recording them as well as the rest point. Leave the tare weights in place.

Remove the flask, insert a funnel that reaches below the calibration mark, and add water of known (and preferably of room) temperature until the mark has almost been reached. Remove the funnel, and with a dropper continue adding water until the bottom of the meniscus is just tangent to the calibration mark. If there are any droplets of water above the mark, they must be removed with filter paper wrapped around a glass rod before making final adjustment. In adjusting the meniscus the same aid should be used as recommended for reading the meniscus position in a buret (Fig. 5-5).

Stopper the flask and return it to the pan of the balance on which it was weighed originally. To the same pan add small weights and adjust the rider, if there is one, until the first rest point has been restored, with a precision corresponding to about one-tenth the value in the limit of errors for volumetric flasks given in Table 5-5.

From the data obtained compute the volume of the flask at 20°C. For highly precise work humidity and barometric pressure of the air must be taken into account in the buoyancy correction.

Repeat the calibration. Duplicate calibrations should agree well within the limits given in Table 5-5.

The Borda substitution method, in the variant described above, is used in this calibration rather than the Gauss double-weighing method, because at the heavy loads involved there is significant distortion of the beam and change in rest point with load. Errors due to such effects are eliminated in the method used.

PROBLEMS

5-1 Concentration units. A solution containing 15.0 weight per cent of $MgCl_2$ has a density of 1.1319 g/ml. Compute volume and weight formalities of this solution. Assuming that the species Mg^{++} and Cl^- predominate to the exclusion of others, give their volume and weight molarities.

5-2 Formal concentration. What is the formality of 98 per cent H_2SO_4 (by weight) whose density is 1.83 g/ml?

5-3 Rinsing of burets. Burets are usually rinsed first with large amounts of distilled water and then with several 5-ml portions of the solution they are to be filled with. Suppose that rinsing with just one such portion has been performed and that the volume of liquid adhering to the inside walls of the 50-ml buret after any rinsing and draining is 0.3 ml. The buret is now filled to a level just above the top mark, requiring 55 ml of the standard solution. What is the percentage concentration change of the standard solution in the buret? Repeat the calculations for rinsing with two and also with three portions of standard solution.

5-4 Buret calibration.* A buret is calibrated at 26°C. Compute the factor by which the apparent weight (in air, with brass weights) of the water delivered

---

* The table on page 398 gives the density of water at various temperatures.

must be multiplied to obtain the corresponding volume of liquid delivered from the same buret at 20°C.

5-5 Temperature dependence of concentration.* The ratio of the densities of a dilute solution at two temperatures is to a good approximation proportional to the corresponding density ratio for pure water. (*a*) A solution of NaCl is 0.1426 *F* at 26°C. What is its formality at 20°C? (*b*) A solution of NaOH is 0.1032 *F* at 20°C. It is used in a buret at 28°C to titrate a solution of HCl, 25.00 ml of which has been transferred, also at 28°C, by means of a pipet into the titration vessel. The concentration of the HCl solution is found by multiplying the NaOH formality by the appropriate ratio of the measured volumes of the two solutions and a correction factor to allow for the different temperatures. What is this factor so that the result is the formality of the HCl at 25°C?

5-6 Determination of vapor density. The apparent weight of a glass bulb filled at 80°C with a certain vapor and sealed is 33.2884 g. The weight of the same bulb filled with air is 32.7241 g, and filled with water at 25°C it is 172.5 g. All weighings are with brass weights and in dry air at 25°C and 740 mm barometric pressure, of density 1.15 g/liter. What is the density, to three digits, of the vapor? The density of brass is 8.4 g/cm^3.

5-7 Molarity. What is the concentration of H_2O in mole/liter in pure water at 20°C?

5-8 Concentration units. The density of an aqueous solution containing 38.0 weight per cent $NaClO_4$ is 1.297 g/ml at 18°C. How many grams of $NaClO_4$ are contained in 1.000 liter of such a solution? How many gram formula weights?

5-9 Calibration of volumetric flask.* A volumetric flask is found to contain 999.29 g of water at 15°C when filled to the calibration mark. (*a*) What is the volume of this water at 20°C? The neck of the flask in the neighborhood of the calibration mark is exactly cylindrical, with a diameter of 1.82 cm at 17.5°C. What is the position of the meniscus relative to the calibration mark when the flask contains exactly 1000.00 ml of water (*b*) at 15°C, (*c*) at 20°C? Cubic expansion coefficient of glass: 2.5 × 10^{-5} (°C)$^{-1}$.

5-10 Solution concentration.* A volumetric flask is filled to the calibration mark with water at 15°C. The true weight of this water is 998.87 g. A standard silver nitrate solution is prepared by dissolving 16.988 g of the pure salt in water and diluting it to the mark in the given flask at 25°C. What is the formality of the solution at 25°C? Cubic expansion coefficient of glass: 2.5 × 10^{-5} (°C)$^{-1}$.

REVIEW QUESTIONS

5-1. Why is the drainage time of pipets and burets important?

5-2. What is the accepted procedure for handling the liquid remaining in the tip of a pipet?

5-3. Why is the use of cleaning solution to be avoided if possible?

5-4. Is a buoyancy correction needed when weighing, for calibration purposes, the water delivered by or contained in volumetric equipment?

5-5. How does the concentration of dilute solutions change with temperature?

5-6. How is the temperature difference allowed for when volumetric equipment is calibrated at temperatures other than the standard temperature of 20°C?

* The table on page 398 gives the density of water at various temperatures.

An exposition of the general aspects
of gas analysis is followed
by a description of
simple equipment for measuring
the volume of gas
evolved in a reaction
and a discussion of the sources of error.
In a laboratory assignment
the volume of nitrogen produced
in a reaction between nitrite
and sulfamic acid is measured.

six

GAS ANALYSIS

GAS ANALYTICAL METHODS

Gas analytical methods are those used when the sample to be analyzed is a gas or when the component to be determined in a liquid or solid sample can be converted into a gas. To measure a quantity of gas, one determines either the volume of the gas at constant temperature and pressure or the pressure of a known volume of gas, again at constant temperature. The number n of moles of gas is computed from the perfect-gas equation in the form

$$n = pV/RT$$

where p is the pressure (atm), V the volume (ml), T the absolute temperature (°K), and R the gas constant, whose value is 82.05 ml atm/mole deg. If the gas is collected above water, the partial pressure of water at the temperature of the experiment has to be subtracted from the barometric pressure (see the table on page 398) and any hydrostatic pressure differences have to be taken into account. The absolute temperature T is obtained by adding 273.2 to the temperature t in degrees centigrade, $T = t + 273.2$.

Although the perfect-gas equation does not describe the behavior of a real gas precisely, deviations from it are negligible in the usual analytical applications. When higher precision is desired, as in the determination of atomic weights, extrapolation to infinite volume is necessary.

In the analysis of air or another mixture of gases, a known quantity of the original gas is shaken with certain solutions or passed over certain solids of large surface area that remove one or the other component gas, and the remaining quantity of gas is measured again. For example, an alkaline solution of pyrogallol, an organic chemical, reacts quantitatively with oxygen. It is also possible to measure the quantity of gas that has reacted with a solid by measuring the weight increase of the solid. An example is a method of determining carbon dioxide in which the gas reacts quantitatively with Ascarite, asbestos coated with sodium hydroxide.

The other application of gas analytical methods is the determination in a solid or liquid sample of a component that can be converted into a gas. For example, some of the nitrogen in biologically important materials is often determined by adding nitrous acid (HNO_2) to the materials. By a reaction similar to that used in the laboratory assignment of this chapter [Eq. (6-1)], the HNO_2 combines with the nitrogen in the material to form gaseous N_2 (method of Van Slyke). In this method the nitrogen that is contained in certain combinations with other atoms (as with hydrogen in amines) is separated from the nitrogen in other such combinations (as with oxygen in nitro groups). Important structural information can be obtained in this way.

Any gas analytical reaction that either evolves or consumes a gas must satisfy the following conditions: (1) It must be *stoichiometric*. The reaction must go to completion, and either it must involve only the gaseous chemical species of interest or it must be possible to separate this species from any other gases present or being evolved. (2) The reaction must be reasonably *fast*, since a method that is wasteful of time is of little practical interest. A further condition is (3) that the *solubility* of a gas whose quantity is to be determined must be *small* in any liquid that comes into contact with it.

GASOMETRIC EQUIPMENT

A simple apparatus that may be used to measure the volume of gas evolved in a reaction is shown in Fig. 6-1. The reactants that produce the gas are contained in the flask *B* and the vial *C* and are kept apart while the apparatus is connected and brought to temperature equilibrium. The vial *C* is held to the wall of the flask by two magnets, one inside the vial and the other on the outside of the flask. The reaction

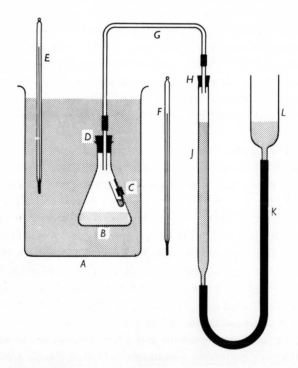

Figure 6-1   Apparatus for nitrogen determination. A, large beaker containing sufficient water completely to cover B, supported by tripod; B, conical flask containing one of the reactants; C, vial containing the other reactant. It is held by a small, plastic-coated magnet on its inside and a small, uncoated magnet on the outside of the flask; D, rubber stopper forming gastight seal; E, thermometer measuring water temperature in A; F, calibrated room thermometer near working space; G, glass tube connected at both ends by Koroseal tubing to short glass tubes; H, rubber stopper forming gastight seal; J, volumetric buret, supported by clamp and ring stand; K, Koroseal tubing, and, L, crucible funnel, supported by clamp and ring stand and usually so adjusted that water level in it is at the same height as that in J.

is initiated by manipulating the magnet on the outside of the flask *B* so that the coated magnet inside the vial *C* slips out of the vial. This causes the vial to overturn so that the reactants mix. The volume of the gas evolved is measured by reading the position of the water level in buret *J* at the beginning and end of the experiment, after adjusting the funnel *L* so that the water levels in *J* and *L* are at the same height. The temperature of the water in beaker *A* is adjusted to room temperature before and after the reaction.

SOURCES OF ERROR

Potentially serious error sources are the two *Koroseal connections* at the ends of glass tube *G*, which may confine different volumes of gas at the beginning and end of the gas evolution. To assess the order of magnitudes involved, assume a total change in these volumes of 0.1 ml and a volume of 30 ml for the gas generated. This corresponds to a relative error of 0.33 per cent. It is expected, however, that with some caution the above volume change can be kept considerably below 0.1 ml.

Another source of error lies in inaccurate *temperature measurements* and in lack of *temperature constancy* in the entire apparatus. For example, suppose that the volume of air initially in the apparatus is 30 ml, that 30 ml of gas has been evolved, and that a uniform temperature change of 1 °C during the experiment has been overlooked. At a room temperature of 27 °C this corresponds to an error of 1 part in 300 in the total gas volume. The entire error will, however, apply to the 30 ml of the gas evolved, even though half of it is due to the volume change of the 30 ml of air. The error in the result will thus be 2 parts in 300, or 0.67 per cent. It is clearly important that the system be at temperature equilibrium at the beginning and end of the experiment and that temperatures be estimated to 0.1°. The water in beaker *A* has to be adjusted carefully to room temperature at the start and finish of the experiment.

Errors of 1 mm in *pressure* are paralleled by errors of about 1 part in 760 in the amount of gas evolved. The *equilibrium pressure of water* must be allowed for (see the table on page 398). Owing to the presence of solutes in the conical flask, the water vapor pressure in it will be below that of pure water by an amount of the order of 1 mm, whereas it reaches its full value over the water surface in the buret. There is thus a continuous minute flow of water vapor to the conical flask, where it condenses. More seriously, the gas in the apparatus may not all be saturated with water. The ensuing error, however, is likely to be small. For example, let the average degree of saturation, or relative humidity, be 90 per cent and constant during the experiment and let the room temperature be 24°C, at which the equilibrium pressure of water is 22.3 mm. Correcting for the full 22.3 mm rather than only for nine-tenths of it would lead to an error in pressure of 2.2 mm, or a relative pressure error of 0.3 per cent.

Another error in pressure results when the *levels* of the water in buret *J* and in funnel *L* are *unequal*. A level difference of 1 mm corresponds to a pressure difference of $1/13.5 \approx 0.07$ mm mercury, where the number 13.5 is the ratio of the densities of Hg and H_2O. The effect of this level difference is negligible.

Surface tension may have more serious effects on the position of the liquid level in the buret. Because of the wide cross section of the filter funnel, the effects of surface tension in it may be disregarded. The buret should be carefully cleaned to such point that liquid draining from it does not leave streaks or droplets. Any effects of surface tension will then be independent of the position of the meniscus, and the meniscus will always have the same shape.

The *partial solubility of the gas evolved in water* is a source of error. The gas produced in the laboratory assignment of this chapter is nitrogen, whose solubility in water at 25°C and 1 atm is 15 ml of N_2 per liter of water, the gas volume measured at 25°C and 1 atm. To form an idea of the size of the error to be expected from this source, we assume that the volume of the liquid in the conical flask is 20 ml, that this liquid is saturated with air at the beginning of the experiment and therefore is 80 per cent saturated with N_2, and that the presence of other solutes does not significantly affect the solubility of nitrogen. We further assume that the liquid in the conical flask is 100 per cent saturated with N_2 after the experiment, since nitrogen has been bubbled through it, but that there is no significant loss of N_2 by solution in the water on the buret side; the gas in the buret has not been bubbled through the water in it and is at worst half air and half nitrogen. With all these assumptions the N_2 lost is computed to be $15 \times 10^{-3} \times 20 \times 0.20 = 0.06$ ml. This amounts to $100 \times 0.06/30 = 0.2$ per cent of the 30 ml N_2 assumed to have been generated.

Incompleteness of reaction may be another source of error. If the reaction mixture is agitated once a minute as indicated in the procedures for the laboratory assignment, the reaction should go to completion quantitatively within about 10 to 15 min.

From this discussion it appears that with careful experimentation the total error should be at most 1 relative per cent and probably less.

The amount of nitrite in a sample is to be determined by reacting it with sulfamic acid and measuring the volume of the nitrogen gas produced.

Laboratory assignment 6
(3 periods)

GAS ANALYTICAL DETERMINATION

OF NITROGEN

DISCUSSION

The sample used in this assignment contains nitrite and is reacted with an excess of sulfamic acid. Nitrogen is evolved quantitatively, and its volume is measured by the apparatus of Figure 6-1 and used to compute the quantity of nitrogen contained in the sample.

The basis of the evolution of nitrogen is the following quantitative reaction:

$$HNO_2 + NH_2SO_3^- = N_2 + HSO_4^- + H_2O \qquad (6\text{-}1)$$

$$\text{nitrous acid} \quad \text{sulfamate ion}$$

The ion reacting with the nitrous acid is the anion of *sulfamic acid,*

$$H-O-\overset{\displaystyle O}{\underset{\displaystyle O}{\overset{|}{\underset{|}{S}}}}-NH_2 \qquad (6\text{-}2)$$

Sulfamic acid can be considered as a derivative of sulfuric acid,

$$H-O-\overset{\displaystyle O}{\underset{\displaystyle O}{\overset{|}{\underset{|}{S}}}}-O-H$$

in which an amine group (NH_2) replaces a hydroxyl group (OH), or as a derivative of ammonia,

$$H-\overset{\displaystyle H}{\overset{|}{N}}-H$$

in which a sulfonic acid group (SO_3H) replaces a hydrogen atom. The lines in the above formulas indicate chemical bonds without regard to whether they are single or double bonds, etc.

Sulfamic acid is a crystalline solid, and the molecular structure has been shown by X-ray methods to correspond to formula (6-3) rather than (6-2),

$$^-O-\overset{\displaystyle O}{\underset{\displaystyle O}{\overset{|}{\underset{|}{S}}}}-NH_3{}^+ \qquad (6\text{-}3)$$

Thus, the H on the O in formula (6-2) is so weakly held (is so strongly acidic) that it has dissociated off as H^+; at the same time the nitrogen atom offers such great attraction to a hydrogen ion (is so strongly basic) that it has taken up an H^+, all this despite the energetically unstable creation of separated charges of opposite sign. The molecule shown by (6-3) is an example of a zwitter ion (German: *zwitter* = hybrid). The over-all charge on the sulfamic acid zwitter ion is, of course, zero.

Sulfamic acid is used in the tanning industry, in the manufacture of dyes and detergents, and as a weed killer. It is a strong acid, and since it can readily be purified and its crystals are stable at temperatures required for drying to constant weight, it is used in volumetric analysis for the standardization of OH^- solutions.

The mechanism of reaction (6-1) is known to involve undissociated HNO_2 molecules rather than $NO_2{}^-$ ions. The tendency of nitrous acid to dissociate into H^+ and NO_2^- is only moderate—it is not a strong acid like sulfamic acid and sulfuric acid. At an H^+ concentration as small as 4×10^{-4} mole/liter half of all nitrous acid present is undissociated, and the higher the H^+ concentration the smaller the percentage of dissociated HNO_2 molecules. Before mixing with the nitrite the concentration of sulfamic acid in this experiment is about $0.25\ F$, and since this strong acid is completely dissociated, the H^+ concentration is about $0.25\ M$. The amount of nitrite used in the reaction, when dissolved in the 20 ml of sulfamic acid solution used, corresponds to about 0.10 gfw/liter. The initial H^+-ion concentration is thus sufficient to change substantially all nitrite, after mixing, to the undissociated form. As reaction (6-1) proceeds, part of the sulfamic acid is converted into sulfuric acid, which is a strong acid also. An excess of at least 0.15 mole/liter H^+ is thus maintained throughout the experiment.

The analogous reaction between nitric acid and sulfamic acid yielding nitrous oxide (N_2O),

$$HNO_3 + NH_2SO_3^- = N_2O + HSO_4^- + H_2O$$

has been reported to proceed in $22\ F\ HNO_3$ but not in $16\ F\ HNO_3$. Again, it is HNO_3 molecules which react rather than NO_3^- ions, and the high concentration of H^+ is needed to keep the strong acid HNO_3 from being completely dissociated. At the H^+ concentrations prevailing in this experiment nitrite can be determined in the presence of nitrate, which will not react.

The nitrogen determination of this assignment is similar to the Van Slyke method mentioned earlier, which is used in biochemistry. The difference is that in the Van Slyke method nitrous acid is added in excess, and the nitrogen determined is chemically similar to the nitrogen in sulfamic acid. It is for simplicity that an inorganic system rather than an organic system has been chosen for quantitative evolution of nitrogen. Aside from the interest of the method itself, the experiment provides experience in the handling of gases.

PROCEDURES

6-1 Construction and testing of apparatus; calibration of thermometer. Hang your 110° thermometer near the calibrated room thermometer by means of some string or wire threaded through the eye at its top end; do not hang it directly from this eye, because the eye might break. Let the 110° thermometer come to equilibrium, and note any difference between the readings of the two thermometers. Use this difference later to correct the readings of your thermometer. In the meantime construct the apparatus shown in Figure 6-1. Fire-polish all the glass tubes used. The two short glass tubes connected to the long tube *G* should come to within about 2 mm of touching it, so that any flexing of the connecting Koroseal tubing causes as little volume change as possible. Place a few drops of water around the rubber stopper *H* to improve the seal.

The use of a Mohr buret for *J* is recommended, because the tips of Geissler burets are quite vulnerable. The buret should be cleaned to the point at which it drains without leaving streaks or droplets. When storing a clean buret, fill it with water.

The amount of water in buret, hose, and funnel tube should be such that the funnel is almost empty when the level in the buret is at the highest etched graduation. Use water that has been standing so that no bubbles of previously dissolved air will form. Check to see that no bubbles are in the system.

To test the apparatus for gas leaks, proceed as follows: Adjust the temperature of the water in beaker *A*, by addition of cold or warm water and by thorough stirring, as closely as you can to that of its surroundings. With the stopper of the conical flask removed, lower the water level in the buret to near the bottom of the graduated portion, insert the stopper tightly in the flask, and raise the funnel until the water-level height difference in buret and funnel is about 20 cm. Read the position of the meniscus in the buret, and repeat this reading after 15 min. If the two readings differ by more than 0.03 ml and the temperature has remained constant, there is a leak that must be repaired. The leak test should then be repeated.

6-2 Evolution of nitrogen gas. Obtain a sample containing $NaNO_2$; record the sample number; and compute the amount that will produce 30 to 45 ml of N_2, assuming a $NaNO_2$ content of 70 to 100 per cent. Since sodium nitrite is hygroscopic, it must be weighed in a covered container. It has been found convenient to dry the sample directly in the $\frac{1}{2}$-dram vial that is to be inserted into flask *B* of the apparatus and to weigh the vial with a 1-dram vial slipped over it to serve as a cover. Thus, obtain three $\frac{1}{2}$-dram vials and a 1-dram vial. Mark the smaller containers with a file, and dry all four vials at 110°C. Weigh each of the $\frac{1}{2}$-dram vials together with the cover vial. Transfer approximately the amount of sample computed into each $\frac{1}{2}$-dram vial. It has been found that 1 g of sample fills about 0.9 cm of such a vial, which may help to estimate amounts. Dry samples and vials at 110°C for 2 hr. It is found that if all four vials are placed standing in a 50-ml beaker none of them can overturn. After cooling in the desiccator, cover each smaller vial with the larger vial in turn, and weigh vials and contents. Store samples not immediately used in the desiccator.

Check out two small magnets, one of them coated with plastic (a small stirring bar about $\frac{3}{8}$ in. in diameter and 1 in. long), the other not coated but of similar dimensions. Return these magnets at the end of the period. Do not mark them in any way.

The following operations should be practiced before using any of the weighed-out samples: Orient the two magnets so that they are antiparallel. Slip the coated magnet into a $\frac{1}{2}$-dram vial, and with the dropper add distilled water until the liquid level is about even with the top end of the coated magnet. Add 20 ml of water to the 50-ml conical flask, and slip the vial without loss of liquid into the flask by suitable manipulation of the uncoated magnet on the outside. Note that there may be sudden and unfortunate motion of the inside magnet if the orientation of the two magnets is not antiparallel, but parallel so that they repel each other. Hold the vial suspended at the side of the flask, and without losing liquid from the vial connect the flask to the equipment of Figure 6-1, having set aside beaker A and the supporting tripod. Manipulate the outside magnet so that the vial turns over.

For each sample, proceed as follows: Adjust the funnel so that the water level in the buret is close to the highest calibration mark. Dissolve 0.5 g of sulfamic acid in the 50-ml conical flask, using 20 ml of water.

Put the coated stirring bar into one of the sample vials and add a few drops of water. Carefully manipulate the uncoated magnet so that the magnet inside the vial acts as stirrer until the nitrite sample is dissolved. Add more water until the liquid level is about even with the top of the coated magnet. Insert the vial into the 50-ml flask as practiced, connect the rubber stopper at D so that a gastight seal is obtained, and replace beaker A and tripod so that the conical flask is completely surrounded by water. Adjust the temperature of the water to room temperature, equalize the levels in buret and filter funnel, and wait for 5 to 10 min to permit temperature equilibrium to establish itself. Readjust the levels, and read the buret, using the device for reading buret levels recommended previously (Fig. 5-5, page 103). To minimize the effects of any potential leak, the two levels should be kept at approximately the same height during the gas evolution. Be ready to lower the funnel and to follow the sinking level in the buret before starting the reaction.

Manipulate the outside magnet so that the vial turns over and the solutions mix. Use the outside magnet to control the rate of mixing and thus to keep the gas evolution from becoming too violent. Finally, cause the inside magnet to slip out of the vial. After the evolution of nitrogen has slowed to a low rate, use the outside magnet to stir the contents of the flask once a minute. Exert caution so as not to change the size of the gas volume defined by the Koroseal tubing. The reaction should be completed after about 10 to 15 min. Allow any gas bubbles in the vial to escape and to combine with the main volume of gas.

Readjust the temperature, let the apparatus stand for 5 to 10 min, equalize the water levels in buret and funnel, and read the buret.

6-3 Computation of the results.   Compute the weight per cent nitrogen for each sample, and average the values. The barometer reading will be provided by the laboratory instructor; the vapor pressure of water as function of the temperature is listed in the table on page 398. Compute the unbiased standard deviation and the relative unbiased standard deviation of your results (see page 398).

PROBLEMS

6-1 Stoichiometry.   Compute the amount of pure $NaNO_2$ which, when treated according to the procedures of this experiment, will yield a volume of 40.0 ml of nitrogen at 25°C and an outside atmospheric pressure of 740 mm.

6-2 Density of a gas mixture.   Compute the density of a mixture of gases containing, by volume, 30 per cent H_2 and 70 per cent CH_4, at 700 mm and 24°C.

6-3 Molecular weight of a gas.   Find the molecular weight of a pure gas of density 2.48 g/liter at 100°C and 740 mm pressure.

6-4 Saturation of gas with water vapor.   Dry air is saturated with water vapor at 50°C. What is the ratio of the volumes of the humid and the dry air if the total pressure is kept constant, at 760 mm? Evaluate the ratio by the numerical method indicated in Appendix I, page 377. $pH_2O = 92.5$ mm at 50°C.

6-5 Stoichiometry.   A volume of 300 ml of O_2 gas is added to 100 ml of a gaseous mixture of CO and C_2H_6. Complete combustion is initiated, and the total volume of the resulting gases is found to be 430 ml. All volume measurements are at the same temperature and pressure, at which both H_2O and CO_2 are gases. What is the volume composition of the original gas mixture?

6-6 Volume correction.   The volume of a gas collected over water at 25°C and 740 mm was 600 ml. The gas was dried and stored at 20°C and 750 mm. What was its volume? (See Table V-3, page 398, for partial vapor pressures of water.)

6-7 Gas law.   A tank filled with 1.000 kg of N_2 at a total pressure of 16 atm and at 0°C is heated to 50°C and the valve is opened. What total weight of N_2 escapes when the tank is kept at 50°C?

6-8   Gas law.   A steel tank of volume 50.3 liters contains 250 g N_2, 355 g O_2, and 73 g CO_2. (*a*) How many moles of gas are in the tank? (*b*) What is the partial pressure of N_2 at 30°C? (*c*) What is the density of the gas mixture?

6-9   Gas law.   An air-filled vessel with an open valve is heated from 0°C to 200°C and the valve is closed, all at a pressure of 1.000 atm. (*a*) What fraction of the gas originally in the vessel remains after closing the valve? (*b*) What is the pressure inside the closed vessel after cooling to 0°C? (*c*) How many moles of gas are in the closed vessel, which has a volume of 10.00 liters?

6-10   Gas constant.   Find the value of R that should be used in the perfect-gas equation if p is given in pounds per square inch, V in cubic feet, T in degrees Rankine, and the quantity of gas in pound moles rather than in gram moles. 1 atm = 14.7 lb/in^2; 1 in = 2.54 cm; 1 lb = 454 g; 1°R = $\frac{5}{9}$°K.

6-11   Stoichiometry.   (*a*) How many milliliters of O_2 at 20°C and 700 mm are required to convert the iodide in a solution containing 10.00 g HI quantitatively to I_2, provided that all O_2 reacts by the equation $4HI + O_2 = 2I_2 + H_2O$? (*b*) How many milliliters of air containing 21.0 volume per cent O_2 would the conversion take under the same conditions?

REVIEW QUESTIONS

6-1.   What is a zwitter ion?

6-2.   Why is the reaction mixture producing the N_2 kept strongly acid?

6-3.   Would the result of the nitrogen analysis be high or low if the partial pressure of water were not corrected for?

6-4.   Assume that the apparatus of Figure 6-1 contains 30.0 ml of air at the beginning of the experiment and that 50.0 ml of N_2 are produced. By how much and in what direction must each of the following measurements be in error to cause the reported quantity of nitrogen to be 0.5 relative per cent higher than the theoretical value? (*a*) Gas volume; (*b*) sample weight; (*c*) temperature measurement, assuming the temperature to be constant during the experiment and neglecting any change of the partial pressure of water with the temperature.

*The general aspects of
volumetric analysis are considered
and an outline of
the mass-action law is presented.
This is followed by discussions
of precipitation titrations
and of volumetric techniques.
In a laboratory assignment Ag^+ is
titrated with SCN^- (Volhard titration).*

seven

VOLUMETRIC ANALYSIS

GENERAL PRINCIPLES

In volumetric analysis a solution is added by means of a buret to a second solution until all the reactant in the second solution has been consumed, within the precision desired. This operation is called *titration*, and the solution being added from the buret is called the *titrant*. The end of a titration is often recognized by the color change of an *indicator* that has been added.

Titrations may be used: (1) to compare the unknown concentration of a solution with the known concentration of a *standard solution* by finding the ratio of the volumes that react quantitatively. Which of the two solutions is used as the titrant depends on the details of the titration reaction and on the means used to recognize the end of the titration. (2) A solution may be standardized by titrating with it a known quantity of a pure dissolved reactant. (3) Inversely, the total quantity of a reactant may be found by dissolving it and then titrating it with standard solution. The concentration of a standard solution is sometimes called its *titer*.

For example, a NaOH solution may be standardized by titrating with it a weighed quantity of sulfamic acid (described in Chap. 6, page 123) dissolved in a convenient volume of water. This standard solution may be used to find the concentration of an HCl solution. The total alkalinity of a water-soluble material containing hydroxides and carbonates of the alkali metals may be determined by titrating a solution containing a weighed quantity of the material with standard HCl solution. In each case the end of the titration may be observed by the change in color of litmus or of another suitable acid-base indicator.

Volumetric methods are popular because they require less experience and fewer special techniques than gravimetric methods. They are rapid once the standard solutions have been prepared. Their precision is, in general, comparable with that of gravimetric methods.

Criteria for volumetric reactions. A reaction and the compounds involved must satisfy the following requirements to be usable as the basis of a volumetric procedure:

The reaction must go to completion. The equilibrium between reactants and products must be highly favorable for the products so that only a negligible excess of standard solution is required to obtain complete reaction, within the desired precision, of the substance being titrated.

The reaction must be stoichiometric. There must be a definite relationship between the quantities of substances reacting. Such a definite relationship may be destroyed by side reactions.

The reaction must be fast. Equilibrium must be established while the titrating solution is added.

A standard solution must be stable if reasonable precautions are exercised, such as protection from atmospheric influences (O_2, CO_2), light, high temperatures, etc.

There must exist a means to recognize the completion of the titration, within the desired precision. Indicators, i.e., substances that change color upon completion of the titration, are often available for this purpose. Or the reactant in one or the other solution may be strongly colored, so that the point at which all the solution being titrated has reacted or at which a slight excess of titrant has been added may be recognized. Physical methods of determining the completion of a titration, such as observing changes in the conductivity or in the electrical potential of the solution, also exist.

It is important to distinguish between the *equivalence point* and the *end point* of a titration. At the equivalence point the quantity of titrant added corresponds exactly to the quantity of substance being determined. The end point is the point at which the titration is terminated because the indicator changes or other observations signal completion. The difference between the end point and the equivalence point represents the *titration error*. It is a matter of theoretical insight and of experimental technique to make the end point of a titration fall as close as possible to the equivalence point.

There are two methods for the *preparation of standard solutions*. (1) A weighed quantity of the pure substance concerned is dissolved and diluted in a volumetric flask to a known volume at a known temperature. (2) A solution of approximately the desired concentration is prepared and standardized either against a suitable standard solution or against a solution containing a weighed quantity of a substance of known purity.

The first procedure may be used when the substance involved can be obtained with high purity, is stable enough to be dried, and can be weighed precisely without major precautions. In addition, the resulting solution must not change its initial concentration, as may occur by reaction with gases or with traces of organic materials that are usually contained in distilled water. The second procedure is more frequently used; for the substances employed in the preparation of standard solutions often do not satisfy the criteria just mentioned.

Primary standards are standards that are suitable for analytical reactions and pure enough so that weighed quantities may be used for preparation of stable standard solutions or for the standardization of other solutions. They must be sufficiently stable to be stored indefinitely without change in composition and to be weighed without special precautions such as excluding air or humidity. Examples are silver nitrate, used to make up standard silver nitrate solution, and sulfamic acid, used in the standardization of base. Solutions that are standardized against a primary standard are called *secondary*, or *derived*, *standards*.

THE MASS-ACTION LAW

The degree of completion of a reaction is governed, under equilibrium conditions, by the mass-action law, which will be used extensively to discuss titration reactions.

Suppose that a chemical reaction is symbolized by the balanced equation

$$aA + bB + \cdots = uU + vV + \cdots \tag{7-1}$$

implying that a molecules of substance A, b molecules of substance B, etc., react to form u molecules of substance U, v molecules of substance V, etc. The condition of equilibrium is that at a given temperature the following combination of the molar concentrations of the substances involved is constant:

$$\frac{[U]^u [V]^v \cdots}{[A]^a [B]^b \cdots} = K(T) \tag{7-2}$$

For example, in the reaction between $Fe^{3+} + Sn^{++}$ to form Fe^{++} and Sn^{4+}, the balanced chemical equation is

$$2Fe^{3+} + Sn^{++} = 2Fe^{++} + Sn^{4+} \tag{7-3}$$

and the mass-action equation has the form

$$[Fe^{++}]^2 [Sn^{4+}]/[Fe^{3+}]^2 [Sn^{++}] = K_3 \tag{7-4}$$

Equation (7-2) is known as the *mass-action law*. The constant $K(T)$, called the equilibrium constant, depends on the temperature T of the system only. Its value may be established by measuring the set of all concentrations at any of the infinite number of combinations at which there is equilibrium. Other methods of determining $K(T)$ for a given reaction are also available.

The mass-action law in the form (7-2) holds only when the concentrations are small. The assumptions made in its derivation are similar to those underlying the perfect-gas equation, such as the absence of forces between the particles involved. Thus, the larger such forces actually are, the larger the deviations from the mass-action law. For solutions the deviations increase with concentration and are the more pronounced the higher the charges on the particles concerned. Interactions between solute and solvent particles may also cause deviations. It is possible to take all these deviations into account by replacing the concentrations of the different species involved in the equilibrium by "effective concentrations" called *activities*. However, these refinements of Eq. (7-2) will not be discussed here. When ionized solutions are involved, quantitative predictions based on Eq. (7-2) are unsafe unless the total ionic concentration is less than about $0.01\ M$. When this equation is applied, as it often is, to solutions of total concentrations approximately between 0.1 and 1.0 M, deviations of 20 per cent and higher may be expected. Nevertheless, the results of applying the mass-action law in its simple form (7-2) are found to be very useful.

Conventions in setting up mass-action expressions.   It is a universally used convention that the concentrations of the products, the substances on the right side of the chemical equation, are always placed in the numerator of the corresponding mass-action expression and the concentrations of the reactants, the substances on the left side of the chemical equation, are placed in the denominator. The following more special conventions are also observed; it is convenient to explain them by examples.

One or more of the substances involved is a gas. Consider the reaction

$$2Fe^{3+} + 2Cl^- = 2Fe^{++} + Cl_2(g) \qquad (7\text{-}5)$$

where the letter g implies that a gas phase containing Cl_2 of a certain partial pressure p_{Cl_2} is at equilibrium with the solution containing the other chemical species. The concentration of Cl_2 in the solution is proportional to p_{Cl_2} (Henry's law), the proportionality constant being k_{Cl_2}.

$$[Cl_2] = k_{Cl_2} p_{Cl_2} \qquad (7\text{-}6)$$

The mass-action equation corresponding to (7-5) would be

$$\frac{[Fe^{++}]^2[Cl_2]}{[Fe^{3+}]^2[Cl^-]^2} = K_5' \qquad (7\text{-}7)$$

but by convention $[Cl_2]$ is replaced by its equivalent from (7-6), and the constant k_{Cl_2} is combined with K_5'.

$$\frac{[Fe^{++}]^2 p_{Cl_2}}{[Fe^{3+}]^2[Cl^-]^2} = \frac{K_5'}{k_{Cl_2}} \equiv K_5 \qquad (7\text{-}8)$$

Thus, when one of the species involved in an equilibrium is a gas, its concentration in the mass-action expression is replaced by the partial pressure of the gas, unless a definite statement to the contrary has been made. The value of the equilibrium constant quoted for such a reaction implicitly contains the proper power of the appropriate Henry's law constant.

A participant in a reaction in a dilute solution is water. An example is the reaction

$$Ti^{3+} + Fe^{3+} + H_2O = TiO^{++} + Fe^{++} + 2H^+ \qquad (7\text{-}9)$$

for which the mass-action equation might be written

$$\frac{[TiO^{++}][Fe^{++}][H^+]^2}{[Ti^{3+}][Fe^{3+}][H_2O]} = K_9'$$

133

However, the concentration of H_2O in a dilute solution may be replaced to a good approximation by its value in pure water, where $[H_2O] = 998/18.02 = 55.4$ moles/liter. By convention this is done and $[H_2O]$ is combined with K_9':

$$\frac{[TiO^{++}][Fe^{++}][H^+]^2}{[Ti^{3+}][Fe^{3+}]} = 55.4K_9' \equiv K_9 \qquad (7\text{-}10)$$

Whenever water participates in a reaction in dilute solution, its concentration is combined with the equilibrium constant so that $[H_2O]$ does not appear in the mass-action expression.

One or more of the species involved is a solid. As an example, consider the reaction

$$AgCl(s) = Ag^+ + Cl^- \qquad (7\text{-}11)$$

The equilibrium expression might be written

$$\frac{[Ag^+][Cl^-]}{[AgCl]} = K_{11}$$

However, in the presence of solid silver chloride the concentration of molecular AgCl is constant at a given temperature, and its value may be combined with K_{11}. The mass-action equation thus becomes

$$[Ag^+][Cl^-] = K_{11}[AgCl] \equiv K_{SP} \qquad (7\text{-}12)$$

the solubility product familiar from the discussion in Chapter 4. Whenever a solid is involved in a reaction, the concentration of the molecular species corresponding to it is constant at equilibrium even though its value may be exceedingly small, and this concentration is combined with the equilibrium constant so that it does not appear in the mass-action expression.

As a combined example of these three conventions, the equilibrium expression of the reaction

$$2I_2(s) + 2H_2O = O_2(g) + 4I^- + 4H^+ \qquad (7\text{-}13)$$

is

$$p_{O_2}[I^-]^4[H^+]^4 = K_{13} \qquad (7\text{-}14)$$

Note, however, that the presence of solid iodine is explicitly prescribed by the s in the parentheses following the I_2 in Eq. (7-13). If the presence of solid iodine cannot be presumed, Eq. (7-13) must be written without this letter s,

$$2I_2 + 2H_2O = O_2(g) + 4I^- + 4H^+ \qquad (7\text{-}15)$$

and the equilibrium condition is

$$\frac{p_{O_2}[I^-]^4[H^+]^4}{[I_2]^2} = K_{15} \qquad (7\text{-}16)$$

The constant K_{15} is, of course, different from K_{13}.

The conventions just given are used for reactions that occur in solutions. Similar conventions apply to other types of reactions as between gases and between gases and solids. Their principal usefulness is that they permit the unambiguous listing of mass-action constants with chemical equations without explicit statement of the mass-action expressions; chemical equations are typographically much easier to handle than mass-action equations.

The *units of mass-action constants* are usually deleted, with the understanding that they are always the same as the units of the corresponding mass-action expressions. For example, the units of K_9 are (mole/liter)^2, those of K_{13} are atm(mole/liter)^8, and those of K_{15} are atm(mole/liter)^6. It is important to realize that the magnitudes of mass-action constants may be compared only when the units of these constants are the same.

When two or more reaction equations are combined into an overall reaction equation, the corresponding mass-action constants may be combined by applying the three rules given below. These rules follow from the way in which the mass-action expression depends on the coefficients of the chemical species in the related reaction equation. They are illustrated by Problem 7-5.

1. When a reaction equation is reversed, the new mass-action constant is the reciprocal of the original constant.

2. When a chemical equation is multiplied by a coefficient n, the original mass-action constant K changes to K^n. The coefficient n may be an integer or a fraction.

3. When two chemical equations are added, the equilibrium constant of the resulting equation is the product of the constants of the original equations.

Aside from the deviations from Eq. (7-2) mentioned earlier, it must never be forgotten that the mass-action law applies only when equilibrium actually is established and that no conclusions can be drawn from it about the rate at which this equilibrium is established. Mass-action considerations thus serve to eliminate reactions and conditions for which the equilibrium is unfavorable for use in analytical procedures. If the results of such considerations are favorable, it is still necessary to establish that the reaction rates are favorable also.

135

PRECIPITATION TITRATIONS

Depending on the reactions underlying a titration, one distinguishes among:

1. Precipitation titrations, to be discussed in this section,

2. *Oxidation and reduction* (*redox*) *titrations*, in which one of the two solutions is oxidized, the other reduced,

3. *Ionization titrations*, which include neutralization, complex-ion formation, and the formation of un-ionized compounds.

Later chapters furnish examples of the second and third categories listed.

In a precipitation titration the reaction between the two solutions goes to completion because a relatively insoluable precipitate is formed. The end point may be determined by several methods.

In the Gay-Lussac titration of silver with standard chloride solution, the *cessation of observable precipitation* of AgCl is used. Although this method yields results of high precision under controlled conditions and is used in certain mints for assaying silver, it is laborious and of little general value.

More often a substance known as *indicator* is added. It produces a visible reaction upon completion of the titration, like the formation of a colored compound or a characteristic precipitate. For example, in the titration of Cl^- with standard silver nitrate solution, a small amount of $CrO_4^=$ can be added to the chloride solution, whence the sequence of reactions is as follows: As long as any but traces of Cl^- remain in the solution being titrated, addition of Ag^+ causes the precipitation of AgCl,

$$Ag^+ + Cl^- = AgCl(s) \qquad \text{titration reaction}$$

When $[Cl^-]$ has decreased below a certain value, addition of Ag^+ produces a precipitate of reddish-brown Ag_2CrO_4,

$$2Ag^+ + CrO_4^- = Ag_2CrO_4(s) \qquad \text{indicator reaction}$$
$$\text{reddish-brown}$$

Silver chromate is much more soluble than silver chloride, so that practically all Cl^- has reacted when the appearance of the characteristic red color of the chromate precipitate signals the completion of the titration. This method is known as the *Mohr titration*. Another example is the method used in the laboratory assignment for this chapter, which will be discussed in the next section.

The end point may also be detected by the use of an *adsorption indicator*, which involves the change in adsorption properties of certain precipitates near the equivalence point. Thus in the titration of Cl^- with standard $AgNO_3$, a small amount of fluorescein, an organic dye of greenish color, may be added to the chloride solution. As long as the halide ions are in excess, they are preferentially adsorbed to the surface of the AgCl precipitate, as discussed in Chapter 4 (page 70). Near the equivalence point the halide concentration is greatly reduced, and fluorescein begins to be adsorbed. Since fluorescein changes its color to pink upon adsorption, the end point is indicated when the white AgCl precipitate takes on a pinkish tinge.

Other methods of end-point detection are available, such as measurement of the conductivity or of the electrical potential of the solution, as mentioned earlier.

Not all reactions that result in a slightly soluble precipitate are suitable for a precipitation titration. Besides being highly insoluble the precipitate must be of stoichiometric composition. The formation of slightly soluable silver salts is the basis of a large majority of precipitation titrations.

The Volhard titration

In the Volhard titration the amount of Ag^+ in a solution is determined by titration with a standard solution of potassium thiocyanate (KSCN). A small amount of $Fe(NO_3)_3$ added to the Ag^+ solution acts as end-point indicator by reacting with SCN^- to form $FeSCN^{++}$, a compound of intense red color. The sequence of reactions is as follows:

The SCN^- ions added combine at first almost exclusively with the Ag^+ ions to form slightly soluble AgSCN,

$$Ag^+ + SCN^- = AgSCN(s) \qquad \text{titration reaction} \qquad (7\text{-}17)$$

When substantially all Ag^+ has been precipitated, further addition of the KSCN solution causes a sudden rise in the concentration of SCN^- and a parallel rise in the concentration of the strongly colored $FeSCN^{++}$,

$$\underset{\text{red}}{Fe^{3+} + SCN^- = FeSCN^{++}} \qquad \text{indicator reaction} \qquad (7\text{-}18)$$

The appearance of the first red tinge is thus a sign that the titration is completed.

The concentrations of the various ions during the titration may be computed from the following mass-action constants:

$$[Ag^+][SCN^-] = K_{SP} = 1 \times 10^{-12} \qquad (7\text{-}19)$$

$$\frac{[FeSCN^{++}]}{[Fe^{3+}][SCN^-]} = 1.4 \times 10^2 \qquad (7\text{-}20)$$

Equation (7-19) may be used to compute the concentrations of Ag^+ and of SCN^- during a titration. Assume, for example, that 100.00 ml of 0.2000 F AgNO$_3$ solution is titrated with 0.2000 F KSCN solution and that 99.99 ml of SCN^- solution has been added. If all the SCN^- were to react with Ag^+, the concentration of the remaining Ag^+ would equal $0.2000(100.00-99.99)/199.99 \approx 10^{-5}$ mole/liter. However, a small quantity of unreacted SCN^- will remain at equilibrium, which can be computed with the aid of (7-19). Let the final concentration of SCN^- due to this unreacted quantity be x, that is, $[SCN^-] = x$; to it correspond x moles/liter of additional unreacted Ag^+, so that $[Ag^+] \approx 10^{-5} + x$. Insertion into (7-19) yields $x(10^{-5} + x) = 10^{-12}$, so that $x = [SCN^-] \approx 10^{-7}$ and $[Ag] \approx 10^{-5}$. At the equivalence point $[Ag^+] = [SCN^-] = 10^{-6}$. When 100.01 ml of SCN^- solution has been added, a calculation similar to the one just explained yields $[SCN^-] \approx 10^{-5}$ and $[Ag^+] \approx 10^{-7}$.

Figure 7-1 shows the results of these and analogous computations; the logarithms of $[SCN^-]$ and of $[Ag^+]$ as functions of the ratio of moles SCN^- added to Ag^+ present originally are plotted. Of great importance is the enormous change, near the equivalence point, of the concentration of SCN^- and of Ag^+ with a given change of this ratio.

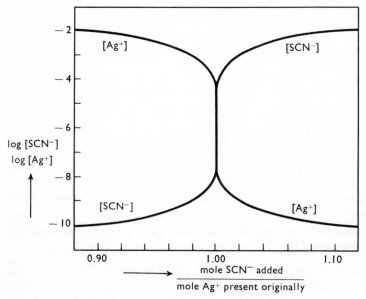

Figure 7-1   The concentration of SCN^- and Ag^+ during a titration of 0.2 F AgNO$_3$ with 0.2 F KSCN.

138

This feature is characteristic of all titrations, and the sharpness of the end point depends on it. The values explicitly calculated above show that, from the point where 1 part in 10,000 of SCN^- remains to be added to the point where 1 part in 10,000 has been added in excess, the value of $[SCN^-]$ changes from 10^{-7} to 10^{-5}, or by a factor 100. By Eq. (7-20) the concentration of $FeSCN^{++}$ changes directly with that of SCN^-,

$$[FeSCN^{++}] = 1.4 \times 10^2 [Fe^{3+}][SCN^-]$$

although the dependence is not one of direct proportionality to the unreacted SCN^-, since some of it is used up in the formation of $FeSCN^{++}$. There is thus an enormous change near the equivalence point in the concentration of the intensely red $FeSCN^{++}$ when minute amounts of SCN^- are added; this rapid change is essential for the precise observation of the end point.

For a quantitative discussion of the functioning of the indicator, information about the intensity of the color of $FeSCN^{++}$ is needed. It has been established that a concentration of $[FeSCN^{++}] = 5 \times 10^{-6}$ corresponds to the faint but clearly visible pink color of the end point.* At the conditions described in the procedures of this assignment, the concentration of Fe^{3+} is about 2.5×10^{-2}, so that at the end point, by Equation (7-20),

$$[SCN^-] = \frac{[FeSCN^{++}]}{1.4 \times 10^2 [Fe^{3+}]}$$

$$= \frac{5 \times 10^{-6}}{2.5 \times 1.4} = 1.4 \times 10^{-6}$$

and, by Equation (7-19),

$$[Ag^+] = \frac{1 \times 10^{-12}}{[SCN^-]} = 7.1 \times 10^{-7}$$

The relative titration error

$$e = \frac{\text{added moles } SCN^- - \text{original moles } Ag^+}{\text{original moles } Ag^+}$$

Most of the added SCN^- ions react to form $AgSCN(s)$, but some turn up as $FeSCN^{++}$ and some remain unreacted. The Ag^+ ions mainly precipitate as $AgSCN(s)$, but some remain in solution. In the titration error e the moles SCN^- in the $AgSCN(s)$ just cancel the moles Ag^+ so that

* E. H. Swift, *Introductory Quantitative Analysis*, Prentice-Hall, Englewood Cliffs, N.J., 1950, pp. 95, 450.

$$e = \frac{\text{unreacted moles SCN}^- + \text{moles FeSCN}^{++} - \text{unreacted moles Ag}^+}{\text{original moles Ag}^+}$$

In the example discussed the quantity of Ag^+ originally contained in 100 ml of 0.2 F $AgNO_3$ solution is $0.2/10 = 2 \times 10^{-2}$ mole, and the quantities in the numerator pertain to 200 ml of solution and are obtained by dividing the corresponding concentrations by 5. Thus

$$e = \frac{1.4 \times 10^{-6} + 5 \times 10^{-6} - 7.1 \times 10^{-7}}{5 \times 2 \times 10^{-2}} \approx 5 \times 10^{-5}$$

Under the circumstances considered the titration error is thus about 5 parts in 100,000. Experimentally, a precision of 1 to 2 parts per 1000 can be achieved readily.

SOME VOLUMETRIC TECHNIQUES

Volumetric equipment and techniques for using it were described in the discussion of the calibration of volumetric equipment (Chap. 5), which should be reviewed. Additional information on techniques follows.

Standard solutions. The concentration of many of the standard solutions used in volumetric analysis is in the vicinity of 0.1 F. The following considerations enter into the choice of the concentration of the titrant and of the amount of substance being titrated. The calibrated portion of the buret (usually 50 ml) should be utilized adequately and the buret should not have to be refilled during a titration, which means that 30 to 40 ml of titrant should be used. It might appear that the precision of a titration could be improved arbitrarily by decreasing the concentration of the titrant and using a larger buret, since to a small quantity of substance as large a volume of titrant as desired could be made to correspond; but the need for a sharp and definite end point sets a lower concentration limit. If the changes in concentration of the ions participating in the titration reaction (such as $[Ag^+]$ and $[SCN^-]$ in the Volhard titration) are plotted not as a function of the ratio of the reactants as in Figure 7-1, but as a function of the volume of titrant added, the slope of the curves depends on the concentration of the titrant. The lower this concentration, the less steep the curves, and therefore the less definite the end point.

Primary standard solutions are prepared by dissolving a weighed quantity of primary standard and diluting it in a volumetric flask to a precise volume. This is a routine operation of general applicability described by the procedure below. Secondary or derived standard solutions are calibrated against a primary standard.

140

PROCEDURE FOR PREPARING A SOLUTION OF ACCURATE VOLUME

Transfer the solid or liquid to be dissolved or diluted to a suitable volumetric flask through a funnel with a long stem so that the part of the neck of the flask above the calibration mark remains clean and dry. If a solid is to be dissolved, wash the particles clinging to the funnel into the flask by sparing amounts of water from the wash bottle. Make sure that all drops that contain dissolved material are washed from the funnel into the flask. Continue adding water until the liquid level in the flask reaches almost to the neck. Remove the funnel and gently swirl the flask until the solution is well mixed and any solids originally present are dissolved. Finally, add water with a dropper or pipet until the bottom part of the meniscus is tangent to the calibration mark. Before making the final adjustment remove with filter paper any water droplets that have reached the neck above the calibration mark. Avoid parallax errors and shade the meniscus with the device shown in Figure 5-5 (page 103). Stopper the flask, swirl, invert the flask, swirl again, and repeat this sequence at least ten times. Determine the temperature of the solution and *record it in your notebook*. The distilled water used in diluting solutions should be close to room temperature. However, heat is often absorbed or evolved during the solution and the dilution processes, and the temperature of the final solution must therefore be measured. Alternatively, the solution may be allowed to attain room temperature *before* the final adjustment of the meniscus to the calibration mark, a procedure that is time consuming.

When a solution is diluted, the resulting volume is not necessarily the sum of the volumes of the original solution and the water added. This is the reason for thoroughly mixing the solution just before the liquid level has reached the neck of the flask.

If inadvertently too much water has been added, the solution may be saved as follows. Paste a piece of paper to the neck of the flask and carefully mark the position of the meniscus with a sharp pencil. Remove the solution and fill the flask with water until the meniscus is tangent to the original calibration mark. Add water from a buret until the meniscus is tangent to the pencil mark. Record the volume added and find the total volume.

Do not store a solution in a volumetric flask. Transfer it to a *clean* and *dry* bottle with a good stopper. *Label the bottle*. Always *mix a solution well* before using it, because frequently there has been evaporation and condensation of water on the glass wall above the solution surface. Use all solutions, and particularly standard solutions, sparingly.

The titration. Since it is advisable not to let a clean and well-wetted buret become dry, the buret should be wet to begin with and must be rinsed with several small portions of a standard solution before being filled with that solution. Pipets are rinsed in the same way before being used to transfer solution. The buret or pipet is held almost horizontally and rotated slowly so that all parts of the walls are reached by the solution. Do not pipet directly from the bottle containing the solution; instead, pour a small amount sufficient to rinse the pipet into a beaker. The solution left is discarded and enough fresh solution is poured into the beaker for the actual transfer by pipet. Use a pipet bulb, but do not suck solution into the bulb. Do not blow out the pipet.

The titration itself is best performed in a conical flask held close to the buret so that losses by splashing are readily prevented. As titrant is added, the solution is swirled to avoid any local excess of titrant. With some burets it takes both hands to operate the valve unless the buret is solidly clamped. Use two clamps in such cases, so that one hand is free to swirl the flask. A general procedure for titrations is given below.

Titrations are usually carried out in triplicate. After completing the first run, it is convenient to compute with a slide rule the volume of titrant to be expected in all subsequent runs. This permits rapid addition of titrant until the equivalence point is close, without fear of overrunning the titration.

In the first titration a small portion of the solution to be titrated is sometimes removed, as a precaution, by sucking it into a long dropper called a *titration thief*. When the indicator appears to be near a permanent color change so that the titration is almost finished, the portion that has been withdrawn is returned to the main solution. If the end point has already been passed, the titration may be rescued in this way. At the end point the liquid in the flask must be sucked into the dropper and expelled again several times to ensure complete reaction of all substance previously in the dropper.

PROCEDURE FOR TITRATIONS

Mix the standard solution with the water that may have evaporated and condensed above the solution surface. Rinse the buret with several small portions of standard solution before filling it. Use a small funnel. Avoid overflow and remove the funnel after filling. Withdraw solution until the meniscus approaches the zero mark. Allow 30 sec for drainage;

adjust the meniscus to the mark; remove any hanging drops from the tip; and check to see that there are no air bubbles in the tip.

Hold the titration vessel close to the buret to minimize splashing, and swirl the solution while adding the titrant. As the titration nears its end point, the local and transient changes characteristic of the indicator used begin to spread through the solution. Wash down the inside walls of the flask with water from the wash bottle at this point. Continue the titration with single drops and later with fractions of a drop that are transferred from the buret tip to the titration vessel by a glass rod. Wash down the walls of the flask during this procedure and again when the end point is reached.

The end point has been reached only if the indicator color change persists for at least 5 to 10 sec while the solution is swirled. Read the buret after allowing time for drainage. *Record this reading in your notebook.* Establish and also record the solution temperatures (usually room temperature), because temperature corrections may be necessary.

*A thiocyanate solution is standardized
by Volhard's method
against several weighed and dissolved
samples of pure silver nitrate.
The thiocyanate solution is then used
to determine by titration
the amount of silver in a sample
of a silver alloy that is dissolved in nitric acid.*

Laboratory assignment 7
(*4 periods*)

VOLUMETRIC DETERMINATION

OF SILVER

DISCUSSION

In this assignment the silver content of an alloy sample is to be determined by dissolving the sample in nitric acid and titrating the Ag^+ in the resulting solution by the Volhard method. The KSCN solution used in this titration is standardized by the Volhard method also, by titrating with it solutions that contain known quantities of $AgNO_3$.

It is important that the Ag^+ solutions used in this titration do not contain nitrous acid, because thiocyanate is oxidized by this substance to form a transitory red color that may be mistaken for the end point. The HNO_3 available may contain HNO_2, and in dissolving the silver

144

alloy HNO_2 may also be formed by the solution reaction, in which NO or NO_2 is an intermediary. Depending on whether the nitric acid is dilute or concentrated, this reaction may be described as follows: In dilute nitric acid,

$$3Ag + 4H^+ + NO_3^- = 3Ag^+ + 2H_2O + NO$$

In more concentrated nitric acid,

$$Ag + 2H^+ + NO_3^- = Ag^+ + H_2O + NO_2$$

Nitric oxide combines with oxygen to form nitrogen dioxide,

$$2NO + O_2 = 2NO_2$$

which in turn combines with cold water to form nitrous and nitric acids,

$$2NO_2 + H_2O = HNO_2 + NO_3^- + H^+$$

Before using the Volhard method the HNO_2 must be boiled off.

Vigorous stirring or swirling of the solution is needed to avoid a premature end point, because of the strong tendency for freshly formed $AgSCN$ precipitate to adsorb Ag^+ ions on its surface.

The solution should be acid to prevent the following reaction of the ferric ions with water,

$$Fe^{3+} + H_2O = Fe(OH)^{++} + H^+$$

since the yellow reaction product tends to obscure the end point. The equilibrium expression for this reaction is

$$\frac{[H^+][FeOH^{++}]}{[Fe^{3+}]} = K$$

An increase of the H^+ concentration caused by adding acid will therefore shift the equilibrium to the left, decreasing the concentration of $Fe(OH)^{++}$ and increasing that of Fe^{3+}.

The solutions should be kept cold, since at elevated temperatures: (1) the concentration of $FeOH^{++}$ is increased, (2) $FeSCN^{++}$ is more dissociated, (3) thiocyanate ion is oxidized more readily by nitric acid and by ferric ion.

The presence of large amounts of Cu^{++}, which is blue, tends to mask the red end point. The solution assumes a green tinge rather than turning red; as the amount of excess SCN^- is increased, the green color deepens. This is mainly due to green compounds that are formed between SCN^- and Cu^{++}, such as $Cu(SCN)_3^-$. When the alloy contains more than about 30 to 40 per cent Cu, the end point is not sharp and the titration must be terminated at the first color change from blue toward green. The precision of the method is impaired under these circumstances. The presence of Cu^{++} may also hasten the fading of the end point by oxidation of SCN^-. The copper content of the alloys used for this assignment is low enough that there should be no difficulty on either account.

PROCEDURES

7-1 Preparation of the samples. Obtain silver-alloy samples from your instructor. Record the sample number. The samples are pieces of wire cut to such size that one piece will require a convenient amount of approximately 0.1 F KSCN solution in the titration. Remove any grease or tarnish with cleaning powder. If there is severe tarnish, abrasive cloth must be used before further cleaning.

Clean three 200-ml conical flasks and mark them with pencil. They need not be dry, but they should have had a final rinse with a small amount of distilled water. Accurately weigh three dry samples of alloy wire and transfer them to the flasks.

Add 15 ml of chloride-free 6 F HNO_3 to each sample. It is wise to test the 6 F HNO_3 for chloride by adding to 1 ml one drop of dilute $AgNO_3$ solution. Obtain for this purpose $\frac{1}{2}$ ml or less of 0.1 F or 0.2 F $AgNO_3$ solution.

Cover the flasks with watch glasses, and heat to near boiling. If the reaction becomes too vigorous and there is danger of spattering, discontinue the heating and, if necessary, cool the outside of the flask with running tap water. Continue the heating until the alloy is completely dissolved and all HNO_2 has been removed. Dilute with distilled water to about 100 ml.

7-2 Preparation of a 0.1 F potassium thiocyanate solution. On a rough balance weigh out 10.0 g of potassium thiocyanate. Transfer the crystals to a beaker and dissolve them in distilled water. Pour the solution into a clean bottle that has a ground-glass stopper, and dilute to 1 liter to make an approximately 0.1 F solution. Thoroughly mix by swirling for a prolonged period. Reverse the swirling motion about twenty times. Many volumetric results are inaccurate because of incomplete mixing. Label the bottle.

7-3 Preparation of silver nitrate samples. Review the general procedure for drying samples and weighing out by difference, page 82. On a rough balance weigh out 2.1 g of $AgNO_3$ and transfer into a clean, dry weighing bottle. Dry at 110°C for 2 hr. After cooling in a desiccator, precisely weigh out three samples of about 0.65 to 0.70 g of $AgNO_3$ into 200-ml conical flasks. Label the flasks and cover them with watch glasses.

7-4   Standardization of the KSCN solution.   Dissolve each of the $AgNO_3$ samples weighed out in Procedure 7-3 in about 25 ml of water. Add to each about 10 ml of 6 F HNO_3. The HNO_3 should be free of nitrous acid and chloride. If it is at all yellowish (indicating nitrous oxides), boil it vigorously for several minutes, replace water lost by evaporation, and cool to room temperature. Also add 5 ml of chloride-free (test!) 0.5 F $Fe(NO_3)_3$ solution to each flask, as well as 25 ml of water.

Carefully mix the thiocyanate solution with the water that has evaporated and condensed above the solution. Rinse the clean buret with two to three portions of this solution and fill the buret. Adjust the meniscus of the full buret to the zero mark; allow at least 30 sec for drainage and check that there are no air bubbles in the buret tip.

Gently swirl the silver nitrate solution and add the thiocyanate from the buret until the local and transient pink color first produced by the thiocyanate shows a tendency to spread throughout the solution. Wash down the inside wall of the titration vessel by means of a jet of water from the wash bottle. Shake vigorously to decrease the amount of Ag^+ adsorbed on the precipitate, and continue adding thiocyanate solution in drops and then in fractions of drops until a color that remains permanent when the mixture is swirled vigorously for 10 sec is obtained. After allowing time for drainage, read the buret, and *immediately record this reading in your notebook.*

Calculate with your slide rule the approximate volumes of titrant required for the remaining runs. Perform these titrations in the manner just described. Compute the formality of the thiocyanate solution at 20°C.

7-5   Titration of the unknowns; computation of results.   Take the three samples of unknown solution prepared in Procedure 7-1 and titrate as described in Procedure 7-4. Compute the weight percentage of silver for each of the samples and average the results. Compute the unbiased standard deviation and the relative unbiased standard deviation of your results (see page 83). Discard the AgSCN precipitate into the bottles provided for that purpose.

Volumetric analysis

PROBLEMS

Note: Values of solubility products are given on page 399.

7-1 Solubility product. What is the solubility of $Al(OH)_3$ in distilled water? Consider only the following reaction:

$$Al(OH)_3(s) = Al^{3+} + 3OH^-$$

7-2 The common-ion effect. Ten grams of $PbSO_4$ and ten grams of $PbCl_2$ are shaken with one liter of distilled water. What are the concentrations of Pb^{++}, $SO_4^=$, and Cl^- at equilibrium, assuming that only solubility-product-type reactions are of importance?

7-3 The Mohr titration. A solution containing Cl^- was titrated with standard $AgNO_3$ solution. A small amount of $CrO_4^=$ had been added to the Cl^- solution as indicator. The end point was recognized by the formation of red $Ag_2CrO_4(s)$. The $CrO_4^=$ concentration was 1.0×10^{-2} mole/liter. Using the solubility product constants, compute the Cl^--ion concentration at the point where $Ag_2CrO_4(s)$ just begins to precipitate.

7-4 The Volhard titration. Assume that a titration of Ag^+ with SCN^-, Fe^{3+} serving as indicator, is ended precisely at the point where the concentration of the red complex $FeSCN^{++}$ is 5×10^{-6} mole/liter. From Equations (7-19) and (7-20) compute the concentration of Fe^{3+} for which this end point would coincide precisely with the equivalence point.

7-5 Relationship between mass-action constants and chemical equations. Consider the two chemical equilibria

$$2Fe^{++} + I_2 = 2Fe^{3+} + 2I^- \qquad\qquad K_1 \qquad\qquad (1)$$

$$4Fe^{++} + O_2(g) + 4H^+ = 4Fe^{3+} + 2H_2O \quad K_2 \qquad\qquad (2)$$

(*a*) What is the equilibrium constant of the reverse of reaction (1)? (*b*) What is the equilibrium constant that corresponds to reaction equation (2) multiplied by $\frac{1}{2}$? (*c*) The reaction

$$\tfrac{1}{2}O_2(g) + 2I^- + 2H^+ = I_2 + H_2O \qquad K_3$$

is the result of the combination $\frac{1}{2}$ [Eq. (2)] $-$ [Eq. (1)]. Show that

$$K_3 = \sqrt{K_2}/K_1$$

7-6 Solubility product. The solubility of AgI in water is 3.0×10^{-6} g/liter. (*a*) Find the value of the solubility product. (*b*) What is the solubility of AgI in a $0.01\ F\ NaI$ solution? Ignore the possible existence in the solution of species like AgI, AgI_2^-.

7-7 Solubility products. The solubilities of $CaSO_4$ and $Ca(IO_3)_2$ are both about 6×10^{-3} gfw/liter, yet their solubility products differ by a factor of about 40. Explain.

7-8 Two slightly soluble salts. Sodium oxalate ($Na_2C_2O_4$) solution is added to a saturated solution of calcium fluoride. What is the oxalate ion concentration at which calcium oxalate just begins to precipitate? Assume that only solubility product equilibria are important and that the CaF_2 solution is kept saturated while the sodium oxalate is added.

7-9 The Mohr titration. To three separate 50.00-ml portions of 0.1000 *F* NaCl solution are added, respectively, (*a*) 49.90 ml, (*b*) 50.00 ml, (*c*) 50.10 ml of 0.1000 *F* $AgNO_3$ solution. Calculate [Cl$^-$] for these three cases. Neglect the existence in the solutions of species such as AgCl and $AgCl_2{}^-$.

REVIEW QUESTIONS

7-1. List requirements that a reaction must satisfy if it is to form the basis of a volumetric method.

7-2. State the conventions that are used for setting up mass-action expressions.

7-3. Briefly explain the following terms: titer, titrant, end point, equivalence point, primary standard, and secondary standard.

7-4. Briefly describe (use balanced ionic equations) the reactions that occur when (*a*) pure silver is treated with dilute nitric acid, (*b*) potassium thiocyanate solution is added to an acid solution of silver nitrate, (*c*) nitric acid is added to a solution of ferric nitrate, (*d*) potassium thiocyanate solution is added to an acid solution of ferric nitrate.

7-5. Indicate whether the deviations from the recommended procedures in the Volhard titration listed below would cause the results to be low, high, or unpredictable in sign and magnitude or whether there will be no error. (*a*) The solution of the silver sample is not boiled after completion of the solution. (*b*) $FeCl_3$ solution is used as indicator. (*c*) The titration is performed in a neutral solution. (*d*) The titration vessel is not vigorously swirled during the titration. (*e*) The titration is carried out at an elevated temperature.

REFERENCES

I. M. Kolthoff and E. B. Sandell, *Textbook of Quantitative Inorganic Analysis*, 3rd ed., Chap. 30, Macmillan, New York, 1952.

H. A. Laitinen, *Chemical Analysis*, Chap. 12, McGraw-Hill, New York, 1960.

E. H. Swift, *Introductory Quantitative Analysis*, Chap. 5, Prentice-Hall, Englewood Cliffs, N.J., 1950.

*Dissociation constants and pH
are defined. A general presentation
of acid and base reactions follows,
and equations are developed
for computing the pH of solutions.
Acid-base indicators and the pH meter
are discussed, and the change in pH
during a titration is examined. In a
laboratory assignment the concentration
and the dissociation constant
of a weak acid are determined.*

eight

ACID-BASE

TITRATIONS

ACID CONSTANTS AND pH

Acid-base titrations are examples of the ionization titrations referred to in the preceding discussion of the general principles of volumetric analysis. The inherent precision of a given acid-base titration depends on the equilibrium constants involved and, in particular, on the choice of the end-point indicator, a choice that requires understanding of the equilibria between acids and bases. Such equilibria will now be discussed.

Acid constants.   An acid may be defined as a substance able to furnish H^+ ions. As discussed earlier, these H^+ ions are actually hydrated

H_3O^+ (hydronium) ions. (Further consideration will shortly be given to this point.) A *monoprotic* acid HA yields one H^+ ion per molecule by the dissociation reaction

$$HA = H^+ + A^- \qquad (8\text{-}1)$$

which corresponds to the mass-action equation,

$$\frac{[H^+][A^-]}{[HA]} = K_a \qquad (8\text{-}2)$$

The constant K_a is called the dissociation constant of the acid, or, more simply, the *acid constant*.

An example is acetic acid, of structure

$$
\begin{array}{c}
\quad\;\; H \quad O \\
\quad\;\; | \quad\;\; \| \\
H-C-C-O-H \\
\quad\;\; | \\
\quad\;\; H
\end{array}
$$

where the hydrogen atom able to leave as H^+ in aqueous solutions is the one attached to the oxygen atom. Henceforth, the acetic acid molecule will be represented by the abbreviated formula HAc, where Ac stands for CH_3COO. The experimental value of K_a for acetic acid is 1.8×10^{-5}.

A *polyprotic* acid H_nA can furnish n hydrogen ions per molecule. The ions are furnished in steps, each of which is governed by a dissociation constant. For example, the successive dissociation of carbonic acid (H_2CO_3) is described by the following chemical equations and their mass-action constants:

$$H_2CO_3 = H^+ + HCO_3^- \qquad K_1 = 4.4 \times 10^{-7} \qquad (8\text{-}3)$$

$$HCO_3^- = H^+ + CO_3^= \qquad K_2 = 4.8 \times 10^{-11} \qquad (8\text{-}4)$$

The constants K_1 and K_2 are called the first and second dissociation constants of H_2CO_3.

An aqueous solution of carbon dioxide is usually treated formally as if all CO_2 had combined with H_2O into H_2CO_3, although in fact most of the carbon dioxide exists as hydrated CO_2 molecules and only a small fraction as H_2CO_3. The reason this is permissible is explained on page 205.

Bases are traditionally defined as substances that yield OH^- ions in aqueous solutions. In the simplest case, a *monohydroxic* base BOH dissociates by the equation

$$BOH = B^+ + OH^- \qquad (8\text{-}5)$$

the equilibrium being governed by

$$\frac{[B^+][OH^-]}{[BOH]} = K_b \qquad (8\text{-}6)$$

where K_b is called the base constant.

The pH. Water itself may be considered an acid or a base, since it is very slightly dissociated into H^+ and OH^- ions:

$$H_2O = H^+ + OH^- \qquad (8\text{-}7)$$

The equilibrium constant for this reaction,

$$[H^+][OH^-] = K_w \qquad (8\text{-}8)$$

is called the ionization product of water. Its value at 24°C is 1×10^{-14} and increases with temperature, being 1×10^{-12} at 100°C. The change with temperature of other dissociation constants of acids is usually smaller than this.

The H^+-ion concentration prevailing in a solution is an important characteristic of the solution, as will become evident from many of the subsequent discussions. Because this concentration may range over many powers of 10, and because these are mainly negative, it is convenient to deal with its negative logarithm (to the base 10), called the pH of the solution.

$$pH = -\log[H^+] \qquad [H^+] = 10^{-pH} \qquad (8\text{-}9)$$

Similarly, the quantity pOH is useful; it is defined by the equation

$$pOH = -\log[OH^-] \qquad (8\text{-}10)$$

By a further convention the negative logarithms of such dissociation constants as K_a and K_w are designated by the symbols pK_a and pK_w, so that, by (8-8),

$$pH + pOH = -\log K_w = pK_w \qquad (8\text{-}11)$$

When the H^+ and the OH^- concentrations are equal, as is the case in pure water, one speaks of a *neutral* medium; by (8-8) or (8-11),

$$[H^+] = [OH^-] = \sqrt{K_w} \qquad pH = pOH = \tfrac{1}{2}pK_w \qquad (8\text{-}12)$$

At 24°C the pH of pure water is thus $-\tfrac{1}{2}\log 10^{-14} = 7$, and, conversely, when the pH of any solution at 24°C is 7, it follows from (8-8) that $[H^+]$ and $[OH^-]$ are equal, so that the solution is neutral.

This statement is exact only to the extent that Equation (8-8) is exact, and as was asserted in the general discussion of the mass-action law, there exist deviations from such relationships as (8-8). These deviations are larger the higher the concentration of solute particles, particularly if these particles are charged. This situation is not serious in the present case, however, and it is practical to consider even rather concentrated solutions to be neutral at pH 7. Similarly, even though K_w changes with temperature, it is practical to assume a pH of 7 as neutral for room temperature in general, and not just at 24°C.

As an example of the magnitudes of the deviations that may be expected, actual neutrality for a 1 F Na$^+$Br$^-$ solution is found to be at pH 6.88. The difference is due not to a direct influence of the Na$^+$ and Br$^-$ ions on [H$^+$] but to deviations from (8-8) caused by the charges on these ions. Differences of a few tenths of a pH unit between predicted and experimentally found values have little bearing on the precision of the experiments described in this text. When higher accuracy of pH values is required, it may be desirable to replace the definition of the pH given above by one that is suited to the experimental methods used to measure the pH of a solution and that takes deviations from Equation (8-8) into account. Several such refined pH definitions have been proposed.

In dilute solutions the pH may range between 0 and 14. In concentrated acid solutions the pH is negative. It has been estimated that the effective pH in concentrated H_2SO_4 is of the order of -10. In concentrated solutions of NaOH or KOH the effective pH has been estimated to reach values of 18 to 19.

The Brønsted-Lowry definition of acids and bases. Following the Danish chemist Brønsted and the English chemist Lowry a *base* may be defined, more generally than by the traditional definition given earlier, as a substance whose molecules or ions *may combine with* H$^+$ *ions or, more precisely, protons*, since the term H$^+$ ion in general connotes a hydrated H_3O^+ ion. Conversely, an acid is defined as a substance whose molecules or ions *may lose protons*. Thus, while the molecule HA of Eq. (8-1) is an acid, the ion A$^-$ is a base; HA and A$^-$ are called a *conjugate pair* of acid and base. An acid and its conjugate base or a base and its conjugate acid are thus related by the equation

$$H_n A^m = H^+ + H_{n-1} A^{m-1} \qquad (8\text{-}13)$$

where n is a positive integer, m (indicating the charge of the particle) is a positive or negative integer or zero, and H$^+$ stands for an unhydrated proton. This double usage of H$^+$ to symbolize, depending on the circumstances, a proton or a hydrated H_3O^+ ion will be discontinued again shortly in favor of the second of these usages. It will be specifically indicated when H$^+$ stands for a proton unless this is clear from the context. Note also that it is irrelevant in the above definition that the particles involved may be charged. Indeed, the charge of an acid particle is always one positive unit larger than that of the conjugate base particle, so that at least one of the two must be charged.

Henceforth the symbols HA and A^- will stand for the general conjugate acid and base particles H_nA^m and $H_{n-1}A^{m-1}$, regardless of the actual charge of the particles or whether A^- may be capable of losing additional protons. If the emphasis is on the base, $H_{n-1}A^{m-1}$ will in general be represented by B and H_nA^m by HB^+, so that (8-13) may be written either as

$$HA = A^- + H^+ \qquad (8\text{-}14)$$

or as

$$HB^+ = B + H^+ \qquad (8\text{-}15)$$

Table 8-1 shows a few examples of conjugate acid-base pairs.

The species HCO_3^- may act either as an acid or as a base, losing or gaining a proton. This behavior is termed *amphiprotic* (Greek, *amphi* = both). Another example of an amphiprotic particle is the water molecule, since it may undergo the reactions

$$H_2O + H^+ = H_3O^+ \qquad (8\text{-}16)$$
$$\text{base} \quad \text{proton} \quad \text{acid}$$

and

$$H_2O = OH^- + H^+ \qquad (8\text{-}17)$$
$$\text{acid} \quad \text{base} \quad \text{proton}$$

The term *ampholyte* (Greek, *lyein* = to lose) is also commonly used to describe species like HCO_3^- and H_2O.

The general reaction between an acid and a base is to form a new acid and a new base, as in the reaction

$$HAc + NH_3 = Ac^- + NH_4^+ \qquad (8\text{-}18)$$
$$\text{acid 1} \quad \text{base 2} \quad \text{base 1} \quad \text{acid 2}$$

in which the proton of the acetic acid is transferred to the ammonia

TABLE 8-1   Conjugate Pairs of Acids and Bases

acid	base
HAc	Ac^-
HNO_2	NO_2^-
H_2CO_3	HCO_3^-
HCO_3^-	$CO_3^=$
NH_4^+	NH_3

molecule. An important case of this type of reaction involves water as a base,

$$HAc + H_2O = Ac^- + H_3O^+ \qquad (8\text{-}19)$$

acid 1   base 2   base 1   acid 2

This is the reaction that occurs when pure acetic acid is mixed with water. It is the same reaction as the dissociation of acetic acid in aqueous solution,

$$HAc = H^+ + Ac^- \qquad (8\text{-}20)$$

in which the proton H^+ reacts with a water molecule to form the H_3O^+ ion, which is then hydrated. The mass-action equation for the reaction (8-19),

$$\frac{[Ac^-][H_3O^+]}{[HAc]} = K_{19} \qquad (8\text{-}21)$$

is identical in its meaning with the one that corresponds to (8-20),

$$\frac{[Ac^-][H^+]}{[HAc]} = K_{20} = K_{19} = 1.8 \times 10^{-5} \qquad (8\text{-}22)$$

since at equilibrium in an aqueous solution a proton that has dissociated off the HAc molecule reacts with water to form a hydronium ion that may be hydrated even further. Thus, as has always been implied, the symbol $[H^+]$ in equations of the type (8-22) refers to the concentration of H_3O^+ ions in the solution, in all its hydrated forms.

The reaction with water of the general acid particle HA is

$$HA + H_2O = H_3O^+ + A^- \qquad (8\text{-}23)$$

Although the mass-action equation for this reaction might be written in the form

$$\frac{[H_3O^+][A^-]}{[HA]} = K_{23} \qquad (8\text{-}24)$$

it is preferable for the sake of brevity and for conformance with the usual tables of acid dissociation constants to replace the symbol $[H_3O^+]$ by $[H^+]$. The acid constants K_a listed in such tables are thus the equilibrium constants for reactions of the type (8-23), and it is understood that the mass-action equation

$$\frac{[H^+][A^-]}{[HA]} = K_a \qquad (8\text{-}25)$$

has precisely the same meaning as (8-24).

Any base $H_{n-1}A^{m-1}$ may react with water to form the conjugate acid and hydroxyl ions,

$$H_{n-1}A^{m-1} + H_2O = H_nA^m + OH^- \qquad (8\text{-}26)$$

or

$$B + H_2O = HB^+ + OH^- \qquad (8\text{-}27)$$

The mass-action constant corresponding to this reaction is the traditional base constant K_b,

$$\frac{[HB^+][OH^-]}{[B]} = K_b \qquad (8\text{-}28)$$

Multiplication of (8-25) and (8-28) yields the important result

$$K_a \cdot K_b = [H^+][OH^-] = K_w \qquad (8\text{-}29)$$

when HB^+ and HA, and B and A^-, are identical particles. *The product of the acid constant of an acid and the base constant of the conjugate base is the ionization product of water.* A special case is the reaction of water with itself, one molecule acting as acid, the other as base,

$$2H_2O = H_3O^+ + OH^- \qquad (8\text{-}30)$$

This reaction is identical with that described by (8-7). Proton transfer reactions—(8-23), (8-27), and (8-30)—are called *protolytic reactions* (Greek, *lyein* = to lose). The particle losing the proton is said to be the *proton donor*; the particle receiving the proton, the *proton acceptor*. Depending on the circumstances, reaction (8-7) or (8-30) is referred to as the *dissociation* of water or the *autoprotolysis* of water.

Strong and weak acids and bases. The values of K_a or K_b determine whether an acid or a base is called weak or strong, as explained by the following examples:

The equilibrium of the reaction between HCl and H_2O,

$$HCl + H_2O = H_3O^+ + Cl^- \qquad (8\text{-}31)$$

lies overwhelmingly to the right. HCl is a much stronger acid than H_3O^+, or, to say the same thing differently, Cl^- is a much weaker base than H_2O. There are essentially no HCl molecules in an aqueous solution of hydrochloric acid. Any acid for which this is true is called a *strong acid*. Other examples are $HClO_4$, HNO_3, and H_2SO_4 (but not HSO_4^-). In aqueous solutions any difference in strengths between these strong acids is completely masked, since they are really all solutions of the same acid, H_3O^+. This is called the *leveling effect* of water on strong acids. The strongest acid that can exist in other than very small concentrations in dilute aqueous solutions is H_3O^+. An acid with a dissociation constant of 100 (estimated K_a for HNO_3) is 0.01 per cent from being completely dissociated in 0.1 F solutions, whereas an acid with $K_a = 10^3$ (estimated value for the first dissociation constant of H_2SO_4) is 0.001 per cent from complete dissociation at the same concentration. Thus there is little practical difference in the degrees of dissociation, and both solutions contain essentially 0.1 mole/liter of H_3O^+.

Differences between strong acids do show up when the acids are dissolved in a solvent that is able, by accepting a proton, to form a stronger acid than H_3O^+. For example, the acetic acid molecule HAc can accept a second proton and thus form the acid H_2Ac^+, which is considerably stronger than H_3O^+. [This proton attaches to the oxygen atom of CH_3COOH (see structural formula on page 151) that is not already part of a hydroxyl group.] When HCl is dissolved in anhydrous acetic acid, the equilibrium of the reaction

$$HCl + HAc = H_2Ac^+ + Cl^- \tag{8-32}$$

is no longer completely in favor of the right side; there are substantial quantities of HCl molecules in this solution. This is true for other strong acids, and their relative strengths are indicated by the following arrangement: $HClO_4 > HCl > H_2SO_4 > H_3O^+$ (see also Table 9-1, page 208).

An acid of *moderate strength* is one whose tendency to dissociate is not much weaker than that of H_3O^+. An example is provided by HSO_4^-, the equilibrium constant of the reaction

$$HSO_4^- + H_2O = SO_4^= + H_3O^+ \tag{8-33}$$

having the value

$$\frac{[H^+][SO_4^=]}{[HSO_4^-]} = K_2 = 1.2 \times 10^{-2} \tag{8-34}$$

(The subscript 2 in K_2 above is a reminder that this is the second dissociation constant of H_2SO_4.)

The tendency of a *weak acid* to dissociate is small compared with that of H_3O^+, so that the acid constants of all weak acids are small compared with unity. Examples are acetic acid, $K_a = 1.8 \times 10^{-5}$; nitrous acid (HNO_2), $K_a = 4.5 \times 10^{-4}$; and hydrocyanic acid (HCN), $K_a = 2 \times 10^{-9}$.

A *strong base* is defined as a substance whose aqueous solutions contain OH^- ions as the only base (other than the H_2O molecules themselves). Examples are aqueous solutions of NaOH and KOH. Another interesting example is provided by the crystalline compound sodium amide ($NaNH_2$), which may be prepared by reacting Na and liquid ammonia (NH_3) with the evolution of H_2 gas, a reaction analogous to that between Na and H_2O, in which NaOH and H_2 are formed. When sodium amide is combined with water, the amide ion NH_2^- reacts vigorously with H_2O molecules.

$$NH_2^- + H_2O = NH_3 + OH^- \qquad (8\text{-}35)$$

The amide ion is a stronger base than the hydroxyl ion, and OH^- is the strongest base able to exist in dilute aqueous solution, just as H_3O^+ is the strongest acid able so to exist. Water thus exerts a leveling effect on strong bases, just as it does on strong acids.

Weak bases are those which are weak compared with the base OH^-, so that the reaction

$$B + H_2O = HB^+ + OH^- \qquad (8\text{-}27)$$

has an equilibrium constant K_b that is small compared with unity. Ammonia is an example of a weak base, as indicated by the mass-action constant

$$NH_3 + H_2O = NH_4^+ + OH^- \qquad K_b = 1.8 \times 10^{-5} \qquad (8\text{-}36)$$

(Note that whereas an aqueous solution of NH_3 in water is sometimes considered to be a solution of NH_4OH, the concentration of NH_4OH molecules in such a solution is very small. See also page 204.)

The terms "strong" and "weak" are seen to be relative and to imply comparison with the acid H_3O^+ or the base OH^-. It also should be noted that, *the stronger an acid, the weaker the base conjugate to it.* The equilibrium in a proton transfer always favors the side with the weaker of the two acids involved, which is also the side of the weaker of the two bases conjugate to these acids.

Other aspects of acid-base reactions such as acid-base behavior in nonaqueous media are discussed in the next chapter, page 206.

COMPUTATION OF HYDROGEN-ION CONCENTRATIONS

In the following examples of pH computations, approximations are used whenever convenient, provided that errors caused by their use are below about 10 to 20 per cent. This is reasonable because of the inaccuracies of the mass-action equations in the form used for simple computations.

Solution of a strong acid or base.   In an aqueous solution of a *strong acid*, practically all acid particles have transferred their protons to water molecules, thus furnishing an equal quantity of hydrogen ions and also of base particles conjugate to the acid [see Eq. (8-31)]. The hydrogen-ion concentration is thus equal to the concentration of the conjugate base, if we neglect the contribution made by the dissociation of water (which will be discussed shortly). In a 1 F solution of HCl, for example, the concentration of H^+ equals that of Cl^-, $[H^+] = [Cl^-] = 1$, so that the pH is 0.

The number of hydrogen ions that are contributed by dissociation of water equals the number of hydroxyl ions present, since there is no other source of hydroxyl ions and since H^+ and OH^- are produced in equal numbers by this dissociation. The part of the hydrogen-ion concentration that results from dissociation of water thus equals $[OH^-]$. In an acid solution $[OH^-]$ is below 10^{-7} mole/liter, and the contribution to $[H^+]$ by dissociation of water is thus less than 10^{-7} mole/liter. In a basic solution $[H^+]$ itself is less than 10^{-7} mole/liter. The maximum contribution to the hydrogen-ion concentration from the dissociation of water is therefore 10^{-7} mole/liter, a value attained in a neutral solution. Such a contribution is negligible except when contributions from other sources are equally small, so that the resultant pH is in the vicinity of 7. A very dilute solution of a strong acid and a less dilute solution of a weak acid are examples.

In a solution of *strong base* the situation is just opposite to that of strong acids. For example, in 0.1 F NaOH the OH^- and the Na^+ concentrations are equal, $[OH^-] = [Na^+] = 0.1$, so that pOH $= 1$ and pH $= 14 - 1 = 13$. The contribution to $[OH^-]$ by the dissociation of water is negligible, the situation being analogous to the one just discussed. The maximum contribution possible is 10^{-7} mole/liter, which is realized at pH 7.

Solution of a weak acid or base.   In a c formal solution of a *weak acid* HA (which may be a charged particle and is assumed here to be able to lose only one proton) the proton transfer to H_2O is incomplete, the acid constant K_a being substantially smaller than 1. Suppose that x mole/liter of original HA molecules have lost their protons. The concentrations of the various species of interest are then as shown on the line below the reaction equation

$$HA = H^+ + A^-$$
$$c - x \quad x \quad x$$

(8-37)

This neglects the contribution made to $[H^+]$ by the dissociation of water, causing an error of less than 10 per cent if $[H^+]$ is larger than 10^{-6} mole/liter, as discussed earlier. Insertion into the mass-action expression for (8-37) results in the equation

$$\frac{[H^+][A^-]}{[HA]} = \frac{x^2}{c - x} = K_a \qquad (8\text{-}38)$$

When x is neglected as small compared with c, it follows that

$$x = [H^+] \approx \sqrt{cK_a} \qquad (8\text{-}39)$$
$$\text{provided that } 10^{-6} \leq [H^+] \ll c$$

If these assumptions are not satisfied, more involved computations are needed. An example of such a situation is given on page 192.

To provide an example in which the assumptions underlying (8-39) are satisfied, the pH in a 0.2 F HAc solution ($K_a = 1.8 \times 10^{-5}$) is computed, as follows:

$$[H^+] = \sqrt{3.6 \times 10^{-6}} = 1.9 \times 10^{-3} \text{ mole/liter} \qquad (8\text{-}40)$$

pH $\approx 3 - \log 1.9 = 2.7$.

In a c formal solution of a *weak base* B (which may be a charged particle), the proton transfer from H_2O to B,

$$B + H_2O = HB^+ + OH^- \qquad (8\text{-}41)$$

is incomplete, the constant K_b for this reaction being substantially smaller than 1. Considerations analogous to those just given lead to the approximate relationship

$$[OH^-] \approx \sqrt{cK_b} \qquad [H^+] \approx \sqrt{K_w^2/cK_b} = \sqrt{K_w K_a/c} \qquad (8\text{-}42)$$
$$\text{provided that } 10^{-6} \leq [OH^-] \ll c$$

The constant $K_a = K_w/K_b$ is the acid constant of the acid HB^+ conjugate to B. If $[OH^-]$ is smaller than 10^{-6} mole/liter, the contribution to $[OH^-]$ from the dissociation of water is no longer negligible.

As an example in which the foregoing assumptions are valid, the pH of 2 F ammonia ($K_b = 1.8 \times 10^{-5}$) is calculated as follows:

$$[OH^-] \approx \sqrt{36 \times 10^{-6}} = 6.0 \times 10^{-3}$$
$$pOH = 3 - \log 6 = 2.2 \qquad pH = 11.8$$

Solution of a salt of a weak acid and a strong base. Salts are electrically neutral combinations of positive particles called *cations* and negative particles called *anions* (excepting H^+ and OH^-). In the cases discussed these particles do not combine to form molecules but, rather,

exist as ions in the solid compound, in its melt, and in solution. However, if the anions A^- in a salt are conjugate to a *weak acid*, some of
them accept protons from water to form acid particles HA. Similarly,
if the cations HB^+ in a salt are conjugate to a *weak base*, some of
them lose their protons to form base particles B.

In solutions of salts of strong acids and bases ($NaCl$, KNO_3, etc.)
neither of these reactions occurs, and the solution thus has a neutral
pH of 7. (This is no longer true when the cation or the anion is amphiprotic. For example, in a solution of $NaHSO_4$ the Na^+ cation cannot
furnish protons and the HSO_4^- anion does not accept protons readily,
but the HSO_4^- anion further dissociates to make the solution acid.)

Consider now a c formal solution of a salt of a *weak acid* HA with
a strong base, for example, NaOH. The salt NaA dissolves as ions
Na^+ and A^-, and the base A^- may accept a proton from water,

$$\underset{c-y}{A^-} + H_2O = \underset{y}{HA} + \underset{y}{OH^-} \qquad (8\text{-}43)$$

If y moles/liter of A^- react in this manner, the concentrations of the
different species are as indicated on the line beneath Equation (8-43).
Any contribution to $[OH^-]$ from the dissociation of water has been
ignored, on the assumption that $[OH^-]$ is at least 10^{-6} mole/liter. The
mass-action constant for reaction (8-43) is the base constant of the
base conjugate to HA, $K_b = K_w/K_a$ [see Eqs. (8-26) to (8-29)]. Upon
inserting into the mass-action equation,

$$\frac{[HA][OH^-]}{[A^-]} = \frac{y^2}{c-y} = K_b = \frac{K_w}{K_a} \qquad (8\text{-}44)$$

and neglecting y as small compared with c, the following results are
obtained:

$$y = [OH^-] \approx \sqrt{cK_b} \qquad [H^+] \approx \sqrt{K_wK_a/c} \qquad (8\text{-}45)$$
$$\text{provided that } 10^{-6} \le [OH^-] \ll c$$

Reaction (8-43) is traditionally known as the *hydrolysis* reaction, but
there is no fundamental difference between it and the general reaction
of a base with H_2O, as comparison between (8-41) and (8-43) or between (8-42) and (8-45) shows.

To give a numerical example, the pH of a $0.1\ F$ solution of
NaAc (K_a for HAc is 1.8×10^{-5}) is calculated as follows:

$$[H^+] \approx \sqrt{1.8 \times 10^{-19}/0.1} = 1.3 \times 10^{-9} \qquad pH = 8.9 \qquad (8\text{-}46)$$

Solution of a salt of a strong acid and a weak base. The salt of
a weak base B of base constant K_b and a strong acid like HCl has the

formula BH^+Cl^-; upon solution of the salt the conjugate acid BH^+ of B reacts with water molecules,

$$BH^+ + H_2O = B + H_3O^+ \qquad (8\text{-}47)$$

with an equilibrium constant that is the acid constant of the acid conjugate to B, $K_a = K_w/K_b$. A development similar to that just given results in the equations

$$[H^+] \approx \sqrt{cK_a} = \sqrt{cK_w/K_b} \qquad (8\text{-}48)$$

Formulas (8-39) and (8-48) are identical, since they deal with the same situation from the Brønsted-Lowry point of view.

Solution containing a weak acid and its conjugate base; buffer solution. Consider a solution that is at the same time c_a formal in an acid HA, of acid constant K_a, and c_b formal in its conjugate base A^-. Rather than start with approximations as in previous computations of $[H^+]$, a precise expression for $[H^+]$ will be developed first and approximations will be introduced at a later stage only. There are two sources of H^+ ions in such a solution: (1) dissociation of H_2O, yielding equal quantities of H^+ and OH^- and (2) dissociation of HA, providing equal amounts of H^+ and A^- By stoichiometry, the contribution to the hydrogen-ion concentration from the first source (H_2O) therefore equals $[OH^-]$; and since the total hydrogen-ion concentration is $[H^+]$, the second source (HA) must contribute the difference, $[H^+] - [OH^-]$. This last quantity must then represent the loss in HA so that the original concentration c_a of HA is decreased and the concentration c_b of A^- is increased by $[H^+] - [OH^-]$:

$$[HA] = c_a - [H^+] + [OH^-] \qquad (8\text{-}49)$$

$$[A^-] = c_b + [H^+] - [OH^-] \qquad (8\text{-}50)$$

The mass-action expression for the dissociation of HA may be combined with these two equations to yield

$$[H^+] = K_a \frac{[HA]}{[A^-]} = K_a \frac{c_a - [H^+] + [OH^-]}{c_b + [H^+] - [OH^-]} \qquad (8\text{-}51)$$

This equation is exact, and inserting $[OH^-] = K_w/[H^+]$ on the right produces a cubic equation in $[H^+]$. It is, however, much less cumbersome not to find and discuss the general solution, but rather to use different approximations for different situations.

For the following two examples it is useful to write (8-51) in the form

$$K_a = [H^+]\{(c_b + [H^+] - [OH^-])/(c_a - [H^+] + [OH^-])\} \qquad (8\text{-}52)$$

Assume first that $c_b = 0$ so that there is no base present at the beginning, and unless c_a or K_a is very small the solution may be expected to be distinctly acidic. Thus [OH$^-$] may be neglected in (8-52), so that

$$K_a = [H^+]^2/(c_a - [H^+])$$

This equation is identical with (8-38), except for changed notation, and leads to (8-39) when [H$^+$] $\ll c_a$.

In the parallel case when $c_a = 0$, there is no acid present at the beginning and the solution may be expected to be distinctly alkaline unless c_b or $K_b = K_w/K_a$ is very small. Neglecting [H$^+$] where possible in (8-52),

$$K_a = [H^+](c_b - [OH^-])/[OH^-] = K_w(c_b - [OH^-])/[OH^-]^2$$

Except for rearrangement and changed notation this expression is identical with (8-44) and leads to (8-45) when [OH$^-$] $\ll c_b$.

In the present situation c_a and c_b are supposed to be large enough that both [H$^+$] and [OH$^-$] may be neglected on the right side of (8-51). Thus,

$$[H^+] \approx K_a c_a/c_b \tag{8-53}$$

provided that [H$^+$] and [OH$^-$] $\ll c_a$ and c_b

and taking negative logarithms

$$pH = pK_a - \log(c_a/c_b) \tag{8-54}$$

An example is represented by a solution that is 0.20 F in HNO$_2$ ($K_a = 4.5 \times 10^{-4}$) and 0.50 F in NaNO$_2$ and thus also 0.50 F in NO$_2{}^-$, the base conjugate to HNO$_2$. The H$^+$-ion concentration in this solution is [H$^+$] = 0.20 $\times$ 4.5 $\times$ 10^{-4}/0.50 = 1.80 $\times$ 10^{-4}, and [OH$^-$] = 5.6 $\times$ 10^{-11}. The assumptions underlying (8-53) are thus satisfied, and the pH of the solution is 3.75.

Solutions like the one being considered have the property of resisting a change in pH when being diluted and when small quantities of acids or bases are added. Such a solution is called a *buffer* solution. Its buffering action may be understood as follows: Within the limitations of the derivation of Equation (8-53) and the mass-action equations underlying it, the pH depends on a ratio of concentrations only and is thus not affected by dilution. Upon addition of H$^+$ ions some of the particles A$^-$ are converted to HA, and addition of OH$^-$ ions causes conversion of some HA particles to A$^-$. As long as the concentrations c_a and c_b are not greatly affected by such conversions, the H$^+$-ion concentration and pH of the solution will not change much.

It is instructive to compute the effects of adding 1 ml of 10 F HCl to 1 liter of the solution of HNO$_2$ and NaNO$_2$ just described, which has a pH of 3.75. This addition corresponds to adding 0.01 mole of H$^+$ ion, making the solution effectively 0.21 M in HNO$_2$ and 0.49 M in NO$_2{}^-$, so that [H$^+$] = 0.21 $\times$ 4.5 $\times$ 10^{-4}/0.49 = 1.93 $\times$ 10^{-4}, pH

= 3.72. Similarly, adding 1 ml of 10 F NaOH to another solution of the original composition results in $[HNO_2] = 0.19$, $[NO_2^-] = 0.51$, $[H^+] = 1.67 \times 10^{-4}$, pH = 3.78. The pH change from the original value of 3.75 in either direction thus amounts to only 0.03 unit. In comparison, an unbuffered solution of pH 3.75 like the original solution is represented by 1.80×10^{-4} F HCl. Diluting by a factor 2 decreases $[H^+]$ to half the original value, a pH change of 0.3 unit; addition of 1 ml of 10 F HCl to a liter of original solution causes $[H^+]$ to be 10^{-2} mole/liter, so that the pH is 2, a change of 1.75 units; adding 1 ml of 10 F NaOH to another liter of 1.80×10^{-4} F HCl changes $[OH^-]$ to 10^{-2} mole/liter or the pH to 12, a change of 8.25 units!

Another example of a buffer solution is one containing adequate amounts of the base NH_3 and the conjugate acid NH_4^+ in a suitable form such as NH_4Cl.

Inspection of the numerical example given confirms that a buffer solution is effective only as long as the number of moles of acid and the number of moles of conjugate base it contains are large compared with the number of moles of acid or of base that are added. A buffer is most efficient when the concentrations c_a and c_b are equal (see Prob. 8-9). Under these conditions the H^+-ion concentration of the buffer equals K_a, pH = pK_a. By changing the ratio c_a/c_b, the pH to be buffered may be changed, but buffering becomes inefficient if this pH differs from pK by more than 1 unit. Buffer solutions are very important in many fields of chemistry and biochemistry. Examples of their use are given in later chapters.

INDICATORS AND THE pH METER

Acid-base indicators. To identify the end point of an acid-base titration, an indicator is often used; an indicator is a substance that has the property of changing color within a certain pH range when acid or base is added. It is thus a substance that may gain or lose a proton and changes color when doing so. This implies that the two forms in which an indicator may exist represent an acid and its conjugate base. If the indicator acid is symbolized by HIn and the conjugate base by In$^-$, the equilibrium between the two forms,

$$HIn = In^- + H^+ \tag{8-55}$$

is governed by the mass-action expression

$$\frac{[H^+][In^-]}{[HIn]} = K_i \tag{8-56}$$

where K_i is called the indicator constant.

A good example of an indicator is methyl orange, whose indicator constant is $K_i = 3 \times 10^{-4}$, or $pK_i = 3.5$. It is intensely red in the acid form and intensely yellow in the basic form; HIn is red, In$^-$ yellow. Equation (8-56) may be rearranged,

$$\frac{[In^-]}{[HIn]} = \frac{[yellow]}{[red]} = \frac{K_i}{[H^+]} \tag{8-57}$$

to give the concentration ratio of yellow to red particles as a function of $[H^+]$.

To understand how the color of this indicator changes with the pH, the concentration ratio of yellow to red particles will be considered at the three pH values, $pK_i + 1$, $pK_i - 1$, and pK_i. (1) When pH $= pK_i + 1$ or $[H^+] = K_i/10$, it follows from (8-57) that [yellow]/[red] $= 10$. Since the color intensities of both HIn and In$^-$ are comparable, the tenfold numerical superiority of yellow particles makes the solution yellow. For more alkaline solutions the ratio of yellow to red particles exceeds 10. (2) When pH $= pK_i - 1$ or $[H^+] = 10K_i$, it follows that [yellow]/[red] $= 1/10$ so that the solution is red. In more acid solutions the red particles are favored even more. (3) At pH $= pK_i$ or $[H^+] = K_i$, the concentration of yellow and red particles is equal, [yellow] $=$ [red]; the indicator is at a transition color of orange, the exact hue depending on the color intensities of the yellow and the red species. The indicator methyl orange is thus expected, as the pH decreases, to undergo a transition from yellow through orange to red in a pH interval of about two units, centered approximately by pK_i. The visually observed transition occurs in the pH interval 3.1 to 4.4, while $pK_i = 3.5$ (see Table 8-2), in reasonable agreement with the semiquantitative considerations just given.

In some indicators, one of the two forms is colorless, and the foregoing considerations have to be modified. For example, the acid form of phenolphthalein ($pK_i = 9.3$) is colorless; the basic form, intensely red. Inspection of an equation analogous to (8-57) shows that there is a tenfold increase in red In$^-$ particles for an increase of the pH by one unit. Experimentally (Table 8-2) it is found that phenolphthalein changes from colorless to red in the pH interval 8.0 to 9.8.

To be of use in an aqueous medium, an indicator must have its indicator constant K_i well within the range 0 to 14; both indicator acid

TABLE 8-2 *Some Common Acid-Base Indicators and Their Transition Ranges*

indicator	color on acidic side	color on basic side	transition range, pH units	pK_i
Bromphenol blue	Yellow	Lavender	3.0–4.6	3.8
Methyl orange	Red	Yellow	3.1–4.4	3.5
Bromcresol green	Yellow	Blue	3.8–5.4	4.7
Methyl red	Red	Yellow	4.2–6.1	5.0
Bromthymol blue	Yellow	Blue	6.0–7.6	7.1
Phenol red	Yellow	Red	6.8–8.1	7.8
Thymol blue	Yellow	Blue	8.0–9.6	8.9
Phenolphthalein	Colorless	Red	8.0–9.8	9.3
Thymolphthalein	Colorless	Blue	9.4–10.5	9.7

and conjugate base must therefore be weak or at most only moderately strong. Unless the indicator concentration is small, the presence of the indicator will affect the pH of the solution. The color of at least one of the two indicator species must therefore be intense so that the color is visible even in dilute solution.

All commonly used acid-base indicators are organic compounds. To give an idea of the structural changes responsible for the color change, the structural formulas of the two forms of methyl orange are shown in Figure 8-1. These structures are rather complicated, and for a complete understanding of them a background in organic chemistry is required. Some of the structural features may, however, be comprehended without much previous knowledge of organic chemistry.

The sulphonic acid group ($-SO_3^-$) attached to one end of the molecule helps to make the substance water soluble. It carries a negative charge in both forms of the indicator, being far too weak a base for a proton to associate with it in an aqueous medium. The same is true of the sulphonic acid group of sulfamic acid (see page 123). In the acid form the molecule is a zwitter ion, and its overall charge is zero; the acid hydrogen atom is attached to one of the N atoms, as shown, and the N atom near the end of the molecule carries a positive charge. In the basic form of the molecule this N atom is no longer charged, and the single bonds and double bonds are arranged differently in part of the molecule from their arrangement in the acid form. The colors of the two particles are related to the regular sequence of single bonds and double bonds, and the color change is due to the change in this sequence, as well as to the difference in the charge of the N atom near the end of the molecule.

Some indicators exist in more than two forms, requiring a more complicated quantitative treatment than that given above. The principles involved remain the same, and as seen by inspection of Table 8-2, the

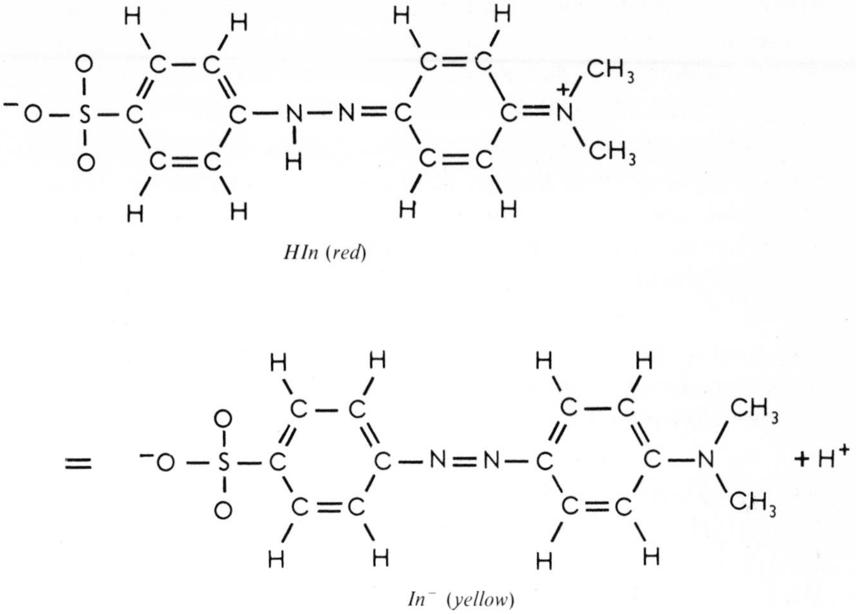

HIn (red)

In⁻ (yellow)

Figure 8-1   Acidic and basic forms of methyl orange.

visible changes of the indicators listed all occur in an interval of 1.1 to 1.9 pH units, with pK_i lying inside this interval.

It is possible to achieve a sharper color indication of certain pH values by using mixtures of indicators or a mixture of an indicator and an inert dye. An example is a mixture of bromcresol green (acidic, yellow; basic, blue) and methyl red (acidic, red; basic, yellow). At a pH of 5.1 the color of methyl red is orange, that of bromcresol green is green-blue. These two colors are complementary, and there is a pronounced color change to a gray of this *mixed indicator* at pH 5.1.

The pH meter.   It has been found experimentally that, when two solutions of different pH are on opposite sides of a membrane made of very thin glass, an electromotive force (emf) is developed across the membrane and that the value of the emf depends on the difference of the pH of the two solutions. This phenomenon permits the construction of the pH-sensitive *glass electrode* (Fig. 8-2a), which contains inside a bulb made of very thin glass a solution of given constant pH, for example, 0.1 *F* HCl. On the other side of the membrane is the solution whose pH is to be measured and into which the glass electrode is inserted. To determine the emf developed across the boundary between these solutions, it would for some purposes be sufficient to insert two wires, one into the bulb and the other into the solution outside. However, for reasons concerning the emf developed across the interface between metal and solution, a more sophisticated procedure is used, and in the *pH meter* the electrical connection between the two solutions and a voltmeter is made by introducing further liquid-liquid interfaces through porous walls. The solution in the glass electrode is usually in contact with a saturated solution of AgCl containing a silver wire connected to the meter. This combination of Ag and AgCl is called a silver–silver chloride electrode. The outside solution is connected by a solution of KCl to a *reference electrode* (Fig. 8-2b). This electrode contains a saturated Hg_2Cl_2 (calomel) solution and a layer of liquid Hg with a Pt wire that is connected to the meter; the combination of Pt, Hg, and Hg_2Cl_2 is called a calomel electrode. Both the AgCl/Ag and the Hg_2Cl_2/Hg electrode develop constant and highly reproducible emf values, and the total emf between the leads to the meter is therefore a function of the pH of the solution only. The detailed theory of these electrodes, and particularly of the processes involving the glass membrane, is complicated.

One important factor is that glass appears to be permeable to H^+ but not to other ions. The H^+ ions have the tendency to migrate from the side of higher H^+-ion concentration to the side of lower concentration. Since no negative ions join in this migration, an emf across the glass membrane arises. This emf increases to the point where the electrical forces on the H^+ ions just balance the effects of the concentration difference that furnishes the driving force for the migration of the H^+ ions. At this point the emf is a measure of the H^+-ion concentration difference.

The emf of different glass electrodes in the same solution varies slightly and may also change from day to day, so that frequent standardization of a given electrode with a buffer solution of known pH is necessary. A convenient reference buffer is a saturated solution of potassium hydrogen tartrate, with a pH of 3.57 at 25°C, as further discussed in Chapter 9 (page 197). In strongly alkaline solutions (pH $\geq$ 9) electrodes made of special glass must be used; otherwise, the pH indicated will be in error (alkaline error). For satisfactory performance, glass electrodes also must have been soaked in distilled water, dilute acid, or an acidic or neutral buffer solution for several hours prior to being used.

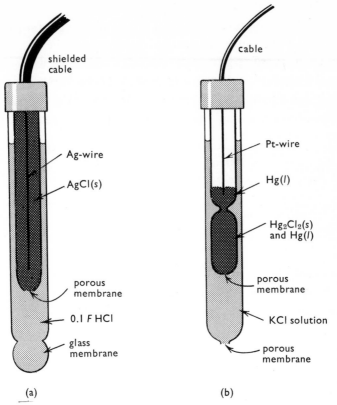

Figure 8-2   (a) Glass electrode.   (b) Calomel reference electrode. The functioning of this electrode including the presence of the KCl solution is discussed on pages 300, 304, and 313.

The electrical resistance of the glass electrode is very high, of the order of 1 to 100 megohms. The emf developed between the leads coming from the two electrodes must therefore be measured by a voltmeter of comparably high internal resistance, such as a quadrant electrometer or a vacuum-tube voltmeter. The latter is much the simpler to use nowadays and is employed in a number of portable pH meters, available commercially, that are accurate to about 0.01 to 0.02 pH units. *Note: The pH meter electrodes are expensive and must be handled with utmost care.*

ACID-BASE TITRATIONS

In this section the methods derived earlier for computing the H^+-ion concentrations of solutions are used to find the pH in a number of acid-base titrations. The use of the resulting titration curves in choosing an indicator will then be considered and the titration precision will be discussed.

Titration of a strong acid with a strong base. The titration reaction is simply the combination of H^+ and OH^-,

$$H^+ + OH^- = H_2O$$

with an equilibrium constant $K_{titration} = K_w^{-1} = 10^{14}$. A typical case is the titration of 100 ml of 0.2 F HCl with 0.2 F NaOH, for which the pH during the course of the titration is computed as follows:

Suppose that to the 100 ml of acid has been added 99.0 ml of 0.2 F NaOH. It is first assumed that all OH^- ions added react with 99.0 ml of the original H^+ ions, and any correction to this assumption is discussed later. This leaves unreacted 1.0 ml of the original solution, 0.2 M in H^+ ions but diluted to 199.0 ml, whence

$$[H^+] = 0.2(1.0/199.0) \approx 10^{-3}$$

The reaction between OH^- and H^+ is, of course, not complete, but the equilibrium is the same as if all OH^- ions added had reacted and then some water had dissociated into OH^- and H^+. However, the contributions of this dissociation are negligible unless the pH is near 7, as was discussed earlier. The pH for other situations on the acid side of the equivalence point is obtained in a similar way.

On the alkaline side of the equivalence point, where an excess of base has been added, the computations are similar to the one just given, except that the roles of OH^- and H^+ are interchanged. At the equivalence point itself the concentrations of H^+ and OH^- are equal, so that $[H^+] = [OH^-] = 10^{-7}$ and the pH is 7.

The curve resulting from such calculations is shown in Figure 8-3, where it is labeled "HCl." It is similar to the titration curves for Ag^+ and SCN^- computed in Chapter 7. The shape of these curves resembles the letter S, and they are therefore said to be of sigmoid nature (Greek, *sigma* = S).

Titration of a weak acid with a strong base. The titration reaction is

$$HA + OH^- = A^- + H_2O \tag{8-58}$$

which leads to an equilibrium expression that is the reciprocal of (8-44),

$$K_{titration} = \frac{[A^-]}{[HA][OH^-]} = \frac{K_a}{K_w} = K_b^{-1} \tag{8-59}$$

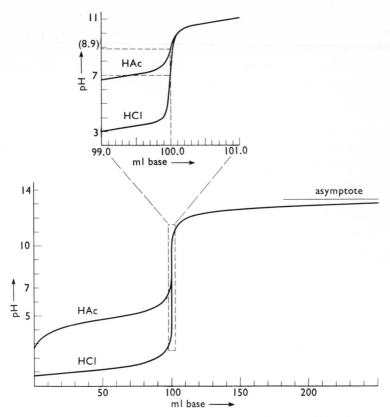

Figure 8-3   Titrations of 100.0 ml of 0.2 F HCl and of 100.0 ml of 0.2 F HAc with 0.2F NaOH.

and in which K_b is the base constant of A^-. It is clear that the equilibrium (8-59) will not be as far to the right as that for the titration of strong acid and strong base, for which the constant was K_w^{-1}. The smaller K_a, the less complete the reaction.

To give an example, we consider the pH variation during the titration of 100 ml of 0.2 F acetic acid ($K_a = 1.8 \times 10^{-5}$) with 0.2 F NaOH. The pH at the start is 2.7, as computed by Equation (8-40). The solution at the equivalence point, at which 100 ml each of 0.2 F HAc and 0.2 F NaOH have been added, precisely represents 200 ml of a 0.1 F NaAc solution. The pH of such a solution is 8.9, as computed by (8-46). In the region between these two points the solution is a buffer containing HAc and NaAc. If V is the volume of base added, in milliliters, the formal concentration c_b of NaAc is proportional to V and the formal concentration c_a of HAc is proportional to $100 - V$. The proportionality factor contains the total solution volume and cancels when the two values for c_a and c_b are inserted into Equation (8-53) for $[H^+]$, so that

$$[H^+] \approx 1.8 \times 10^{-5}(100 - V)/V$$

except very close to the equivalence point and to the starting point of the titration.

On the alkaline side of the equivalence point $[OH^-]$ is determined by the excess of OH^- ions added, and the computation of $[H^+]$ is the same as in the titration of HCl with NaOH.

Instead of computing the pH as a function of V, it may be of interest to find the volume of base to be added for a given pH to result. This problem is solved by combining the relation

$$\frac{[Ac^-]}{[HAc]} = \frac{1.8 \times 10^{-5}}{[H^+]} \tag{8-60}$$

with the stoichiometric conditions of the case considered. Particularly instructive is the case of pH 7 at which $[OH^-] = [H^+]$ so that $[Na^+]$ exactly equals $[Ac^-]$. Since the solution is not electrically charged, the total concentration of positive charges must equal that of the negative charges

$$[Na^+] + [H^+] = [Ac^-] + [OH^-] \tag{8-61}$$

(This condition of *charge conservation* often expresses a stoichiometric condition that is useful in the discussion of equilibria.) At pH 7 $[H^+]$ just cancels $[OH^-]$, so that $[Na^+]$ exactly equals $[Ac^-]$, and (8-60) yields $[Ac^-]/[HAc] = 180$. It follows that, of any representative 181 acetate particles in either form, 180 are Ac^- ions, and the remaining 1 is an HAc molecule. Thus, at the neutrality point $100.0(180/181)$ = 99.45 ml of 0.2 F NaOH has been added, leaving the titration 0.55 per cent short of the equivalence point.

At other pH values between about 4 and 10 the same problem can be attacked in a similar way, because the concentrations of both H^+ and OH^- are small compared with those of Na^+ and Ac^-. Both $[H^+]$ and $[OH^-]$ may thus be neglected in (8-61), and $[Na^+]$ is approximately equal to $[Ac^-]$.

The titration curve computed in this way is shown in Figure 8-3. The equivalence point is, to a good approximation, an inflection point of the curve (see Prob. 8-11).

Titration of a weak base with a strong acid. The titration reaction is of the form

$$H^+ + B = HB^+ \qquad (8\text{-}62)$$

with the equilibrium expression

$$K_{\text{titration}} = \frac{[HB^+]}{[B][H^+]} = K_a^{-1} \qquad (8\text{-}63)$$

where K_a is the dissociation constant of HB^+. The pH during the titration may be computed by applying Equations (8-42), (8-48), and (8-53).

Alternatively, it is of interest to compare the titration reactions of the weak acid–strong base and the weak base–strong acid cases, (8-58) and (8-62), and the corresponding mass-action expressions (8-59) and (8-63). Inspection shows that the titration curve of an acid of constant K_a with strong base must be identical with the titration curve of a base of base constant K_b with strong acid, provided that the roles of $[H^+]$ and $[OH^-]$ and of K_a and K_b are interchanged.

For example, the base constant of NH_3 is approximately equal to the acid constant of acetic acid. Thus, if the ordinates in Figure 8-3 are labeled "pOH" and the abscissas "ml of acid added," the curve labeled "HAc" applies to the titration of 100 ml of 0.2 F NH_3 with 0.2 F HCl and the curve labeled "HCl" describes the pOH in the titration of 100 ml of 0.2 F NaOH with 0.2 F HCl. The equivalence point of the titration of NH_3 with HCl is at pOH 8.9 or at pH 5.1.

End points and precision of acid-base titrations. The end point of a titration may be recognized by the color change of an acid-base indicator. This color change must be sharp and as close as possible to the pH of the equivalence point. As discussed earlier, the color change of an indicator occurs in a pH interval of almost two units approximately centered by the pK_i of the indicator. The indicator must therefore be chosen with pK_i close to $-\frac{1}{2}\log(K_w K_a/c)$ for the titration of a weak acid with strong base [Eq. (8-45)] or to $-\frac{1}{2}\log cK_a$ for the titration of a weak base with strong acid [Eq. (8-48)]. For good precision of a titration the steep portion of the titration curve must extend over at least two pH units.

For the example of acetic acid shown in Figure 8-3, the equivalence point has a pH of 8.9 and phenolphthalein or thymol blue is a suitable indicator (see Table 8-2). The steep portion of the titration curve that extends over two pH units goes approximately from the 99.9-ml to the

100.1-ml abscissa, so that a precision of the order of 1 part in 1000 may be expected for this titration.

The titration of HCl with NaOH is seen to be much less sensitive to the choice of indicator, and a precision of the order of 0.1 per cent can be expected if indicators of pK_i in a range from 5 to 9 are used.

The pH of the equivalence point of a titration of $0.2\ F\ NH_3$ with $0.2\ F$ HCl lies at 5.1, as mentioned earlier. Methyl red and bromcresol green are thus suitable indicators.

The pH curve for the titration of a weak acid with strong base depends mainly on the dissociation constant of the acid. The smaller this constant, the more alkaline is the pH of the equivalence point and the shorter the steep part of the curve. If the dissociation constant of the acid is less than about 10^{-5}, the steep part of the sigmoid pH curve is no longer very pronounced and the precision of the titration falls below the order of 0.1 per cent. With an acid dissociation constant of about 10^{-7}, for example, a precision of the order of 1 per cent only can be expected. This may be improved to some extent by terminating the titration when the indicator color is the same as that of a reference solution containing, in appropriate concentrations, indicator and the other components that the solution being titrated contains at the equivalence point, or by using a mixed indicator. The same applies, *mutatis mutandis*, to the titration of weak bases with strong acids.

The pH curves discussed depend on the concentrations of the acids and bases involved also. The steep part of the sigmoid curve will be less steep the smaller the concentrations, and it disappears entirely in the limiting case of infinite dilution. This concentration dependence is not very important and can be neglected as long as all solutions are not much more dilute than $0.1\ F$. A tenfold concentration change will cause, by (8-45) or (8-48), a change of the pH of the equivalence point by 0.5 unit.

If the dissociation constant of the acid to be titrated is unknown, it is not possible to choose the most suitable indicator for the purpose. The safest indicator choice under these circumstances is one with pK_i about 9, such as phenolphthalein, although this procedure may result in slightly high titration results (see Fig. 8-3). A more accurate procedure is to use a pH meter, to plot the pH during the titration, and to obtain from the resulting graph an approximate value of the dissociation constant of the acid being titrated. This value may be used to select the proper titration indicator. The graph also contains, of course, stoichiometric information that may be used directly.

The following factors may change the pH range in which indicators change color. (1) Change of temperature changes the dissociation constants of the indicators; in particular, an increase in temperature increases the ionization product of water. The transition range of methyl orange, for example, is changed in hot solutions, and it is advisable to observe end points in cold solutions. (2) Changes in the concentrations of the ionic constituents of the solution change the effective concentrations, called *activities*, that have to be used in the mass-action equations to make them precise. Such effects are termed *salt effects*. (3) A change in the nature of the solvent resulting, for example, from the addition of alcohol changes activities as well as dissociation constants.

In general, these effects are not troublesome in titrations but are important if indicators are used to determine the pH values. Conversely, owing to activity effects, the pH curve of a titration as obtained, for example, by a pH meter will lead only to approximate values of the dissociation constants of the acids or bases involved unless special precautions are taken.

The logarithmic nature of the pH scale makes it relatively insensitive to changes in the values of the actual constants. A change of pK by ± 0.1 represents a change of K by 26 per cent ($10^{0.1} = 1.26$). However, the pH scale is more representative of the chemical phenomena observed than is the H^+-ion concentration scale. The pK values obtained without special refinements are valuable even though inaccurate, since many important effects are consequences of the order of magnitudes of mass-action constants rather than of their accurate values.

Titration of a weak acid with a weak base. The titration reaction is

$$HA + B = A^- + HB^+$$

TABLE 8-3 *The Different Cases of Acid-Base Titrations*

case	acid	base	titration reaction	equilibrium constant $K_{titration}$
1	Strong	Strong	$H^+ + OH^- = H_2O$	$1/K_w$
2	Weak	Strong	$HA + OH^- = A^- + H_2O$	$1/K_b(A) = K_a(HA)/K_w$
3	Strong	Weak	$H^+ + B = HB^+$	$1/K_a(HB^+) = K_b(B)/K_w$
4	Weak	Weak	$HA + B = HB^+ + A^-$	$K_a(HA)/K_a(HB^+)$ $= K_a(HA)K_b(B)/K_w$

and the equilibrium is controlled by the equation

$$K_{\text{titration}} = \frac{[A^-][HB^+]}{[HA][B]} = K_{a\text{HA}}K_{a\text{HB}^+}^{-1}$$

where the constants on the right are the respective acid constants of HA and HB$^+$. The correctness of the equation may be established by multiplying the numerator $[A^-][HB^+]$ and the denominator $[HA][B]$ by $[H^+]$.

The titration reactions and equilibrium constants for the different cases of acid-base titrations are summarized in Table 8-3. The equilibrium constants $K_{\text{titration}}$ for cases 2 and 3 are small by powers of 10 compared with that of case 1, because K_a and K_b are small for weak acids and bases; similarly, $K_{\text{titration}}$ for case 4 is smaller yet by powers of 10. It is expected that the slope of the steep portion of the pH curve of a titration of a weak acid with a weak base is so small that such a titration is impractical. This is indeed the case.

Consider, for example, the pH curve of the titration of 100.0 ml of 0.2 F HAc with 0.2 F NH$_3$, whose form can be guessed by considering Figure 8-3. The part of the curve that is in the acid region closely follows that shown for HAc, deviating from it to go through pH 7 at the equivalence point, because of the approximate equality of K_a for HAc and K$_b$ for NH$_3$. If now the branch of the curve just discussed is inverted through the equivalence point, the resulting curve approximately represents the pH curve of the titration in the alkaline region, the correspondence being inexact because of dilution. The resulting sigmoid curve does not have a particularly steep portion, so that this titration would be highly imprecise. Whenever the choice of titrant is open, as it usually is, a strong acid or base should be chosen.

Displacement titrations. As discussed earlier, the slope of the titration curve of a weak acid HA with a strong base is not large enough for a precise titration if K_a of the acid is substantially below 10^{-5}. However, it may be possible to titrate with strong acid the solution of the salt of HA with a strong base, like the salt Na$^+$A$^-$. This is a titration with strong acid of the weak base A$^-$ conjugate to HA, with the titration reaction H$^+$ + A$^-$ = HA.

Such titrations are called *displacement titrations*, because the reaction underlying them used to be viewed as a displacement of the weak acid from its salt by the strong acid. It is, of course, in no way different from any other titration of a weak base with strong acid. The base constant of A$^-$ is given by $K_b = K_w/K_a$, and if K_b is not substantially smaller than 10^{-5} or K_a not substantially larger than 10^{-9}, the titration is expected to have a precision of 0.1 per cent.

For example, the titration of 100 ml of a 0.2 F solution of the salt NaA of an acid HA of constant $K_a = 5 \times 10^{-9}$ with 0.2 F HCl follows a pOH curve like the pH curve labeled "HAc" in Figure 8-3, with the ordinates indicating the pOH and the abscissas the milliliters of HCl added. Methyl red or bromcresol green would thus be suitable end-point indicators.

In a similar way the salt of a weak base B with strong acid, like HB^+Cl^-, may be titrated with a strong base, provided that K_b of B is not substantially larger than 10^{-9}.

*A sodium hydroxide solution is to be prepared
and then standardized by titrating
a weighed quantity of
potassium hydrogen
phthalate, with phenolphthalein
serving as indicator. This standard base
is used in the preliminary titration
of a solution of a weak acid
whose concentration and identity are not known.
Phenolphthalein is again used as
the indicator even though its choice
may not be ideal, depending on the
value of the dissociation constant
of the weak acid. To determine this
constant approximately, a titration
is run with a pH meter. The indicator
most appropriate for the situation
is then chosen and used
in a further titration or two.*

Laboratory assignment 8
(4 periods)

DETERMINATION OF THE CONCENTRATION AND THE DISSOCIATION CONSTANT OF A WEAK ACID

DISCUSSION

Carbonate-free sodium hydroxide solutions.   In this assignment all titrations of the unknown weak acid are performed with a standard solution of strong base. Such solutions are usually prepared with NaOH, because KOH is more expensive and because it is harder to remove carbonate impurities from KOH. Solutions of NaOH are stored in polyethylene bottles, because they tend to attack glass containers.

178

It is important to prepare NaOH solution as free as possible of carbonate and to protect the solution from reacting with CO_2 of the atmosphere,

$$2NaOH + CO_2 = Na_2CO_3 + H_2O$$

The reason is that in the titration the carbonate may be converted, depending on the indicator used, to HCO_3^-,

$$CO_3^= + H^+ = HCO_3^- \qquad\qquad (8\text{-}64)$$

or to H_2CO_3,

$$CO_3 + 2H^+ = H_2CO_3 = H_2O + CO_2 \qquad (8\text{-}65)$$

using up one or two equivalents of H^+, respectively, per formula weight of Na_2CO_3. The two dissociation constants of H_2CO_3 are $K_1 = 4.4 \times 10^{-7}$ and $K_2 = 4.8 \times 10^{-11}$. From the discussion of polyprotic acids in the next chapter it follows that the $[H^+]$ of a $NaHCO_3$ solution is

$$[H^+] \approx \sqrt{K_1 K_2} = 4.5 \times 10^{-9}$$

and that of a 0.1 F solution of H_2CO_3 is

$$[H^+] \approx \sqrt{cK_1} = 2.1 \times 10^{-4}$$

For indicators with a pK_i of the order of 9 the titration stoichiometry is thus represented by (8-64), whereas (8-65) indicates the stoichiometry for indicators with a pK_i of the order of 4. The stoichiometry for intermediate indicators is between these limits. There exists the additional complication that the pH curve of the titration of Na_2CO_3 with acid has only two rather short steeper portions, which are centered around the HCO_3^- and H_2CO_3 equivalence points. Such titrations can be made relatively accurate only by taking special precautions, particularly if the HCO_3^- equivalence point is involved.

A suitable method of preparing a NaOH solution relatively free of carbonate is based on the small solubility of Na_2CO_3 in 50 per cent NaOH solution. The Na_2CO_3 precipitate in such a solution may be removed by filtration through an asbestos or sintered-glass filter, by centrifuging, or by simple decantation or siphoning off of the supernatant after allowing the precipitate to settle. This concentrated solution is then diluted by the desired amount of water that has been boiled free of carbon dioxide.

Standardization. In this laboratory assignment the NaOH solution is standardized against potassium hydrogen phthalate

$$(K^+[OOC(C_6H_4)COOH]^-)$$

with phenolphthalein used as an indicator. Phthalic acid

$$[C_6H_4(COOH)_2]$$

is a diprotic acid with acid constants $K_1 = 1.2 \times 10^{-3}$ and $K_2 = 3.1 \times 10^{-6}$. The $[H^+]$ of the equivalence point of the standardization is that of 0.05 F potassium sodium phthalate (about 4 meq phthalate in 90 ml water), or approximately equal to

$$\sqrt{K_2 K_w/c} = \sqrt{62 \times 10^{-20}} = 8 \times 10^{-10} \text{ (see Chap. 9)}$$

This is seen to lie inside the range in which phenolphthalein changes its color.

The accuracy of a titration of a relatively weak acid may be improved by using what is known as a *blank*, a solution that closely matches the composition, at the end point, of the solution being titrated. It consists here of 90 ml of a 0.05 F solution of K_2Ph, Na_2Ph, or sodium succinate $(Na_2C_4H_4O_4 \cdot 6H_2O, K_2 = 2.8 \times 10^{-6})$ that contains the same concentration of phenolphthalein as the solution being titrated does at the equivalence point. When an end point that is stable for several minutes has been reached in the actual titration, NaOH solution is carefully added to the blank until a matching color has been obtained. The amount of NaOH used for the blank is then subtracted from that used in the original titration. It is important that the quantity of phenolphthalein added and the total volume at the end point be the same in the actual and the blank titration. Since phenolphthalein is actually a good indicator for the titration of potassium acid phthalate with strong base, the blank correction is negligible unless the titration has been carried past the end point.

PROCEDURES

8-1 Preparation of carbonate-free NaOH solution. In a 1500 ml conical flask or beaker boil 1 liter of distilled water for 5 min, and let it cool to room temperature. Obtain from the laboratory instructor 6 ml of the carbonate-free 50 per cent NaOH solution described, and add it to the boiled water. Stir until the solution is homogeneous, but avoid stirring so vigorously that air bubbles enter the solution. Transfer the solution to a clean, 1-liter polyethylene bottle, securely close the bottle with its screw cap, and gently swirl the container, occasionally inverting it, until the solution is completely mixed. The result is an approximately 0.1 F NaOH solution.

Do not be wasteful of this solution, because it is needed in further assignments.

8-2 Standardization of the NaOH solution. (Review the general procedure for drying samples and weighing out by difference, page 82, and the procedure for titrations, page 142.) Dry 4 to 5 g of the primary standard potassium hydrogen phthalate at 120°C for 1 to 2 hr. Accurately weigh out 0.7- to 0.9-g portions into each of four 200-ml conical flasks. It is best to do two standardizations of the NaOH solution before the titration of the weak acid and two afterward, to check whether the NaOH solution has absorbed atmospheric CO_2. Add to each portion of phthalate about 50 ml of freshly boiled distilled water which is still hot, swirl until the solid has dissolved, and cool to room temperature. Add 4 to 5 drops of 0.1 per cent phenolphthalein indicator solution, and titrate with the carbonate-free NaOH solution until a stable end point has been reached. (The color will fade after a while, owing to absorption of CO_2 from the air.) Be careful not to expose the NaOH solution to the air unduly while filling the buret, and do not leave it in the buret longer than necessary, particularly if the buret is provided with a glass stopcock. If desired, run a blank as discussed in the last paragraph preceding the Procedures. After the first run compute with the slide rule, as always, the approximate volumes of titrant expected for the later runs. Remember to determine the temperature of the solution. Compute the concentration at 20°C, and label the bottle. The average of the deviations of all of the determinations from their mean should be within 2 parts per 1000.

8-3 Titration of an unknown acid. Obtain a sample of the solution of an unknown acid. Pipet a 25.00-ml portion of the acid into a 200-ml flask, add an equal volume of water and 4 to 5 drops of phenolphthalein indicator, and titrate with standard base. The accuracy of the result depends on the pK of the unknown acid as well as on the pH of the phenolphthalein end point as observed by you.

8-4 Determination of the pK of a weak acid. In this experiment you will use a pH meter to follow the change in pH in the solution during the course of the titration. The operation of the pH meter will be explained to you by the laboratory instructor.

These instruments are expensive, and the electrodes in particular are fragile and should be handled with the greatest of care. Be absolutely certain you understand the correct technique for using the meter.

Since the number of pH meters available is limited, each student will be restricted to 45 min use of an instrument. This is more than ample time if the experiment is well thought out in advance.

Prepare a table in your notebook and enter the milliliters of base to be added, as computed from the result of Procedure 8-3, for the following ratios of meq base added to meq acid present: 0.20, 0.40, 0.60, 0.80, 0.90, 0.95, 1.00, 1.05, 1.10, 1.20. This table is to serve as a guide in the actual titration.

Rinse the glass electrode with distilled water, and carefully wipe it with soft tissue. Calibrate it with the buffer solution provided, and adjust the temperature compensation of the pH meter to the temperature

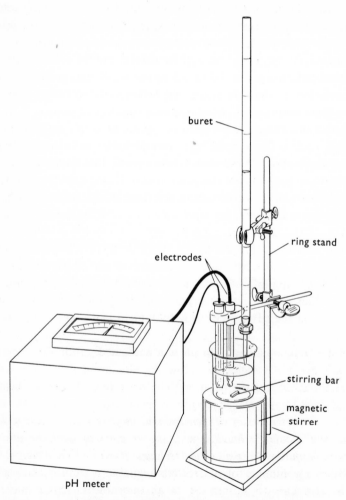

Figure 8-4   Titration with a pH meter.

of the solution. Pipet 25.00 ml of the unknown acid into a 150-ml beaker, and add 25 ml of water and 4 to 5 drops of phenolphthalein solution. Repeat the rinsing and careful drying of the glass electrode, and insert the electrodes into the solution to be titrated.

Make absolutely certain that the electrodes are situated sufficiently above the stirring bar that there will be no damage.

Mount the buret in an appropriate position for the addition of standard base to the titration vessel (Fig. 8-4). Adjust the temperature control of the pH meter to the temperature of the solution. Determine the initial pH; and after 15 to 30 sec, check the reading. The stirring motor should not disturb the pH meter reading if everything is carefully grounded and the resistance across the glass electrode is not too high. Check this and fix the ground if necessary. Add standard base to the unknown acid and record the amount added and the resulting pH. Aim to record pH changes of 0.2 to 0.3 units or volume increases of about 5 ml, whichever comes first. Use the table prepared earlier as a rough guide. Note also the pH of the phenolphthalein end point.

Label the axes of an $8\frac{1}{2}$- by 11-in. piece of graph paper as follows: abscissa, "(equivalents base)/(equivalents acid)," with values from 0 to 1.20; ordinate, "pH," with values from 1 to 12. Plot the points observed, and draw a smooth line through them. Determine the equivalence point on the graph by finding the midpoint of the steep portion of the titration curve that can be represented by a straight line. Locate the abscissa of the equivalence point, and find the pH corresponding to half the volume of base added at equivalence. At this halfway point the solution is a buffer with equal concentrations of HA and A^-, and its pH equals the pK_a of the unknown acid [see Eqs. (8-53) and (8-60) and the discussion pertaining to them]. Although the value for pK_a should be reproducible within 0.1 pH units, it may be as much as 1 pH unit different from the true pK_a that is usually found in tables and is sometimes called the *thermodynamic* pK_a. The difference is due to activity effects.

It is also of interest to calculate pK_a values for other experimental points in the buffering region, for which $pK_a = pH + \log ([HA]/[A^-])$ $\approx pH + \log [(V_{eq} - V)/V]$, where V is the volume of base added at the point considered and V_{eq} that added at the equivalence point.

8-5 Additional titrations of the weak acid.   From the pH at the equivalence point just found determine whether or not phenolphthalein was a satisfactory indicator for the titration of Procedure 8-3. If not, choose a more suitable indicator from those available. In either case, repeat the titration twice, and again compute the concentration of the acid. Compare the results with the one obtained from the pH curve. Report the concentration values computed from all titrations, possibly excepting the preliminary run. Compute and report the average of these values and their absolute and relative standard deviations (see page 83). Also report the value of pK found. Save the remaining standard base in a well-stoppered polyethylene bottle.

PROBLEMS

8-1 Equivalents.   A 0.500-g sample of a metal dissolves completely in 500 ml of 1.000 F HCl with the evolution of 623 ml H_2 gas, measured at STP. (*a*) What is the equivalent weight of the metal? (*b*) How many equivalents of acid are remaining in the solution?

8-2 pH values.   Give the pH of (*a*) 0.5 F HCl; (*b*) 1.0×10^{-8} F NaOH.

8-3 Acid constant of a weak acid.   Formic acid (HCOOH) is 4.5 per cent dissociated in a 0.10 F solution. Compute the constant K_a for the dissociation reaction

$$\text{HCOOH} = \text{H}^+ + \text{HCOO}^-$$

8-4 Buffer solution and indicator.   A small amount of phenolphthalein is added to a solution prepared by mixing 20 ml of 1 F NH$_4$Cl solution and 3 ml of 1 F NH$_3$ solution. Find [H$^+$] and the fraction of indicator HIn that is dissociated into H$^+$ and In$^-$. K_b for NH$_3$ is 1.8×10^{-5}; K_i for HIn is 5.0×10^{-10}.

8-5 Buffer solution.   It is desired to buffer 1 liter of a solution at pH 5.0 by using benzoic acid (symbolized by HBz) and sodium benzoate (NaBz). The formal concentrations of HBz (c_1) and of NaBz (c_2) are to add up to 0.1 F, and K_a of HBz is 6.3×10^{-5}. How many formula weights of HBz and of NaBz are needed?

8-6 The pH during a titration.   The dissociation constant of a certain acid is 2×10^{-4}. A 100.0-ml sample of 0.1000 F solution of this acid is titrated with 0.1000 F NaOH. Compute the pH for (*a*) the initial solution, (*b*) the point where 70.0 ml of base has been added, and (*c*) the equivalence point. What would be a suitable indicator for this titration?

8-7 The titration error.   Hydroxylamine (H$_2$NOH) is a weak base of base constant $K_b = 6.6 \times 10^{-9}$. The N atom may accept a proton to form the conjugate acid hydroxylammonium ion (H$_3$NOH$^+$). In a titration of hydroxylammonium chloride (H$_3$NOH$^+$Cl$^-$) with NaOH the indicator bromthymol blue was used, and the titration was stopped at a pH of 7.0. The initial solution volume was 25.00 ml, and 30.00 ml of 0.1000 F NaOH was used in the titration. Estimate the additional volume of NaOH that is needed to reach the equivalence point. What indicator is suitable in this titration?

8-8 Determination of the pH by observation of the indicator color.   The substance *p*-nitrophenol is a weak acid of constant 6.9×10^{-8}. It is colorless in its acid form and yellow in its basic form. To 100.0 ml of a certain solution 1.00 ml of a dilute solution of *p*-nitrophenol was added, and the resulting color was found to match that obtained by adding 0.42 ml of the same *p*-nitrophenol solution to 100.0 ml of 0.1 *F* KOH solution. Estimate the pH of the solution of the unknown acid.

8-9 Buffer capacity. Consider a buffer solution that is c_1 *F* in the weak acid HA and c_2 *F* in the salt NaA. To a volume *V* of this solution is added strong acid or strong base; let the variable *x* indicate, when positive, the gram equivalents of base added; and let a negative *x* indicate that $|x|$ equivalents of acid have been added. (*a*) Begin with Equation (8-53) and find an approximate equation for $d(\text{pH})/dx$, the rate of change of the pH upon addition of base or acid. The volume change may be neglected, particularly since its inclusion can be shown to have no effect on the result. The smaller $d(\text{pH})/dx$, the better the buffering action. The reciprocal of this derivative is therefore called the buffer capacity. (*b*) As acid or base is added, the derivative $d(\text{pH})/dx$ changes. Find the value x_m of *x* at which $d(\text{pH})/dx$ is a minimum or the buffer capacity a maximum. How are the concentrations of HA and A^- related to each other when x_m equivalents of base or acid have been added [in the approximation in which (8-53) is valid]?

8-10 Titration to pH 7. How many milliliters of 0.0500 *F* H_2SO_4 are needed to neutralize exactly 100.00 ml of 0.1000 *F* NH_3 solution ($K_b = 1.8 \times 10^{-5}$)? How many milliliters of base are needed to reach a pH of 7.00 in the titration of Problem 8-6?

8-11 Symmetry of acid-base titration curve. Show by the following steps that near the equivalence point an acid-base titration curve is approximately symmetrical relative to that point. (*a*) Consider the case of a weak acid titrated with NaOH, and let the total concentration of acid be *c* and that of NaOH be $(c + x)$. A negative *x* represents a surplus of acid, a positive *x* a surplus of base, and at equivalence $x = 0$. Show that near equivalence, where both $[H^+]$ and $[OH^-]$ are small compared to $(c + x)$,

$$[H^+] \approx K_a([OH^-] - [H^+] - x)/(c + x) \qquad (8\text{-}66)$$

[This is closely related to Eq. (8-51).] (*b*) Let *p* be the solution pH and p_{eq} be the (approximate) pH at the equivalence point,

$$10^{-p_{eq}} = \sqrt{K_a K_w/(c + K_a)}$$

Show that (8-66) can be given the form

$$[H^+](c + x + K_a) - K_a K_w/[H^+] = -K_a x \qquad (8\text{-}67)$$

and that further, when $x \ll c$,

$$10^{\Delta p} - 10^{-\Delta p} \approx \sqrt{K_a/K_w(c + K_a)}x \qquad (8\text{-}68)$$

where $\Delta p = p - p_{eq}$. (*c*) Discuss the symmetry properties evident in Equation (8-68) and show that in the approximation considered the equivalence point is an inflection point of the titration curve.

8-12 Mixtures of acids and bases. To different 10.0-ml portions of 0.1 *F* HBrO ($K_a = 2 \times 10^{-9}$) are added (*a*) 10.0 ml of 0.1 *F* NaOH, (*b*) 20.0 ml of 0.1 *F* NaOH, (*c*) 5.0 ml of 0.1 *F* NaOH, (*d*) 5.0 ml of 0.1 *F* HCl. What is the H^+-ion concentration in the resulting four solutions?

8-13 pH of a solution. An excess of solid $Zn(OH)_2$ is added to 0.1 *F* HCl.

What is the pH of the resulting solution? Assume that the only equilibrium involving Zn that needs consideration is the solubility-product equilibrium.

8-14 Buffer solution. Derive a simple expression for the pH of a solution that is c_b formal in the weak base B (base constant K_b) and c_a formal in the salt BH^+Cl^-. Make suitable simplifying assumptions and state under what conditions they hold.

8-15 Titration of a weak acid. A 0.1 F solution of HNO_2 ($K_a = 4.5 \times 10^{-4}$) is titrated with 0.1 F NaOH, using methyl red as indicator. Estimate $[H^+]$ at the end point by using the value of the indicator constant given in Table 8-2 and estimate (within a few per cent) the degree to which the titration is complete or past completion. If the indicator used is unsatisfactory, suggest a better one.

8-16 Buffer solution. One liter of a buffer solution is to be prepared. It is to be buffered at $[H^+] = 1.8 \times 10^{-5}$ by using HAc/NaAc buffer. The solution should not change $[H^+]$ by more than 10 per cent, even though 5 mmoles of H^+ or 5 mmoles of OH^- may be added to it. What are the minimum amounts of HAc and of NaAc needed to give the required buffer action? (K_a of HAc: 1.8 $\times 10^{-5}$.)

REVIEW QUESTIONS

8-1. Briefly explain the following terms: pH, amphiprotic, mixed indicator, autoprotolysis, displacement titration, buffer.

8-2. Why should NaOH standard solutions be protected from the atmosphere? (Give equations.) Why are such solutions kept in polyethylene bottles?

8-3. A number of deviations from the recommended procedures in the titration of a weak acid with NaOH are given. Indicate whether these deviations cause the results to be low, high, or unpredictable in sign and magnitude or whether there will be substantially no error. Give reasons for your answers and indicate approximate magnitudes of deviations, if possible. (a) The indicator used was methyl red. (b) The indicator was phenolphthalein. (c) Phenolphthalein was used as indicator and the NaOH solution had absorbed atmospheric CO_2 after it had been standardized. (d) The indicator was appropriate for 20°C, but the titration was carried out at 90°C. (e) An air bubble was in the tip of the buret at the beginning of the titration, but not at the end.

8-4. (a) A solution of NaOH was prepared without removing impurities of Na_2CO_3. This solution was standardized with standard HCl, using methyl orange as indicator. Give equations showing the titration reactions. (b) The NaOH solution was then used to titrate acetic acid, using phenolphthalein as indicator. Give equations showing the titration reactions. Was the concentration of the acetic acid, found in this way, too high or too low?

*The pH is computed for a solution
of the salt of a weak acid
with a weak base and for a solution
of a polyprotic acid or of one of its salts.
The discussion of the Brønsted-Lowry
concept of acids and bases
is pursued further. In a laboratory
assignment the pH is measured
during the titration
of a polyprotic acid with strong base.*

nine

POLYPROTIC

ACIDS

THE pH IN A SOLUTION OF A
POLYPROTIC ACID OR ONE OF ITS SALTS

Before considering polyprotic acids, the pH of a solution of the salt of a weak acid with a weak base is examined. The result is of interest in its own right and also applies directly to solutions involving polyprotic acids, as will be shown later.

Solution of a salt of a weak acid and a weak base. Consider a c formal solution of the salt A^-HB^+ of the weak acid HA (acid constant K_{a1}) with the weak base B (base constant K_{b2}). This solution contains the six species HA, A^-, B, HB^+, H^+, and OH^-. Thus six equations are needed to find the concentrations of the six species.

All these species must have originated from H_2O molecules and the two ions A^- and HB^+ by the following three reactions: (1) the ionization or autoprotolysis of water furnishing H^+ and OH^-; (2) the reaction of A^- with H^+,

$$A^- + H^+ = HA \tag{9-1}$$

for which it is convenient to write the equilibrium condition:

$$[HA] = \frac{[H^+][A^-]}{K_{a1}} \tag{9-2}$$

and (3) the dissociation of HB^+,

$$HB^+ = H^+ + B \tag{9-3}$$

for which the equilibrium condition will be given the form

$$[B] = \frac{K_{a2}[HB^+]}{[H^+]} \tag{9-4}$$

The constant $K_{a2} = K_w/K_{b2}$ is the acid constant of the acid HB^+ conjugate to the base B.

Three of the required six equations are furnished by the equilibrium conditions (9-2), (9-4), and that governing the autoprotolysis of water, $[H^+][OH^-] = K_w$. The other three equations are stoichiometric in nature. The first expresses the conservation of the total quantity of acid,

$$[HA] + [A^-] = c \tag{9-5}$$

and the second that of base,

$$[B] + [HB^+] = c \tag{9-6}$$

Equation (9-7) may be obtained from the condition for charge conservation

$$[H^+] + [HB^+] = [OH^-] + [A^-]$$

Replacing $[HB^+]$ by $c - [B]$ and $[A^-]$ by $c - [HA]$ and rearranging results in

$$[H^+] = [OH^-] + [B] - [HA]. \tag{9-7}$$

This equation has the following direct interpretation. Since all the species in the solution must have originated from reactions of H_2O, HB^+, and A^-, the concentration of H^+ in particular must equal the sum of the contributions from the dissociation of water (measured by $[OH^-]$) and the dissociation of HB^+ by reaction (9-3) (measured by $[B]$), diminished by the concentration of H^+ ions lost through the formation of acid particles HA by reaction (9-1) (measured by $[HA]$).

All concentrations on the right of (9-7) are now expressed in terms of $[H^+]$ by using (9-2), (9-4), and the ion product for water

$$[H^+] = \frac{K_w}{[H^+]} + \frac{K_{a2}[HB^+]}{[H^+]} - \frac{[H^+][A^-]}{K_{a1}}$$

Solving for $[H^+]$ results in the expression

$$[H^+] = \sqrt{\frac{K_{a1}(K_w + K_{a2}[HB^+])}{K_{a1} + [A^-]}} \qquad (9\text{-}8)$$

which is exact but which still contains two unknowns on the right. At this point it is convenient to make assumptions that are appropriate to the value of c and to the values of the equilibrium constants. Often the following assumptions are suitable: The concentration $[HB^+]$ and the value of K_{a2} are such that K_w may be neglected, and $[A^-]$ is large compared with K_{a1} so that K_{a1} may be neglected in combination with $[A^-]$. This results in the approximation

$$[H^+] \approx \sqrt{\frac{K_{a1}K_{a2}[HB^+]}{[A^-]}} \qquad (9\text{-}9)$$

The two neglected terms correspond to neglecting $[H^+]$ and $[OH^-]$ in Equation (9-7), so that on the same level of approximation $[B]$ and $[HA]$ are almost equal to each other. It follows from (9-5) and (9-6) that $[HB^+]$ and $[A^-]$ are also almost equal and cancel each other approximately in (9-9). Hence,

$$[H^+] \approx \sqrt{K_{a1}K_{a2}} \qquad (9\text{-}10)$$

provided that $K_w \ll K_{a2}[HB^+]$ and $K_{a1} \ll [A^-]$

where K_{a1} is the acid constant of HA and K_{a2} is the acid constant of HB^+.*

In the situation considered, the H^+-ion concentration is almost independent of the concentration c and the H^+ ions produced by the reaction (9-3) are almost exactly used up in the reaction (9-1).

The value of $[H^+]$ obtained from (9-10) may be inserted into Equations (9-2) and (9-4), yielding

$$\frac{[B]}{[HB^+]} = \frac{K_{a2}}{\sqrt{K_{a1}K_{a2}}} = \sqrt{\frac{K_{a2}}{K_{a1}}} = \frac{[HA]}{[A^-]} \qquad (9\text{-}11)$$

This may be combined with (9-5) and solved for $[HA]$ and $[A^-]$, whereas the solutions to (9-11) and (9-6) furnish $[HB^+]$ and $[B]$.

To give an example, the pH of a $0.200\ F$ solution of NH_4NO_2 is computed. The constants, which have been given earlier, are

* It is of interest that the first condition can be written $[HB^+] \gg K_w/K_{a2} = K_{b2}$, where K_{b2} is the base constant of B.

$K_{a1} = 4.5 \times 10^{-4}$ and $K_{a2} = 5.5 \times 10^{-10}$. Inserting these values into (9-10) yields $[H^+]$ and the pH,

$$[H^+] \approx \sqrt{25.0} \times 10^{-7} = 5.0 \times 10^{-7} \qquad \text{pH} = 6.3$$

It follows that $[OH^-] = 2.0 \times 10^{-8}$ and, from (9-11), that

$$[HA]/[A^-] = [B]/[HB^+] = \sqrt{K_{a2}/K_{a1}} = 1.1 \times 10^{-3}.$$

Thus, $[NH_4^+] = [NO_2^-] = 0.2$, and $[NH_3] = [HNO_2] = 2.2 \times 10^{-4}$. Inspection shows that all equations are satisfied in the approximation used.

Note that formula (9-10) also gives the pH at the equivalence point of the titration of a weak acid with a weak base, a type of titration that was shown in the preceding chapter to have very low precision.

Solution of a polyprotic acid. Consider first the special case of a c formal solution of a *diprotic* acid H_2A that dissociates in the two steps

$$H_2A = HA^- + H^+ \tag{9-12}$$

and

$$HA^- = A^= + H^+ \tag{9-13}$$

with the mass-action equilibria

$$\frac{[H^+][HA^-]}{[H_2A]} = K_1 \tag{9-14}$$

and

$$\frac{[H^+][A^=]}{[HA^-]} = K_2 \tag{9-15}$$

Although it is possible to set up an equation for $[H^+]$ and to solve it rigorously, such a procedure proves to be cumbersome and it is better to make assumptions appropriate to the situation considered and to find an approximate solution. Usually, K_2 is much smaller than K_1, and it may be assumed that $[H^+]$ is determined by the first step of dissociation alone. The pH of a c formal solution of a monoprotic acid has been discussed in the preceding chapter (page 160), with the result (8-39),

$$[H^+] \approx \sqrt{cK_1} \approx [HA^-] \tag{9-16}$$

provided that $10^{-6} \leq [H^+] \ll c$ and $K_1 \gg K_2$

Insertion of the values just obtained for $[H^+]$ and $[HA^-]$ into (9-15) leads to

$$[A^=] \approx K_2 \tag{9-17}$$

Since for each H_2A molecule that dissociates to $A^=$ two H^+ ions are produced, the contribution to $[H^+]$ by this dissociation is $2[A^=] \approx 2K_2,$* which is usually small compared with $\sqrt{(cK_1)}$ and which may be neglected, as assumed earlier.

As an example, the concentrations of the different ions and molecules in a $0.034\ F$ solution of H_2CO_3 are calculated. Such a solution is just saturated with CO_2 at 1 atm pressure; and to maintain equilibrium, CO_2 gas of this pressure must be bubbled through the solution or otherwise be in contact with it. The dissolved CO_2 is at equilibrium with H_2CO_3, and indeed the symbol $[H_2CO_3]$ is defined as the total concentration of both species, H_2CO_3 and CO_2. The two dissociation constants of H_2CO_3 are $K_1 = 4.4 \times 10^{-7}$ and $K_2 = 4.8 \times 10^{-11}$. The pH of the $0.034\ F\ H_2CO_3$ solution is determined by the equilibrium governed by K_1, and it is found that

$$[H^+] = \sqrt{0.034 \times 4.4 \times 10^{-7}} = 1.2 \times 10^{-4} = [HCO_3{}^-]$$

$$pH = 3.9 \tag{9-18}$$

$$[OH^-] = 0.8 \times 10^{-10} \qquad [H_2CO_3] = 0.034 \qquad [CO_3{}^=] = 4.8 \times 10^{-11}$$

This set of values satisfies all mass-action equations as well as the stoichiometric condition, total carbonate $= [H_2CO_3] + [HCO_3{}^-] + [CO_3{}^=] = 0.034$. The pH computed furnishes a point on one of the titration curves discussed later, as will many of the pH values in the examples to follow.

In a solution of a polyprotic acid that can yield more than two protons the situation is similar, provided that the successive dissociation constants differ by several powers of 10, as is often the case. Again $[H^+]$ is determined by the dissociation of the first hydrogen. An example is furnished by H_3PO_4, with the three equilibrium equations

$$\frac{[H^+][H_2PO_4{}^-]}{[H_3PO_4]} = K_1 = 7.1 \times 10^{-3} \tag{9-19}$$

$$\frac{[H^+][HPO_4{}^=]}{[H_2PO_4{}^-]} = K_2 = 6.2 \times 10^{-8} \tag{9-20}$$

$$\frac{[H^+][PO_4{}^{3-}]}{[HPO_4{}^=]} = K_3 = 4.4 \times 10^{-13} \tag{9-21}$$

* Statements of this kind may usually be checked by applying conservation equations. In this case the charge-conservation equation $[H^+] = [HA^-] + 2[A^=] + [OH^-]$ shows that the total H^+-ion concentration is the sum of the contributions from the reactions $H_2A = HA^- + H^+$ (measured by $[HA^-]$), $H_2A = 2H^+ + A^=$ (measured by $2[A^=]$), and $H_2O = H^+ + OH^-$ (measured by $[OH^-]$).

The H^+ concentration is obtained by considering the equilibrium underlying Equation (9-19) only. The contributions from the equilibria corresponding to (9-20) and (9-21) will be seen to be negligible. Since K_1 is relatively large, the depletion in H_3PO_4 by dissociation may be considerable and the assumptions leading to the approximation (9-16) are suspect. Thus the complete quadratic equation has to be solved to obtain $[H^+]$. If $0.4\ F\ H_3PO_4$ is considered as an example and the moles per liter of H_3PO_4 that have lost one H^+ are denoted by x, the concentrations of the species involved in (9-19), the expression for K_1, are approximately as indicated beneath the chemical equation

$$H_3PO_4 = H^+ + H_2PO_4^-$$
$$0.4 - x \qquad x \qquad\quad x$$

Therefore,

$$x^2/(0.4 - x) = K_1$$

which is solved to give

$$x = [H^+] = [H_2PO_4^-] = 0.050 \qquad pH = 1.3 \qquad\qquad (9\text{-}22)$$
$$[H_3PO_4] = 0.35 \qquad [OH^-] = 2 \times 10^{-13} \qquad [HPO_4^=] = 6.2 \times 10^{-8}$$
$$[PO_4^{3-}] = 4.4 \times 10^{-13}[HPO_4^=]/[H^+] = 5.5 \times 10^{-19}$$

This set of values is in agreement with all mass-action equations and with the condition that

$$\text{total phosphate} = [H_3PO_4] + [H_2PO_4^-] + [HPO_4^=] + [PO_4^{3-}]$$
$$= 0.4\ \text{mole/liter}$$

Solution of an acid salt of a polyprotic acid. The anion of an acid salt of a polyprotic acid is, by definition, an acid and is thus capable of furnishing protons by dissociation; it is also a base, because it can accept protons. An example is the salt Na^+HQ^- of the diprotic acid H_2Q. The species HQ^- in a solution of this salt may act as acid,

$$HQ^- = H^+ + Q^= \qquad\qquad (9\text{-}23)$$

with acid constant K_2; its base reaction is

$$HQ^- + H^+ = H_2Q \qquad\qquad (9\text{-}24)$$

with the mass-action constant K_1^{-1}, where K_1 is the first dissociation constant of H_2Q. Comparison of this situation with that discussed earlier of a solution of the salt A^-HB^+ of a weak acid and a weak base reveals a close similarity. H_2Q is identical with the acid HA of (9-1); $Q^=$ is identical with the base B of (9-3); and HQ^- plays the role of both the base A^- in (9-1) and the acid HB^+ in (9-3). The formula (9-8) for the H^+-ion concentration derived earlier applies here also, with the change that $[HB^+]$ and $[A^-]$ are now identical and represented by $[HQ^-]$, so that

$$[H^+] = \sqrt{\frac{K_1(K_w + K_2[HQ^-])}{(K_1 + [HQ^-])}} \qquad (9\text{-}25)$$

Usually the approximations that hold are the same as those that led from (9-8) to (9-10), with the difference that now $[HB^+]$ and $[A^-]$ are exactly equal, since both are identical with $[HQ^-]$. For the conditions listed following the next equation, $[H^+]$ is given by an equation identical with (9-10),

$$[H^+] \approx \sqrt{K_1 K_2} \qquad (9\text{-}26)$$

provided that $K_w \ll K_2[HQ^-]$ and $K_1 \ll [HQ^-]$

Note that $[H^+]$ is independent of c in the approximation considered. In the same approximation

$$\frac{[H_2Q]}{[HQ^-]} = \frac{[Q^=]}{[HQ^-]} = \sqrt{\frac{K_1}{K_2}} \qquad (9\text{-}27)$$

which is analogous to (9-11). It follows that $[Q^=] = [H_2Q]$; the extent of dissociation of HQ^- to $Q^=$ is just about balanced by the extent to which HQ^- accepts protons to form H_2Q. The following examples are of interest. In particular, cases 1, 2, and 3 furnish points on the titration curves to be discussed later.

    1.   *c formal solution of* $NaHCO_3$.   Inspection of the constants K_1 and K_2 given earlier [preceding Eq. (9-18)] reveals that the assumptions leading to (9-22) are satisfied if $c \gtrsim 10^{-2}$, so that

$$[H^+] = \sqrt{K_1 K_2} = 4.6 \times 10^{-9} \qquad pH = 8.3$$

$$[OH^-] = 2.2 \times 10^{-6} \qquad [HCO_3^-] = c \qquad (9\text{-}28)$$

$$[CO_3^=] = [H_2CO_3] = [HCO_3^-]\sqrt{K_2/K_1} = 1.1 \times 10^{-2}c$$

    2.   *c formal solution of* NaH_2PO_4.   In view of the large differences between the constants K_1, K_2, and K_3 [Eqs. (9-19) to (9-21)] it is reasonable to assume that the pH of this solution is governed by the association of $H_2PO_4^-$ to H_3PO_4 and its dissociation to $HPO_4^=$ and that further dissociation to PO_4^{3-} affects the pH very little. The conditions underlying Equation (9-26) are satisfied if c is of the order of 0.1 F or larger. The following concentrations are found to obtain:

$$[H^+] = \sqrt{K_1 K_2} = 2.1 \times 10^{-5} \qquad pH = 4.7$$
$$[OH^-] = 4.8 \times 10^{-10} \qquad [H_2PO_4^-] = c$$
$$[HPO_4^=] = [H_3PO_4] = \sqrt{K_2/K_1}\,[H_2PO_4^-]$$
$$= 4.6 \times 10^{-3}c \qquad [PO_4^{3-}] = [HPO_4^=]K_3/[H^+]$$
$$= c \times 10^{-10} \qquad\qquad (9\text{-}29)$$

3. *c formal solution of* Na_2HPO_4. The reasonable assumption here is that the pH is determined by the dissociation of $HPO_4^=$ to PO_4^{3-} and its association to $H_2PO_4^-$, whereas further association to H_3PO_4 has only little effect. The assumptions leading to Equation (9-26) are satisfied if c is at least of the order of 0.1 F. The following concentrations are calculated:

$$[H^+] = \sqrt{K_2 K_3} = 1.6 \times 10^{-10} \qquad pH = 9.8$$
$$[OH^-] = 6.2 \times 10^{-5} \qquad [HPO_4^=] = c$$

(9-30)

$$[H_2PO_4^-] = [PO_4^{3-}] = \sqrt{K_3/K_2} \qquad c = 2.2 \times 10^{-3}c$$
$$[H_3PO_4] = [H^+][H_2PO_4^-]/K_1 = 6.1 \times 10^{-11}c$$

This set of values is consistent with all requirements.

For all situations that do not satisfy the requirements specified in the foregoing, different approximations need to be made in solving (9-25) and the related equations. Two examples follow.

4. 0.1 F $NaHSO_4$ *solution.* In this example approximations different from those made earlier are needed. The constant K_1 for H_2SO_4 is much larger than 1, and $K_2 = 1.2 \times 10^{-2}$. Comparison of the different terms in (9-25) shows the following results: $K_1 \gg [HSO_4^-]$ and $K_w \ll K_2[HSO_4^-]$. Neglecting the items suggested by this comparison,

$$[H^+] \approx \sqrt{\frac{K_1 K_2[HSO_4^-]}{K_1}} = \sqrt{K_2[HSO_4^-]} = 3.5 \times 10^{-2}$$

Comparison with (8-39) (page 160) shows that the important reaction in the solution considered is dissociation of HSO_4^-. Because of the large magnitude of K_1, there are practically no HSO_4^- particles that accept protons to form H_2SO_4.

5. 0.01 F $NaHS$ *solution.* The dissociation constants of H_2S are $K_1 = 9.1 \times 10^{-8}$, $K_2 = 1.2 \times 10^{-15}$. Since $[HS^-]K_2 \lesssim 0.01 \times 1.2 \times 10^{-15}$ is small compared with K_w, $[HS^-]K_2$ may be neglected in (9-25) rather than K_w. This leads to

$$[H^+] \approx \sqrt{K_1 K_w/[HS^-]} \approx \sqrt{9.1 \times 10^{-22}/0.01} = 3.0 \times 10^{-10}$$

Comparison with (8-42) (page 160) shows that the important reaction in this solution is protonation of HS^- to form H_2S; since K_2 is so small, the contribution to $[H^+]$ by dissociation of HS^- is negligible. The concentrations of the other species in the solution are $[OH^-] = [H_2S] = 3.3 \times 10^{-5}$; $[HS^-] = 0.01$; $[S^=] = 4.0 \times 10^{-8}$.

Solution of a polyvalent anion. In computing the H^+-ion concentration of a solution of a polyvalent anion A^{-n}, a base that can add n protons in steps, all but the first of the steps may usually be ignored. Thus from Equation (8-42) (page 160),

$$[H^+] = \sqrt{K_w K_n / c} \qquad (9\text{-}31)$$

provided that $10^{-6} \leq [OH^-] \ll c$ and $K_n \ll K_{n-1}$

where K_n is the constant for the nth step in the dissociation of H_nA; in addition,

$$[HA^{n-1}] = [OH^-] \qquad (9\text{-}32)$$

The extent to which HA^{n-1} adds further protons follows from inserting (9-31) and (9-32) into the appropriate mass-action equations; the pH is, in general, affected very little by this. A particularly simple result is the equation analogous to (9-17),

$$[H_2A^{n-2}] = K_w / K_{n-1} \qquad (9\text{-}33)$$

To give an example, the following concentrations are calculated for a $0.1\ F$ solution of Na_2CO_3 ($K_1 = 4.4 \times 10^{-7}$, $K_2 = 4.8 \times 10^{-11}$):

$$[H^+] = \sqrt{10^{-14} \times 4.8 \times 10^{-11} / 0.1} = 2.2 \times 10^{-12} \qquad pH = 11.7$$
$$\qquad (9\text{-}34)$$

$$[OH^-] = [HCO_3^-] = 4.5 \times 10^{-3} \qquad [CO_3^=] = 0.096 \approx 0.1$$
$$[H_2CO_3] = 4.4 \times 10^{-7}$$

Another example, the $0.1\ F$ solution of Na_3PO_4, leads to a somewhat more involved computation [for constants see Eqs. (9-19) to (9-21)]. Insertion into Equations (9-31) to (9-33) shows that $[PO_4^{3-}]$ is sufficiently depleted by the protolysis

$$PO_4^{3-} + H_2O = HPO_4^= + OH^-$$
$$0.1 - x \qquad\qquad x \qquad\quad x$$

so that x in the quadratic equation $x^2/(0.1 - x) = K_w/K_3 = 0.1$ is not negligible compared with 0.1, as is assumed in deriving (9-31). (The symbols beneath the chemical equation stand, as usual, for the concentrations of the respective species.) It is thus necessary to solve the quadratic explicitly, with the result

$$x = [OH^-] = [HPO_4^=] = 0.038$$

The remaining concentration values are

$$[H^+] = 2.6 \times 10^{-13} \qquad pH = 12.6 \qquad (9\text{-}35)$$
$$[PO_4^{3-}] = 0.062 \qquad [H_2PO_4^-] = K_w/K_2 = 1.6 \times 10^{-7}$$
$$[H_3PO_4] = [H_2PO_4^-][H^+]/K_1 = 6 \times 10^{-18}$$

Buffer solutions. A solution containing substantial amounts of a weak acid as well as the conjugate weak base is usually a buffer, whether or not the acid or the base, or both of them, are amphiprotic (can gain or lose protons). An example is a solution that is c_1 formal in NaH_2PO_4 and c_2 formal in Na_2HPO_4. The H^+-ion concentration in this solution is governed by the interaction between the $H_2PO_4^-$ and $HPO_4^=$ ions,

$$H_2PO_4^- = HPO_4^= + H^+ \qquad (9\text{-}36)$$

and its value closely equals the result expressed by Equation (8-53) (page 163),

$$[H^+] = K_2[H_2PO_4^-]/[HPO_4^=] \approx K_2 c_1/c_2 \qquad (9\text{-}37)$$
$$\text{provided that } [H^+] \text{ and } [OH^-] \ll c_1 \text{ and } c_2$$

There will, of course, be some $H_2PO_4^-$ ions that gain protons, some $HPO_4^=$ ions that lose protons, and some H_2O molecules that furnish H^+ ions by dissociation. All these effects do not change $[H^+]$ appreciably. For example, the concentrations of the different species in a solution 0.1 F in NaH_2PO_4 and 0.2 F in Na_2HPO_4 are the following [see Eqs. (9-19) to (9-21) for K_1, K_2, and K_3]:

$$[H^+] = K_2[H_2PO_4^-]/[HPO_4^=] = 6.2 \times 10^{-8} \times 0.1/0.2$$
$$= 3.1 \times 10^{-8}$$
$$[PO_4^{3-}] = [HPO_4^=]K_3/[H^+] = 2.8 \times 10^{-6}$$
$$[H_3PO_4] = [H_2PO_4^-][H^+]/K_1 = 4.4 \times 10^{-7}$$
$$[OH^-] = 3.2 \times 10^{-7}$$

Changes in $[H^+]$ caused by the formation of PO_4^{3-} and H_3PO_4 are seen to be negligible. Any contribution to $[H^+]$ from the dissociation of H_2O causes a small shift in the equilibrium (9-36). Since the concentrations $[H_2PO_4^-]$ and $[HPO_4^=]$ are hardly affected by this shift (by assumption, $[H^+]$ and $[OH^-]$ are negligible compared with c_1 and c_2), the H^+-ion concentration is changed very little.

For buffer solutions containing other components than in the example discussed the H^+-ion concentration is given by expressions analogous to (9-37).

Solution of an acid salt of a polyprotic acid as pH standard. As shown by (9-26), in the solution of a salt NaHA, $[H^+] = \sqrt{(K_1 K_2)}$ is independent of the concentration of the salt, provided that the conditions listed beneath (9-26) are satisfied. The solution is thus expected to maintain its pH upon dilution, at least approximately. Such salts when well crystallized and easily purified are often used to prepare pH standards, for example, in the calibration of the glass electrode of a pH meter. It should be noted that solutions of these salts are not buffer solutions in the ordinary sense, and although they hardly change pH when diluted, there is little buffering against addition of acid or base. On the contrary, as will appear from the following discussion of the pH change during titrations of polyprotic acids, a solution of NaHA is on a portion of the pH curve where the change in pH upon addition of acid or base is *larger* than anywhere else (e.g., Fig. 9-1, at 100 ml HCl added).

As an example, a solution of potassium hydrogen tartrate has been recommended for the standardization of glass electrodes. Tartaric acid is a diprotic acid whose pK values have been reported to be p$K_1 = 2.52$ and p$K_2 = 4.16$, so that the pH for a solution of the potassium hydrogen salt is expected to be $\frac{1}{2}(2.52 + 4.16) = 3.34$. It is found that

$$pH = 3.57 \qquad \text{at } 25°C \tag{9-38}$$

in a saturated solution, the different value being due to deviations from the mass-action equations used in obtaining (9-26). The pH of this solution is found to change very little with temperature (about $+0.0015$ pH unit per degree centigrade), and dilution by a factor 2 changes it by only 0.02 unit.

TITRATIONS INVOLVING POLYPROTIC ACIDS

Two examples are considered: the titration of the base $CO_3^=$ with strong acid and that of the acid H_3PO_4 with strong base.

Titration of Na_2CO_3 with HCl. The pH change during such a titration may be computed by applying the methods discussed earlier. To give a numerical example, it will be assumed that 100.0 ml of 0.1 F Na_2CO_3 is titrated with 0.1 F HCl. The pH at the start is 11.7, as shown by (9-34). After adding 100.0 ml of HCl, the solution is identical with 200.0 ml of 0.05 F NaHCO$_3$, with a pH of 8.3, as given by (9-28). When another 100.0 ml of HCl is added, 300.0 ml of a 0.033 F solution of H_2CO_3 results, with a pH of 3.9, as given by (9-18). This solution, incidentally, is saturated with CO_2 at 1 atm pressure, so that it would be

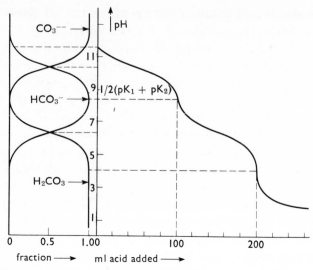

Figure 9-1   Titration curve for Na₂CO₃ with HCl, and distribution of carbonate species.

necessary to bubble CO_2 at 1 atm through it if maintenance of the equilibrium were essential. At other points of the titration curve the pH can be computed by equations analogous to (9-37) and (8-53) (page 163).

The resulting pH curve is shown in Figure 9-1 with a graph giving the fractions of total carbonate that exist at different pH values as H_2CO_3, HCO_3^-, and $CO_3^=$. These fractions are obtained by inserting a specified value of $[H^+]$ into the equilibrium expressions for the dissociation of H_2CO_3. The concentrations of the different carbonate species may then be expressed in terms of one of them, for example, $[HCO_3^-]$,

$$[H_2CO_3] = \frac{[HCO_3^-][H^+]}{K_1} \tag{9-39}$$

$$[CO_3^=] = \frac{[HCO_3^-]K_2}{[H^+]} \tag{9-40}$$

If the total carbonate in all different forms is denoted by T, it follows that

$$T = [H_2CO_3] + [HCO_3^-] + [CO_3^=]$$

$$T = [HCO_3^-]\left(\frac{[H^+]}{K_1} + 1 + \frac{K_2}{[H^+]}\right) \tag{9-41}$$

198

and thus, for the different fractions,

$$\frac{[H_2CO_3]}{T} = \frac{[H^+]^2}{[H^+]^2 + [H^+]K_1 + K_1K_2} \tag{9-42}$$

$$\frac{[HCO_3^-]}{T} = \frac{[H^+]K_1}{[H^+]^2 + [H^+]K_1 + K_1K_2} \tag{9-43}$$

and

$$\frac{[CO_3^=]}{T} = \frac{K_1K_2}{[H^+]^2 + [H^+]K_1 + K_1K_2} \tag{9-44}$$

The following special points of the distribution curves are immediately obtained: When $[H^+] = K_1$, it follows from (9-39) that $[H_2CO_3] = [HCO_3^-]$, and since $[CO_3^=]$ can be neglected, $[H_2CO_3]/T = [HCO_3^-]/T \approx 0.5$. Similarly, $[HCO_3^-]/T = [CO_3^=]/T \approx 0.5$ when $[H^+] = K_2$. It can also be shown that when $[H^+] = \sqrt{(K_1K_2)}$, $[HCO_3^-]/T$ is a maximum and $[H_2CO_3] = [CO_3^=]$ (see Problem 9-8).

As already mentioned, the distribution of carbonate over the three possible species as a function of $[H^+]$ is shown in Figure 9-1. The figure shows that at most two of the three carbonate species, $CO_3^=$ and HCO_3^-, or HCO_3^- and H_2CO_3, can be present in significant concentrations at the same time. This follows from the large ratio between the two constants K_1 and K_2.

At the beginning of the titration, $CO_3^=$ exists to the practical exclusion of the other carbonate species. When one equivalent of acid has been added, almost all the $CO_3^=$ has been changed to HCO_3^-. Addition of a further equivalent of acid changes practically all HCO_3^- to H_2CO_3 and to CO_2, part of which may escape. The slope of the titration curve is large in the neighborhood of these two equivalence points and small whenever substantial concentrations of either $CO_3^=$ and HCO_3^- or of HCO_3^- and H_2CO_3 are present, as is expected for buffer solutions.

The steep portions of the titration curve near the equivalence points are not so steep and do not extend over so large a pH range as is required for a titration precision of 0.1 relative per cent. Near the HCO_3^- equivalence point, of pH 8.3, the change in pH caused by adding 1.0 ml of acid is only about 0.3 units, and the slope becomes rapidly less steep on either side of the equivalence point, so that 10 ml of acid is needed for a pH change of 1 unit. In a titration making use of this first equivalence point and an indicator changing in a range of 1.5 to 2.0 pH units, an accuracy of only 5 to 10 relative per cent may be expected. The situation near the second equivalence point at pH 4.0 is somewhat more favorable. About 4 ml of acid is needed for a pH change of 1 unit, so that, with an indicator changing in a range of 1.5 to 2.0 pH units and considering that at equivalence 200 ml of acid is used, an accuracy of 1 to 2 relative per cent may be expected.

The accuracy of the titration can be improved considerably by removal of the carbon dioxide just before the second equivalence point has been reached. An accuracy of better than 0.1 per cent may be obtained experimentally as follows: Phenolphthalein indicator is first added and the carbonate solution titrated with HCl until the red color has just disappeared, which is at an approximate pH of 8. Since the equivalence point is at pH 8.4, an amount of acid somewhat in excess of one equivalent is used, and the titration gives a rough idea of the carbonate content of the original solution. Next, bromcresol green (basic, blue; acidic, yellow) is added and the titration is continued to the first indication of green color, which is at a pH of about 5 and corresponds by Figure 9-1 to about 195 ml or 97 to 98 per cent of two equivalents of acid. The solution is boiled to remove the CO_2, which changes the pH back to somewhere between 8 and 9 and the indicator color back to blue (there may also be some red mixed in from the phenolphthalein). The solution is cooled and the titration is continued to the green end-point color of bromcresol green. Removal of the carbon dioxide changes the aspects of this last titration to one of a *strong base* with strong acid, which explains the accuracy of better than 0.1 per cent that may be obtained.

Since sodium carbonate of high purity can readily be prepared, this substance is often used as a primary standard for the standardization of strong acids.

By a suitable choice of indicators it is also possible to titrate separately for carbonate and bicarbonate. A titration to pH 8.4 yields the carbonate, and further titration to pH 4, after removal of the carbon dioxide, indicates the bicarbonate. This second titration may be carried out in a separate sample, so that it shows the total of carbonate and bicarbonate. Respectable accuracy in these titrations may be reached by using mixed indicators or comparison solutions containing indicator at the pH of the equivalence point aimed for. (See Problem 9-4 for an example of a titration of this type.)

Titration of H_3PO_4 with NaOH.   The titration of 100.0 ml of 0.4 F H_3PO_4 with 0.4 F NaOH is considered. The pH for a number of important points of the titration has already been calculated and is given in Table 9-1. At other points of the titration the pH may be calculated by equations like (9-37) and (8-53). Figure 9-2 shows the pH, as a function of the quantity of base added, and the distribution of the total

TABLE 9-1   *Equivalence Points in the*
H_3PO_4 Titration

equivalents base added	pH	equation
0	1.3	(9-22)
1	4.7	(9-29)
2	9.8	(9-30)
3	12.6	(9-35)

phosphate over the four species H_3PO_4, $H_2PO_4^-$, $HPO_4^=$, and PO_4^{3-} for the different pH values. These distributions were computed from equations analogous to (9-42) to (9-44).

It is seen from Figure 9-2 that at the first equivalence point practically all the phosphate present exists as $H_2PO_4^-$ and at the second equivalence point practically all as $HPO_4^=$. At the third equivalence point, however, only about one-third the phosphate is in the form of PO_4^{3-} and two-thirds still exists as $HPO_4^=$. The reason is that there is serious competition between the reactions

$$HPO_4^= = H^+ + PO_4^{3-}$$

and

$$H_2O = H^+ + OH^-$$

as sources of protons, the acid strength of H_2O being comparable with that of $HPO_4^=$. This is also the reason why there is no steep slope of the titration curve in the vicinity of the third equivalence point as there is for the first and the second equivalence points. In a medium of lower acid strength than that of H_2O (or of higher base strength than that of OH^-) there would be a third steep portion of the pH curve in the vicinity of the PO_4^{3-} equivalence point also.

The portions of the pH curve near the first and second equivalence points are steep enough for titration accuracies of about 1 per cent, without special precautions. For better accuracy, comparisons with indicator solutions of suitable pH are required as follows: At the first equivalence point methyl orange (acidic, red; basic, yellow) or bromcresol green may be used, the comparison solution containing the indicator at the same concentration in a solution of KH_2PO_4. The precise concentration of this salt is unimportant, since $[H^+] = \sqrt{(K_1 K_2)}$ is to a good approximation independent of it. For the second equivalence point thymolphthalein (acidic, colorless; basic, blue) may be used. It is added to a comparison solution of K_2HOP_4 until a faint but distinct tinge of blue is obtained. The same final indicator concentration is used in the titration, which is stopped at the same tinge of blue as in the comparison solution. It is possible to titrate to the first equivalence point with methyl orange, to add thymolphthalein, and to continue the titration to the second equivalence point. The comparison solution should, of course, contain the same mixture of indicators. Alternatively, it is possible to use a pH meter in titrations of polyprotic acids, as described in the laboratory assignment.

It is even feasible to titrate to the third equivalence point if the PO_4^{3-} is removed by precipitation. The PO_4^{3-} may be removed by the presence of Ca^{++} of the proper concentration, so that slightly soluble $Ca_3(PO_4)_2$ is formed.

Instead of titrating H_3PO_4 or $H_2PO_4^-$ with standard NaOH, PO_4^{3-} or $HPO_4^=$ may be titrated with standard HCl. The titration curve is substantially the reverse of that shown in Figure 9-2, the only difference, apart from possible different initial concentrations, being that the solution becomes more dilute as

Polyprotic acids

more acid is added, whereas previously the dilution increased upon addition of base. The pH curve is again steep at the $HPO_4^=$ and the $H_2PO_4^-$ equivalence points and quantitative titrations are possible, with suitable precautions against reaction of the strongly basic PO_4^{3-} or $HPO_4^=$ solution with atmospheric CO_2. There is, however, no steep portion of the pH curve at the H_3PO_4 equivalence point. In addition, as seen from Equation (9-22), at this equivalence point only about half the phosphoric acid exists as H_3PO_4, the other half being $H_2PO_4^-$. The reason for both these facts is that the base strengths of H_2O and $H_2PO_4^-$ are comparable, so that there is an extensive transfer of protons from H_3PO_4 to H_2O to form H_3O^+. In a medium of lower base strength than that of H_2O (or of higher acid strength than that of H_3O^+) there would be a steep portion of the pH curve at the H_3PO_4 equivalence point, and at that point practically all the phosphoric acid would exist as H_3PO_4.

As seen from the distribution curves in Figure 9-2, only species that are neighbors in the series H_3PO_4, $H_2PO_4^-$, $HPO_4^=$, and PO_4^{3-} may exist at the same time in substantial concentrations. This is related to the large ratios of the constants for the successive dissociation of H^+ ions, K_1/K_2 and K_2/K_3. For example, when $H_2PO_4^-$ is present in significant concentration, either H_3PO_4 or $HPO_4^=$ may also exist at substantial concentration levels, but not PO_4^{3-}. If Na_3PO_4 is added to such a solution, PO_4^{3-} reacts with $H_2PO_4^-$ to form $HPO_4^=$,

$$H_2PO_4^- + PO_4^{3-} = 2HPO_4^= \qquad K_2/K_3 = 1.4 \times 10^5$$

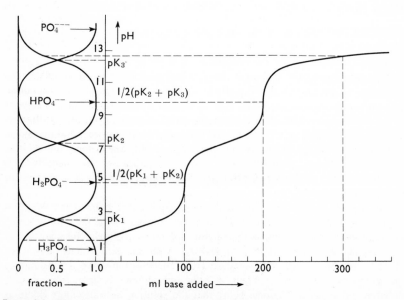

Figure 9-2 Titration curve for H_3PO_4 with NaOH, and distribution of phosphate species.

This reaction proceeds quantitatively to the right because the reaction constant is about 10^5, and as a result either practically all $H_2PO_4^-$ or practically all PO_4^{3-} is converted to $HPO_4^=$, or both. It is possible, by separate or consecutive titrations with end points near the $HPO_4^=$ and the $H_2PO_4^-$ equivalence points and by using strong acid, strong base, or both as titrants, to determine the two constituents in mixtures of different phosphate species. (See Prob. 9-3 for examples.)

Inspection of Figure 9-2 shows that the slope of the pH curve is relatively small whenever two phosphate species coexist at other than negligible concentrations. These are the regions of buffering action of phosphate solutions discussed earlier.

Mixtures of acids. The discussion in the foregoing section applies not only to those polyprotic acids for which the ratio of successive acid constants is not larger than about 10^{-4} but also to mixtures of acids. With suitable indicators and at similar concentrations two or three acids may be titrated separately in the same solution when their acid constants differ by more than a factor of about 10^4. Water is itself a very weak acid, of course, and titration of c formal acids in aqueous solutions is not feasible unless cK_a is at least 10^{-10}. For titrations of weak bases the situation is analogous.

For inorganic polyprotic acids the ratio of successive acid constants is generally about 10^{-5}, but for organic acids these constants are often much closer to each other. There have been synthesized diprotic acids for which removal of the first proton leads to an unstable particle that tends to lose the second proton also (G. Schwarzenbach); K_2 is larger than K_1. In essence the two protons come off in one step.

Statistical factors. In a diprotic acid HQH that is symmetrical so that the dissociable hydrogens are equivalent the existence of *statistical factors* should be noted. Consider, for example, the first acid constant K_1 of HQH that is defined as usual without specifying which of the two H atoms is concerned, and the first dissociation constant K_1^* for a specific hydrogen. If in each HQH molecule the two hydrogens are labeled l and r, the acid constant for H_l,

$$[H^+][QH_r^-]/[H_lQH_r] = K_1^*$$

equals that for H_r,

$$[H_lQ^-][H^+]/[H_lQH_r] = K_1^*$$

by assumption. However, in the definition of K_1 only the total concentration of HQ^- enters, or the sum of $[H_lQ^-]$ and $[QH_r^-]$. Therefore,

$$K_1 = [H^+]([H_lQ^-] + [QH_r^-])/[HQH] = 2K_1^*$$

There is thus a statistical factor of 2. Similarly, if $Q^=$ has two equivalent but distinct sites for the attachment of H^+ ions, a statistical factor turns up in the dissociation constant for the second hydrogen. The equilibrium constant referring to an H atom at a specific site will be called K_2^* and that without regard to site K_2. For example,

$$K_2^* = [H^+][Q^=]/[H_lQ^-]$$

The reciprocal of K_2 is then

$$K_2^{-1} = ([H_lQ^-] + [QH_r^-])/[H^+][Q^=] = 2(K_2^*)^{-1}$$

so that $K_2 = \frac{1}{2}K_2^*$.

In the special case that the dissociation of the first H^+ has no effect on that of the second, $K_1^* = K_2^*$, but

$$K_1 = 4K_2$$

When there are more than two equivalent H atoms, or more than two equivalent sites, the values for the statistical factors will be different. For nonequivalent H atoms or sites, similar considerations can be made. Such considerations are of importance in discussing the relationship between acid strength and molecular structure but do not, of course, affect the computation of H^+-ion concentrations from experimental values of acid constants.

HYDRATION OF IONIC SPECIES

Often an equilibrium is complicated because it concerns the reactions of ions or molecules of several degrees of hydration, and the pertinent hydration-equilibrium constants are known only approximately, if at all, or are of secondary interest. Consider, for example, the dissociation of H_2SO_3

$$H_2SO_3 = H^+ + HSO_3^- \tag{9-45}$$

with the equilibrium expression

$$\frac{[H^+][HSO_3^-]}{[H_2SO_3]} = K_{45} \tag{9-46}$$

In addition, H_2SO_3 is at equilibrium with dissolved SO_2

$$H_2O + SO_2 = H_2SO_3 \tag{9-47}$$

an equilibrium governed by

$$\frac{[H_2SO_3]}{[SO_2]} = K_{47} \tag{9-48}$$

(The symbol $[SO_2]$ is used rather than p_{SO_2} because of the specific reference to dissolved SO_2.) In a solution of sulfurous acid the total concentration T of SO_2 and H_2SO_3

$$T = [SO_2] + [H_2SO_3] \tag{9-49}$$

may be known (e.g., from the way the solution was prepared), but not the individual concentrations of SO_2 and H_2SO_3. Equations (9-48) and (9-49) yield expressions for these concentrations,

$$[SO_2] = \frac{T}{1 + K_{47}} \qquad (9\text{-}50)$$

$$[H_2SO_3] = \frac{TK_{47}}{1 + K_{47}} \qquad (9\text{-}51)$$

but to find their values, K_{47} is needed. However, if (9-51) is combined with (9-46), the result may be rearranged to

$$\frac{[H^+][HSO_3^-]}{T} = \frac{K_{47}K_{45}}{1 + K_{47}} = K_{52} \qquad (9\text{-}52)$$

an equation of the same structure as (9-46). It is customary to redefine $[SO_2]$ and $[H_2SO_3]$ so that both really stand for T. Thus by definition

$$[H_2SO_3] = [SO_2] = T \qquad (9\text{-}53)$$

By the same convention K_{52} is considered to be the first acid constant of H_2SO_3, $K_{52} = K_1 = 1.3 \times 10^{-2}$, with the equilibrium expression written exactly like (9-46).

A second example of the same situation is provided by carbonic acid, except that the constant for the equilibrium $CO_2 + H_2O = H_2CO_3$ is actually known: 2.6×10^{-3}. Nevertheless, unless explicitly stated, $[H_2CO_3]$ and $[CO_2]$ both mean by definition the same thing: the total concentration of H_2CO_3 *and* CO_2. The first acid constant for H_2CO_3 usually given, $K_1 = 4.4 \times 10^{-7}$, refers to this definition of $[H_2CO_3]$. The *true* first acid constant of the species H_2CO_3 has a value that can be found by rearranging an equation similar to (9-52): $4.4 \times 10^{-7} \times (1 + 2.6 \times 10^{-3})/2.6 \times 10^{-3} = 1.7 \times 10^{-4}$.

Further examples concern the equilibria between H^+, H_3O^+, $H_5O_2^+$, ..., $H_3O^+ \cdot nH_2O$, where by definition

$$[H^+] = [H_3O^+] = \text{total concentration of hydrated protons}$$

and none of the equilibrium constants are known. Similarly, for ions like Cu^{++} the constants governing hydration equilibria are unknown, and by definition $[Cu^{++}]$ stands for the total of the concentrations of Cu^{++}, $Cu \cdot H_2O^{++}$, ..., and $Cu(H_2O)_n^{++}$.

ACIDS AND BASES IN NONAQUEOUS MEDIA

As indicated in Chapter 8, the Brønsted-Lowry point of view permits a quantitative description of acids and bases in any solvent that is able to donate or to accept protons, not just in an aqueous medium. Any such solvent is of the form HSlv and reacts with an acid or a base according to the equations

$$HA + HSlv = A^- + H_2Slv^+ \qquad (9\text{-}54)$$

and

$$B + HSlv = HB^+ + Slv^- \qquad (9\text{-}55)$$

with acid and base constants

$$\frac{[A^-][H_2Slv^+]}{[HA]} = K'_a \qquad (9\text{-}56)$$

$$\frac{[HB^+][Slv^-]}{[B]} = K'_b \qquad (9\text{-}57)$$

By its amphiprotic nature the solvent also undergoes the autoprotolysis reaction

$$2HSlv = H_2Slv^+ + Slv^- \qquad (9\text{-}58)$$

with the autoprotolysis constant

$$[H_2Slv^+][Slv^-] = K_{Slv} \qquad (9\text{-}59)$$

all analogous to the corresponding reactions in water [(8-23) to (8-30), pages 155 ff.]. Examples of such solvents are acetic acid, reacting as indicated in (8-19) (page 155) and (8-32) (page 157), liquid ammonia, reacting as shown by Equations (8-35) and (8-36) (page 158), and

TABLE 9-2   *Approximate Values of Autoprotolysis Constants*

compound	formula	constant
Water	H_2O	$[H_3O^+][OH^-] = 10^{-14}$
Methyl alcohol	CH_3OH	$[CH_3OH_2^+][CH_3O^-] = 2 \times 10^{-17}$
Ethyl alcohol	CH_3CH_2OH	$[C_2H_5OH_2^+][C_2H_5O^-] = 3 \times 10^{-20}$
Formic acid	$HCOOH$	$[HC(OH)_2^+][HCOO^-] = 6 \times 10^{-7}$
Acetic acid	$HAc \equiv CH_3COOH$	$[CH_3C(OH)_2^+][CH_3COO^-] = 4 \times 10^{-15}$
Sulfuric acid	H_2SO_4	$[H_3SO_4^+][HSO_4^-] = 2 \times 10^{-4}$
Ammonia	NH_3	$[HN_4^+][NH_2^-] = 10^{-33}$

sulfuric acid. This last solvent may accept a proton to form $H_3SO_4^+$ as well as donate one to form HSO_4^-. Note that the values of acid and base constants depend on the medium, and so does the product of conjugate constants, $K_a' \cdot K_b' = K_{Slv}$. Approximate values of K_{Slv} are given in Table 9-2.

These facts are basic to acid-base titrations in nonaqueous media. For example, it is possible to titrate in liquid ammonia the acid NH_4^+, as existing in NH_4NO_3, with the base NH_2^-, as existing in potassium amide (KNH_2) by using phenolphthalein as indicator. Another example concerns anhydrous acetic acid as solvent. Since acetic acid is a weaker base than water (H_2Ac^+ a stronger acid than H_3O^+), all bases are stronger in anhydrous acetic acid solution than they are in aqueous solution and all acids are weaker. It is thus possible to titrate in anhydrous HAc as solvent many bases that are too weak to be titrated in water. As titrant a solution of $HClO_4$ in anhydrous HAc is suitable. Owing to its exceptional strength, $HClO_4$ is still a strong acid and almost completely dissociated in this medium. The titrant is thus effectively a solution of H_2Ac^+, the strongest acid that may exist in reasonable concentrations in anhydrous acetic acid. (The strongest base that may exist in reasonable concentrations in anhydrous acetic acid is Ac^-.)

Acid and base constants in water. When the protolysis constants of two acids in two different solvents are compared, their ratios are often found to be nearly independent of the solvent. The reason they are not precisely independent is that aside from the proton transfer there are other interactions between solvent molecules and acid and base particles. However, the approximate constancy of the ratios just mentioned permits semiquantitative comparison of acids that are stronger than H_3O^+ and of bases that are stronger than OH^-. It is also possible to estimate values of K_a on structural grounds. Table 9-3 contains values of the acid constants in water for a number of conjugate pairs of acids and bases listed in sequence of decreasing acid strengths.

Water as a buffer. The leveling effect of water on strong acids and bases discussed on pages 156 and 158 is related to a buffering action of water, even though water is not a useful buffering agent in the conventional sense. There is always buffering when both an acid and its conjugate base are present in substantial amounts. In an aqueous solution of a strong acid the acid is essentially replaced by H_3O^+, and since H_2O is the conjugate base, there is buffering. Similarly, a solution of strong base contains substantial quantities of OH^- as well as its

TABLE 9-3 *Acid Constants in Water**

(See also table on page 397)

conjugate pair of acid and base		acid constants
$HClO_4$	ClO_4^-	ca. 10^9
HI	I^-	ca. 10^7
HBr	Br^-	ca. 10^6
HCl	Cl^-	ca. 10^5
H_2SO_4	HSO_4^-	ca. 10^3
$HClO_3$	ClO_3^-	ca. 10^3
HNO_3	NO_3^-	ca. 10^2
H_3O^+	H_2O	55.5†
H_2CrO_4	$HCrO_4^-$	1.2
H_2SO_3	HSO_3^-	1.3×10^{-2}
HSO_4^-	$SO_4^=$	1.2×10^{-2}
$HClO_2$	ClO_2^-	1.0×10^{-2}
H_3PO_4	$H_2PO_4^-$	7.1×10^{-3}
H_2CO_3	HCO_3^-	1.7×10^{-4}‡
HF	F^-	6.7×10^{-4}
HNO_2	NO_2^-	4.5×10^{-4}
HAc	Ac^-	1.8×10^{-5}
HSO_3^-	$SO_3^=$	5.0×10^{-6}
$HCrO_4^-$	$CrO_4^=$	3.2×10^{-7}
H_2S	HS^-	9.1×10^{-8}
$H_2PO_4^-$	$HPO_4^=$	6.2×10^{-8}
$HClO$	ClO^-	1.1×10^{-8}
HCN	CN^-	2.0×10^{-9}
H_3BO_3	$H_2BO_3^-$	6.4×10^{-10}
NH_4^+	NH_3	5.5×10^{-10}
HCO_3^-	$CO_3^=$	4.8×10^{-11}
H_2O_2	HO_2^-	2.4×10^{-12}
$HPO_4^=$	PO_4^{3-}	4.4×10^{-13}
HS^-	$S^=$	1.2×10^{-15}
H_2O	HO^-	1.7×10^{-16}§
NH_3	NH_2^-	ca. 10^{-23}
HO^-	$O^=$	ca. 10^{-35}

* Estimated values mainly by G. Schwarzenbach.
† $K_a = [H_2O][H^+]/[H_3O^+] = [H_2O]$ (by definition of $[H^+]$).
‡ Acid constant of the species H_2CO_3. The conventional first acid constant involving the total concentration of H_2CO_3 and CO_2 is $K_1 = 4.4 \times 10^{-7}$ (see page 205).
§ $K_a = [HO^-][H^+]/[H_2O]$. ($[H_2O]$ is retained in the denominator by analogy with other acid constants.)

conjugate acid H_2O. The buffering action of H_2O in both circumstances is illustrated by the relatively level portions of the titration curve for HCl with NaOH in Figure 8-3, page 171.

Comparison of different concepts of acids and bases. In the classical theory of electrolytes, which goes back to *Arrhenius*, acids are defined as (uncharged) substances capable of furnishing H^+ ions and bases are defined as (uncharged) substances capable of furnishing OH^- ions. The symmetry between H^+ and OH^- ions is lost in the *Brønsted-Lowry* point of view, which has the advantage, however, of stressing the unique character of the proton and thus making possible a consistent description of proton acids in media other than water. A further advantage of the Brønsted-Lowry concept is its economy of description. Since charged as well as uncharged particles may be acids or bases, several reactions that are described differently in the Arrhenius system are unified by the Brønsted-Lowry view. Hydrolysis, displacement of a weak acid by a stronger acid, and neutralization reaction between an acid and a base all are examples of the same fundamental acid-base reaction,

$$\text{acid } 1 + \text{base } 2 = \text{base } 1 + \text{acid } 2$$

G. N. Lewis has proposed another important definition of acids and bases, one that does not restrict these concepts to substances that are able to donate or to accept protons. A particle that can accept a proton also has a free electron pair, and this is considered by Lewis to be the characteristic property of a base. Any particle able to attach itself to such an electron pair is called an acid. These concepts are useful in describing many reactions, but they will not be discussed further here.

*Phosphoric acid is to be titrated
with a sodium hydroxide solution
using methyl orange
and thymolphthalein as indicators.
The pH during a second titration
is measured with a pH meter.*

*Laboratory assignment 9
(1 period, optional)*

TITRATION OF A POLYPROTIC

ACID

PROCEDURES

9-1 Preliminary titration of a solution of H_3PO_4. Obtain a
sample of H_3PO_4 of unknown concentration, and pipet 25.00 ml into a
200-ml flask. Add 25 ml of distilled water and two drops of methyl
orange indicator. Titrate with standard 0.1 F NaOH until the color
changes from red to orange (see procedure for titrations, page 142).
Better accuracy is obtained if a comparison solution of reagent-grade
KH_2PO_4 containing the same concentration of methyl orange indicator
is prepared and the titration is terminated when the colors of the two
solutions match. This refinement, however, is not necessary if the results

210

are to be used only as a basis for Procedure 9-2, the titration of H_3PO_4 with a pH meter.

To a second 25.00-ml sample add 3 to 5 drops of thymolphthalein indicator and titrate with the standard NaOH until the solution shows a faint but distinct blue tinge. Avoid excessive shaking so that atmospheric CO_2 is not absorbed near the end of the titration. Again the accuracy is improved by the use of a comparison solution of reagent-grade K_2HPO_4 or Na_2HPO_4 containing indicator at the same final concentration as in the titration. The comparison solution should be well stoppered, so that no CO_2 is absorbed.

The results of these two titrations are used to compute the concentration of H_3PO_4 in the sample.

9-2   Titration of H_3PO_4 with the pH meter.   Prepare a table in your notebook similar to that described on page 182, with entries for the following ratios of equivalents base added to equivalents acid present: 0.20, 0.40, 0.60, 0.80, 0.90, 0.95, 1.00, 1.05, 1.10, 1.20, 1.40, 1.60, 1.80, 1.90, 1.95, 2.00, 2.05, 2.10, 2.20. These values are to serve as a guide in the titration with the pH meter. Prepare a sheet of graph paper so that the pH measured can be plotted as ordinate against the quantity of base added as abscissa.

Calibrate the glass electrode of the pH meter with the buffer provided; the temperature compensation of the instrument should be adjusted for the temperature of the buffer. If available, employ a buffer well inside the pH range of the subsequent titration. Rinse the electrode with distilled water, and carefully wipe it with soft tissue.

Pipet 25.00 ml of the phosphoric acid sample into a 250-ml beaker. Add 25 ml of distilled water and two drops of methyl orange indicator. Insert the stirring bar, and mount buret and electrodes in appropriate positions. Check to be sure that the electrodes cannot be damaged by the stirring bar or the walls of the beaker.

Adjust the temperature compensation of the pH meter to the temperature of the solution and determine the initial pH; repeat after 15 to 30 sec. Add portions of standard NaOH to obtain either pH changes of 0.2 to 0.3 units or volume increases of about 5 ml, whichever occurs sooner. Use the table prepared earlier as guide. Record and plot values measured immediately afterward, and, if necessary, change the quantities of base added near the equivalence point from those suggested earlier so that enough points will be available on the graph to draw a smooth curve. Note the pH at which the indicator color begins to change and the pH beyond which no further change occurs. Add four drops of thymolphthalein after having passed the first equivalence point. Note the pH at which the first faint but distinct green tinge appears, indicating a change to blue of the thymolphthalein.

Carefully plot the titration curve, and find the midpoints of the two steep portions of the titration curve that can be represented by straight lines. These are the two equivalence points.

Find the pH values that correspond to ratios 0.5 and 1.5 of equivalents base to equivalents acid. These represent apparent values of pK_1 and pK_2. The other experimental points in the buffer regions may also be used to compute values for pK_1 and pK_2, in a way analogous to that described at the end of Procedure 8-4.

Compute the concentration of H_3PO_4 in the sample, and report it with the values of pK_1 and pK_2.

PROBLEMS

9-1 The pH during a titration. A 25.00-ml sample of a 0.100 F solution of Na_3PO_4 is titrated with 0.100 F HCl. Calculate the pH for the following quantities of acid added: 0.00, 15.00, 25.00, 35.00, and 50.00 ml.

9-2 The pH of a phosphate mixture. To 500 ml of water are added 0.15 gfw H_3PO_4, 0.20 gfw Na_2HPO_4, and 0.10 gfw Na_3PO_4. After the salts have dissolved, water is slowly added to make a total of 1000 ml of solution. What are the concentrations of the various phosphate species in the solution, and what is the pH of the solution?

9-3 Analysis of phosphate solutions. Several solutions are known to contain one or more of the following compounds: HCl, H_3PO_4, NaH_2PO_4, Na_2HPO_4, Na_3PO_4, and NaOH. Each solution is analyzed by the following steps: (1) The pH is determined approximately with pH paper or with a pH meter. (2) Twenty-five milliliters of the solution is titrated to the $HPO_4^=$ end point. Depending on the pH, 0.100 F HCl or 0.100 F NaOH is used for this purpose. The volume of titrant used is p ml. (3) Twenty-five milliliters of the solution is similarly titrated to the $H_2PO_4^-$ end point, which uses q ml of titrant, 0.100 F HCl or NaOH, as the case may be. Given below are the pH values of the different solutions as determined by step 1. For each case indicate whether standard acid or base was used in step 2 and what titrant was used in step 3. Furthermore, indicate in terms of p and q the formality in the possible constituents of each solution. Indicate any internal checks between p and q (such as $p \geq q$), whenever such checks exist. The pH values of the different solutions are as follows: (*a*) pH < 1; (*b*) pH ~ 3; (*c*) pH ~ 7; (*d*) pH ~ 11; (*e*) pH > 13. Consider Figure 9-2 in working this problem.

9-4 Analysis of a carbonate solution. The possible constituents of a solution are NaOH, Na_2CO_3, and $NaHCO_3$. The solution is titrated to the HCO_3^- end point with 0.1000 F HCl, which requires 19.34 ml for an original sample of 25.00 ml. Another 25.00-ml sample of the original solution is titrated with the same acid to the H_2CO_3 end point, the resulting CO_2 being removed by brief boiling just before the end point, which requires a total of 35.77 ml of titrant. What are the concentrations of the possible constituents of the original solution?

9-5 Distribution of phosphate species. What are the concentrations of H_3PO_4, $H_2PO_4^-$, $HPO_4^=$, and PO_4^{3-} in a 1.0 F phosphate solution buffered at pH 7?

9-6 Arsenic acid solution. To different 100.0-ml portions of 0.2 F H_3AsO_4 are added (a) 100.0 ml of H_2O; (b) 100.0 ml of 0.1 F NaOH; (c) 100.0 ml of 0.2 F NaOH. What is $[H^+]$ in the three resulting solutions? (See page 400.)

9-7 Zwitter ion. The amino acid glycine has the zwitter-ion formula $^+H_3$—CH_2—COO^- and is amphiprotic. The base constant of its —COO^- group is $K_b = 10^{-11.6}$ and the acid constant of its —NH_3^+ group is $K_a = 10^{-9.8}$. At what pH are the concentrations of the ions H_2N—CH_2—COO^- and ^+H_3N—CH_2—$COOH$ equal to each other?

9-8 Ionic and molecular species in diprotic acid solution. Consider the diprotic acid H_2Q with acid constants K_1 and K_2. Assume that the conditions underlying Equation (9-26) are valid and show that when $[H^+] = \sqrt{(K_1K_2)}$ the concentrations of H_2Q and $Q^=$ are equal and $[HQ^-]$ has its maximum value.

REVIEW QUESTIONS

9-1. Why is a titration of H_3PO_4 that goes all the way to PO_4^{3-} not satisfactory?

9-2. What are the common features of a solution of a salt of a weak acid and a weak base and a solution containing an ampholyte like $H_2PO_4^-$?

9-3. What is the reason that in a phosphate solution at most two phosphate species may exist in substantial concentrations at the same time?

9-4. What are the advantages of using anhydrous acetic acid as solvent in acid-base titrations?

9-5. State the definitions of acids and bases given by Arrhenius, by Lowry and Brønsted, and by Lewis.

REFERENCES

H. A. Laitinen, *Chemical Analysis*, Chaps. 3 to 5, McGraw-Hill, New York, 1960.

R. P. Bell, *Acids and Bases, Their Quantitative Behavior*, Methuen, London, and Wiley, New York, 1952.

*The properties and applications
of ion-exchange resins are discussed.
In a laboratory assignment
the total concentration of cation equivalents
in a solution is determined.*

ten

ION-EXCHANGE
RESINS

STRUCTURE AND PROPERTIES OF EXCHANGE RESINS

In this assignment a material known as an *ion-exchange resin* is
employed. Such a resin consists of practically insoluble giant organic
molecules, so-called high polymers, that contain certain active groups of
atoms capable of taking up ions from solutions and exchanging them
for other similarly charged ions already on the resin. There are *cation
exchangers*, which are able to interchange positively charged ions, or
cations, and there are *anion exchangers*, which can do the same for
anions, or negative ions. The relative tendency of a resin to hold different
types of ions depends on the nature of the resin, ions, and solvent.

These resins are made of chains of carbon atoms,

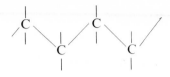

or of carbon and nitrogen atoms,

to which are attached:

1. The active groups referred to above.
2. H atoms or other inactive groups such as methyl groups ($-CH_3$).
3. Neighboring chains, a cross-linked three-dimensional network thus being formed.

The active groups are acidic for cation exchangers, basic for anion exchangers. Common examples of such groups are

the carboxyl group, R-COOH

the sulfonic acid group, R-SO$_3$H

} for cation exchangers

the amine group, R-NH$_2$ for anion exchangers

In all these cases the groups are attached to carbon atoms of the resin, represented by R. The acidic H atoms of a cation exchanger are held to the O atoms of the acidic groups by chemical bonds, or they may have dissociated off as H^+ ions, and the same O atoms, which are now charged negatively, attract them electrostatically and keep them close. The amine groups of an anion exchanger are able to accept protons to form charged groups $R-NH_3{}^+$ and to hold anions by electrostatic forces.

If a cation exchanger is immersed in a solution containing cations, such as Na^+ or K^+, some of the hydrogens of the acidic groups of the resin will be exchanged for the cations in the solution. Figure 10-1 shows this cation exchange reaction between a solution containing Na^+ ions and a resin with sulfonic acid groups.

Cations with two or three positive charges, such as Cu^{++} or Fe^{3+}, liberate two or three H^+ respectively, requiring two or three carboxyl or sulfonic acid groups on the resin to be held. The negative charges of

215

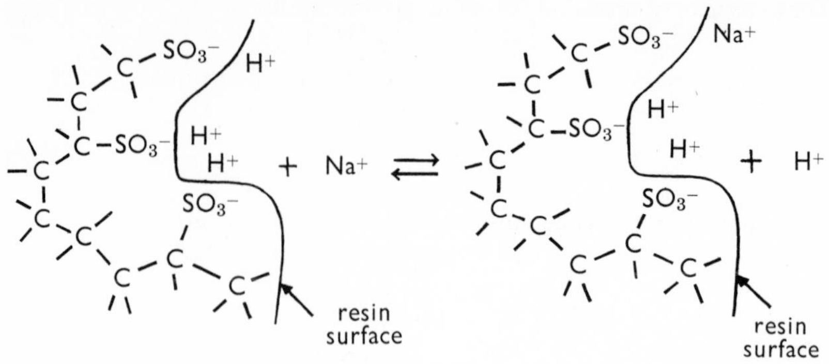

Figure 10-1 Interaction between ions on resin surface and in solution.

the active groups on the resin are always balanced by the positive charges of the small movable ions attracted by them, either the original H^+ ions or the cations that have replaced them. These ions are free to move from one active site to another and may be further exchanged with ions of like charge in the solution surrounding the resin. Since the resin as a whole is electrically neutral, the exchange of the ions in the solution for ions on the layer is *stoichiometric*.

As indicated by the double arrows in Figure 10-1, the reaction is reversible, and if particles of the original resin are stirred with a solution containing Na^+ ions, an equilibrium is eventually established: as many H^+ ions are given off by the resin as are taken up by it, and similarly for Na^+ ions. If more Na^+ ions are added to the solution from the outside, some of them will be exchanged for further H^+ ions on the resin until equilibrium is established again; similarly, H^+ ions added to the solution will be exchanged in part for Na^+ ions on the resin.

The equilibrium is governed, at least approximately, by the mass-action equation

$$\frac{[Na^+]_R[H^+]}{[Na^+][H^+]_R} = K_1 \tag{10-1}$$

where the subscript $_R$ to a bracket implies an effective concentration of the ion specified in the bracket corresponding to its surface concentration on the resin. Rearrangement leads to a relation between the effective concentration ratios of adsorbed ions and of ions in the solution,

$$\frac{[Na^+]_R}{[H^+]_R} = K_1 \frac{[Na^+]}{[H^+]} \qquad (10\text{-}2)$$

Similar equilibrium expressions exist for any pair of cations, e.g.,

$$\frac{[K^+]_R}{[H^+]_R} = K_2 \frac{[K^+]}{[H^+]} \qquad (10\text{-}3)$$

for the pair H^+ and K^+, and by division of (10-2) by (10-3),

$$\frac{[Na^+]_R}{[K^+]_R} = K_3 \frac{[Na^+]}{[K^+]} \qquad K_3 = \frac{K_1}{K_2} \qquad (10\text{-}4)$$

for the pair K^+ and Na^+.

The constants K_1, K_2, and K_3 quantitatively describe the preference that the resin exhibits toward cations of one kind over cations of another kind. For example, K_3 is smaller than 1 for the usual cation exchangers, indicating preference of the resin for K^+ over Na^+; more generally, the preference of the resins for cations is as follows:

$$Cs^+ > Rb^+ > K^+ > Na^+ \quad \text{and} \quad Ba^{++} > Sr^{++} > Ca^{++} > Mg^{++}$$

Ion-exchange columns. Suppose that grains of a cation exchanger are stirred with a solution containing many kinds of salts, such as NH_4Cl, Na_2SO_4, and $Cu(NO_3)_2$. At equilibrium many of the original cations, NH_4^+, Na^+, Cu^{++}, etc., have been stoichiometrically replaced by H^+ ions of the resin; the salts originally in solution have partly been changed into the corresponding acids, HCl, H_2SO_4, HNO_3, etc. If the resin is filtered off and replaced by fresh resin, additional salt is converted to acid, as is clear by application of equations like (10-2) and (10-3). For example, for fresh resin the value of $[Na^+]_R$ is very small, so that the left side of (10-2) is very small; Na^+ in solution is replaced by H^+ from the resin until the left side of (10-2) has increased sufficiently and the right side decreased sufficiently so that they match. By repeating this process many times, it is possible to replace with H^+ practically all other cations in the solution. For a given total amount of original resin it is more efficient to use small portions of the resin and repeat the above process many times rather than use large portions and repeat it a few times only. It is least efficient to use the total amount of resin all at once.

However, repeating this process many times would be quite laborious, and it is fortunate that there is an elegant and efficient way to achieve essentially the same result. The resin is packed into a vertical glass tube, forming a so-called ion-exchange column. The solution is added to the top and passes through the resin. As a given portion of solution proceeds through the column, it interchanges more and more of its cations with the H^+ ions of the resin and gets into contact with portions of the resin that have lost fewer and fewer of their H^+ ions. The replacement of solution cations by H^+ ions will be essentially complete if the rate of flow is slow enough to allow exchange equilibrium to establish itself all along the column and if all portions of the solution have been in contact with fresh resin before leaving the column. The resin can be *regenerated* again by passing acid through the column.

Anion exchangers are analogous to cation exchangers. They are capable of replacing by OH^- ions any other anions in a surrounding solution, as shown by the example of an amine group (NH_2) attached to the resin R,

$$\underset{\underset{H}{|}}{\overset{\overset{H}{|}}{R\text{—}N}}: + H_2O + Cl^- \rightleftharpoons \underset{\underset{H}{|}}{\overset{\overset{H}{|}}{R\text{—}N}}\text{—}H^+ \mid Cl^- + OH^-$$

Again, this reaction is reversible, and if anion-exchange resin is left in contact with a solution, an equilibrium will establish itself just as in the parallel case of cation exchangers.

Applications. A combination of both types of exchange resins is used industrially to deionize water. Water with salt impurities is first passed through a tank containing grains of a cation exchanger, which replaces with H^+ practically all other cations in the water. The now-acid solution is then passed through a tank filled with grains of an anion exchanger, and OH^- ions take the place of practically all other anions in the original water. Most of these OH^- ions combine with the H^+ ions already in the solution to form H_2O. The product contains very few anions or cations and is often used in industry or in chemical laboratories in the place of distilled water. Both tanks have to be *regenerated* from time to time by washing with acid or base, respectively. A method of desalting ocean water is also based on the use of ion-exchange resins.

It is possible to replace ions in a solution with any other similarly charged ions by using a column of exchanger that has previously been washed with a solution containing the ions desired in high concentration. It is also possible to *separate* cations of different kinds by means of a column of a cation-exchange resin. The solution with the cations to be separated is poured through a resin column of suitable length, so that practically all cations are retained on the column. This is followed by passing an acid or another suitable solvent through the resin, which serves to bring the cations back into solution, or to *elute* them. As the eluent passes through the column, there is a continuous exchange of ions between resin and solution, governed by equilibrium expressions like (10-2) and (10-3). Some kinds of ions move down the column faster than others, and a full or at least a partial separation of the ions results. The stronger the preference of the resin for a given kind of ions, the slower those ions travel down the column.

The relative preference of a resin for different kinds of ions, and therefore the sequence in which the ions emerge upon being eluted, depends on the nature of not only the resin but also the eluent. For example, it is sometimes possible to improve a separation of cations, or even to change the sequence of their emergence, by adding substances to the eluent which form complexes of different stability with the different ions.

The eluent passing through the column is collected and the receiving vessel is changed whenever a new kind of ion begins to emerge. This may be discovered by observing or measuring appropriate characteristics of the ions in question, such as their color, or by making frequent chemical tests on the solution flowing out of the column. Many difficult analytical separations, for instance, in the field of rare-earth chemistry, have been achieved by this method. It is, of course, possible to separate anions by a similar use of anion-exchange resins.

The physical nature of an exchange resin is usually different in the dry and in the wet state, inasmuch as the resin can take up considerable amounts of solvent and solute, causing it to swell. This swelling is largely due to an osmotic effect resulting from the solute concentration in the pores of the resin being higher than in the main body of the solution. More solution tends to enter the pores to decrease this higher solute concentration, causing the pores to swell. The swelling is counteracted by the elastic forces of the cross-linked network of atoms making up the skeleton of the resin, and equilibrium is reached when the swelling pressure due to these elastic forces equals the osmotic pressure, which may amount to more than 1000 atm.

Exchange resins are synthetic products. In the design of their structure the desirability of a resin of high exchange capacity, with a large number of fixed ionic groups, runs counter to the desirability of a resin that does not swell excessively and that has a framework strengthened by many cross-linkages. If the number of cross-linkages is of the order of 1 for every 100 atoms in the chain, the resin may swell as much as tenfold upon addition of solvent. The number of cross-links is usually about 1 for every 10 chain atoms, in which case the swelling may amount to about 20 per cent of the dry volume.

The use of exchange resins is not restricted to aqueous solutions, and mixed solvents are at times useful also. Besides the organic exchange resins other materials can be used for similar purposes; examples are certain coals, lignine, and certain aluminosilicate minerals.

At least three types of aluminosilicate exchangers can be distinguished: permutites, clays, and zeolites. *Permutites* are prepared artificially and contain a negatively charged network of Al, Si, and O atoms that is arranged randomly. They swell like organic exchange resins. In one variety the cations in the original permutite are Na^+ ions. When ordinary tap water is passed through a column of such permutite grains, the Ca^{++}, Mg^{++}, and other doubly and triply charged cations in the tap water are interchanged for an equivalent amount of Na^+ ions. This treatment of the original water is called *water softening* because Ca^{++} and Mg^{++} form a "hard," or insoluble, precipitate with soap. After some use as water softeners, the permutite grains become suffused with Ca^{++}, Mg^{++}, and other ions. They can be regenerated by treatment with NaCl solution. *Clays* have a fibrous or a layered structure, their aluminosilicate frameworks showing one- or two-dimensional regularity. When in contact with water, they undergo two- or one-dimensional swelling, respectively. Their exchange characteristics are different from those of the permutites. For that reason and because they tend to form fine suspensions in water, they cannot be used for water softening. Their exchange properties are, however, of great importance in soil chemistry. *Zeolites* are crystalline and show practically no swelling. They preferentially take up monovalent ions and may be used in separations of alkali metals (for example, Rb^+ and Cs^+). They occur naturally and can also be made artificially. Their most important application is in the separation of hydrocarbons that are highly branched or have bulky groups of atoms attached to the main chain of carbon atoms, from hydrocarbons that are unbranched and have at most small groups attached to the main chain. The straight-chain molecules will pass through the long channels in the zeolites, whereas the branched molecules will not. The zeolites are said to act as *molecular sieves*.

A cation-exchange column is to be prepared
and used in the stoichiometric exchange
of the cations in a neutral solution
for the H^+ ions on the resin.
The resulting acid solution
is titrated with the standard NaOH solution
prepared in Assignment 8. The data
obtained permit computation of the total concentration
of cation equivalents
contained in the original solution.

Laboratory assignment 10
(2 periods)

DETERMINATION OF TOTAL CATION

EQUIVALENTS BY ION EXCHANGE

PROCEDURES

10-1 Preparation of a column of ion-exchange resin.   Obtain an auxiliary buret; clean it with detergent; remove the detergent with tap water; and finally rinse with distilled water. Obtain a solution sample from the laboratory instructor, as well as about 10 g of the sulfonic acid resin designated commercially as Amberlite 120 H or Dowex 50.

Add the resin to a mixture of 150 ml of water and 50 ml of 6 F HCl. Let it stand for 15 min, and stir occasionally. Decant the acid, and wash the resin four to five times with water, carefully decanting each time.

Fill the lowest 5 cm of the buret with distilled water. Insert a plug of glass wool and push it down with a glass or wooden rod so that it rests just above the stopcock and is completely covered by the water. Add distilled water to the washed resin, and transfer it to the buret. It is important never to let the liquid level in the column fall below the upper surface of the resin; otherwise, air pockets will form and cause uneven flow and poor efficiency of ion exchange later on. The finished resin column should be 20 to 25 cm long.

Do not waste resin. Resin not used and resin discarded after completion of the assignment should be placed in marked bottles provided for the purpose.

Wash the resin with distilled water until the effluent gives, with universal indicator paper, a pH test that is the same as that of the distilled water used. This step is very important. Never let the liquid level in the column sink below about 1 cm above the top of the resin column, and add liquid carefully so as not to disturb the resin.

10-2 Determination of the total cation equivalents in a solution. Depending on the circumstances, proceed as follows: (1) If the column has been freshly prepared, it has sufficient capacity for several exchange runs with the unknown sample, and the next paragraph may be skipped. (2) If the column has not been used, but has been left standing overnight, it must be washed free of the yellow-brownish decomposition products of the resin before proceeding. Regeneration as described in the next paragraph is not needed. (3) If the column has been used for exchange and then left standing overnight, it must be regenerated prior to further use, because there is danger of undesirable cations having diffused down the column during standing.

To regenerate the column, lower the water level to about 1 cm above the resin and slowly pass 50 ml of 3 F HCl through the column at a rate not exceeding 2 to 3 ml/min. Follow by distilled water at a rate of 5 to 8 ml/min until the pH of the effluent matches that of the distilled water. **Caution:** Do not use HNO_3 for regeneration, because it causes copious gas evolution by oxidation. The resin is likely to be ejected explosively from the buret. Contact with nitric acid also impairs the efficiency of the resin.

Before introducing sample solution into the column, lower the water level to about 1 cm above the resin. Carefully pipet 25.00 ml of the sample solution into the column without unduly disturbing the resin. The stopcock of the buret should be so regulated that the solution passes through the column at a rate not exceeding 1.5 to 2.5 ml/min.

Collect the effluent in a 250-ml flask so arranged that the liquid runs down along the inside wall of the flask and splashing and loss of solution are avoided.

When the level of the sample solution is within 1 cm of the top of the resin, rinse the upper portion of the buret with 2 to 3 ml of distilled water and let it drain through the column at the same rate as before. Repeat the rinsing whenever the liquid level is within 1 cm of the top of the resin until about 25 ml of water has been used. Finally, continue washing the resin with distilled water at a rate of 5 to 8 ml/min, until the effluent gives the same pH test as the distilled water used. About 25 to 100 ml of distilled water will be required.

The flow rate should never be above the prescribed limits; otherwise, incomplete exchange may result, causing serious errors.

Add four to five drops of phenolphthalein to the effluent and titrate with the standard sodium hydroxide solution as described in Procedure 8-3, page 181.

Repeat the entire procedure with two or more additional samples of the solution.

10-3 Computation of the results.   Compute the total cation concentration in equivalents per liter for the three samples run. Find the average and the absolute and relative unbiased standard deviations (see page 83).

REVIEW QUESTIONS

10-1. What causes channeling in a bed or column of ion-exchange resin? What effect could this have on the determination? How can channeling be prevented?

10-2. Why are polymers of high molecular weight used to make ion-exchange resins? What distinguishes a cation-exchange resin from an anion-exchange resin?

10-3. What method may be used to determine whether the exchange of metal cations by hydrogen ions has been complete? What should be done if, as a result of this test, the exchange appears incomplete?

10-4. In a titration the eluent, a strong acid, is titrated with a strong base and the base is standardized, as in Procedure 8-2, by titrating with it a solution of the weakly acid hydrogen phthalate ion. Nevertheless, the same indicator is used in both titrations. Explain.

10-5. What effect, if any, would the following changes from the recommended procedures have? (*a*) The column used was not regenerated completely. (*b*) The NaOH used in the titration was standardized with standard HCl using phenolphthalein indicator, but in the titration of the eluent bromcresol green is used as indicator. (See Table 8-2 for values of the indicator constants.) (*c*) The indicator in both standardization with standard HCl and titration of the eluent is bromcresol green, but the NaOH has absorbed substantial amounts of atmospheric CO_2 between its standardization and its use as a titrant.

*The general laws of colorimetry
and the laws of absorption of radiation
by a homogeneous medium are considered
and experimental techniques for measuring this
absorption are described. A laboratory assignment
consists of the colorimetric determination
of manganese in steel,
after conversion of the Mn to MnO_4^-.*

eleven

COLORIMETRIC
ANALYSIS

PRINCIPLES OF COLORIMETRIC ANALYSIS

The concentration of a substance in a solution may be measured by visual or instrumental comparison of the absorption of light by the solution with that by the solvent or that by a standard solution. In simple colorimeters white light is used, or light that has been passed through colored filters. In more refined work so-called monochromatic light is employed; such light contains only a narrow band of wavelengths. Instruments that use monochromatic radiation are called spectrophotometers.

Colorimetric methods are rapid once standard solutions have been prepared and are particularly suited for analyses performed in large series, like routine control analyses. In certain cases of very intense colors, determinations can be carried out with quantities so minute that ordinary gravimetric and volumetric methods fail. This is of particular importance in biological chemistry and in clinical analysis.

Some compounds are colored so strongly that they can be determined unchanged, as, for example, permanganate can. If not, it is often possible, by means of a suitable reaction, to change a colorless or only slightly colored substance to one that is highly colored; an example is Fe^{3+} to which SCN^- is added. Colorimetric methods may also be used when the concentration of a certain molecular or ionic species affects the equilibrium between two substances of different color or between a colored and an uncolored substance. An example is the effect of the H^+-ion concentration on acid-base indicators, which permits colorimetric pH determination.

The relative precision of colorimetric methods is usually not very high, of the order of 1 to 5 per cent. In many determinations of practical importance this is not a serious limitation. With precautions and a good spectrophotometer, relative precisions of a few tenths of a per cent may be reached.

The Laws of Bouguer, Lambert, and Beer. All colorimetric work depends on the laws to be described in the following paragraphs.

Consider a beam of monochromatic radiation passing through a homogeneous solution contained in an absorption cell with walls that are transparent to the radiation. Let the intensity of the incident radiation be I_1 and that of the emergent radiation be I_2 (Fig. 11-1). Part of the radiation is reflected at the interfaces, and part (usually negligibly small)

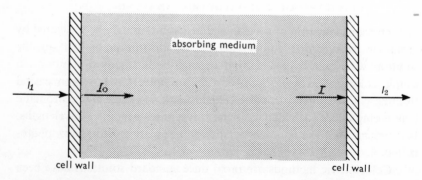

Figure 11-1 Intensities of the beam at different points of the absorbing system.

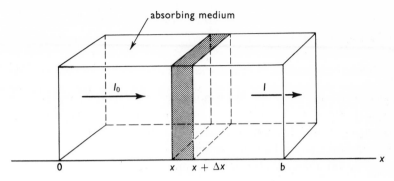

Figure 11-2   Internal absorption of radiation.

is absorbed by the cell walls, so that the intensity I_0 of the beam actually entering the medium of interest is less than I_1 and the intensity I of the beam that is just about to leave the medium is larger than I_2. The ratio I_2/I_1 of the beam intensities upon leaving and entering the *cell* is called the *transmittance T*,

$$T = I_2/I_1 \qquad (11\text{-}1)$$

The ratio I/I_0 of the intensities just before the beam is leaving the *medium* and just after it has entered it is called the *internal transmittance* T_i of the *sample*,

$$T_i = I/I_0 \qquad (11\text{-}2)$$

The beam intensities lost upon entering and leaving the cell and the solution can be corrected for by determining the intensity loss for the absorption cell filled with solvent. If the absorptions of two solutions or of a solution and solvent are compared directly, the two liquids can be placed in matched cells so that the reflected intensity losses are equal and cancel. Although the intensities reflected at the boundaries of different solutions are not precisely the same, the differences are negligible as long as the index of refraction is smaller than 1.5.

The internal transmittance I/I_0 of a homogeneous medium is governed by the following laws: Let a beam of monochromatic radiation traverse a layer of thickness Δx that is oriented perpendicularly to the beam (Fig. 11-2). It was discovered by Bouguer (1729) and Lambert (1760) that $-\Delta I$, the loss in intensity of radiation due to its passage through the layer, is proportional to the total intensity I, as well as, for a very thin layer, the path length Δx. Thus,

227

$$-\Delta I = kI\Delta x$$

or, more precisely,

$$-\frac{dI}{dx} = kI \tag{11-3}$$

where k is known as the absorption coefficient (units, reciprocal centimeters). Since the intensity decreases continuously as the beam passes through the medium, a differential law, (11-3), is needed to express the appropriate relationships in a simple way.

The variables in (11-3) may be separated,

$$-\frac{dI}{I} = k\, dx$$

and the equation integrated,

$$-\ln\left[I(x)/I_0\right] = kx \tag{11-4}$$

where I_0 is the intensity of the incident radiation and $I(x)$ is the intensity in the medium at a depth x (see Fig. 11-2).

For practical reasons the natural logarithm (ln) is usually replaced by the decadic logarithm (log); since by (11-4),

$$I(x)/I_0 = e^{-kx} = 10^{-(\log e)kx}$$

it follows that

$$\log\left[I(x)/I_0\right] = -(\log e)kx = -ax \tag{11-5}$$

where
$$a = k\log e = 0.4343k = k/2.303 \tag{11-6}$$

is called the *absorptivity* (units, reciprocal centimeters) of the medium. Although both k and a are used in the literature, only a will be used in the subsequent discussions. If the absorbing medium is bounded by two parallel planes oriented perpendicularly to the beam and a distance b apart, the intensity $I = I(b)$ of the beam that is about to leave the medium follows the equation

$$-\log(I/I_0) = \log(I_0/I) = ab \tag{11-7}$$

or, solved for I,

$$I = I_0 10^{-ab} \tag{11-8}$$

This law holds not only for electromagnetic radiation but also for other kinds, such as sound radiation and radiations consisting of particles like neutrons or electrons, as long as the wavelength range of the radiation is small enough so that the absorptivity a is constant. It holds for homogeneous liquids, gases, and solids.

According to Beer (1852) the exponent in Equation (11-8) is proportional to the total quantity of absorbing material in the path of the radiation beam. If this medium is a solution of molecular or ionic species of molarity c, the quantity of absorbing material in the path of length b is proportional to the product cb, so that

$$\text{exponent} = ab = \varepsilon cb \qquad (11\text{-}9)$$

or

$$a = \varepsilon c$$

where ε, in liter/mole cm, is called the *molar absorptivity*. Combining Equations (11-8) and (11-9) yields

$$I = I_0 10^{-\varepsilon cb} \qquad (11\text{-}10)$$

which is often called the law of Lambert and Beer or of Bouguer and Beer, or, as it will be referred to here, *Beer's law*.

The negative logarithm of T_i is called the absorbance A_i of the medium,

$$A_i = \log(I_0/I) = -\log T_i$$

By (11-10) and (11-2) the molar absorptivity ε is related to T_i and A_i by the equation

$$\varepsilon = -(1/cb)\log(I/I_0) = -(1/cb)\log T_i = A_i/cb \qquad (11\text{-}11)$$

Table 11-1 contains a brief summary of colorimetric terms and their relationship. The names and symbols used conform to accepted usage, but different terminology is still found. For example, the term *optical density* is used for absorbance.

TABLE 11-1   *Definitions of Colorimetric Terms*[a]

symbol	name	definition
T_i	Internal transmittance	I/I_0
A_i	Absorbance	$-\log T_i$
a	Absorptivity	A_i/b
ε	Molar absorptivity	a/c

[a] I and I_0 are defined in Figures 11-1 and 11-2; b is the length of the absorption path; and c is the concentration of the solution.

Colorimetric analysis

If more than one absorbing species is present, Equation (11-9) for the molar absorptivity is replaced by

$$a = \sum \varepsilon_j c_j \qquad (11\text{-}12)$$

where c_j is the molar concentration of species j with the molar absorptivity ε_j. This *additivity law* of absorptivities is of great importance. For example, by subtracting the contributions of the contaminants from the total absorbance, it permits colorimetric analysis of a solution containing colored contaminants in addition to the colored species of interest. In practice, this may be handled by measuring the absorbances of both the solution of interest and a solution containing the contaminants only. If c_0 and ε_0 are the concentration and the molar absorptivity of the component being determined and c_i and ε_i ($i = 1, 2, \ldots, n$) the analogous quantities of the contaminants, the two absorbances measured may be represented as follows:

Solution being analyzed:

$$A_i \text{(unknown)} = (\varepsilon_0 c_0 + \sum \varepsilon_i c_i)b$$

Comparison blank containing contaminants only:

$$A_i \text{(blank)} = \sum \varepsilon_i c_i b$$

The difference between these two absorbances is the absorbance that would be observed if only the component of interest were present:

$$A_i \text{(component of interest)} = \varepsilon_0 c_0 b$$

In the photoelectric instrument to be described later it is possible to set the instrument reading for the *blank* solution, containing contaminants only, at zero absorbance. When the solution to be analyzed is inserted, the instrument reading shows directly the absorbance of the component of interest.

In looking up absorption data in the literature it is important to establish whether they are based on the decadic or the natural logarithm (i.e., whether they refer to ε or k) and to what units of concentration and length they refer. Wavelength, solvent used, and temperature should also be specified.

Absorption spectra. The molar absorptivity ε of a substance depends on the wavelength λ, as just implied; and a plot of ε against λ or the frequency is called the *absorption spectrum* of the substance. Knowledge of the absorption spectrum is useful for a number of reasons. A substance may be identified by its absorption spectrum, and under favorable circumstances the absorption spectrum of a mixture may be resolved into the portions contributed by each component, so that the mixture can be analyzed in this way. Even more important, information relating to the molecular structure of a substance can often be obtained by an analysis of its absorption spectrum. Depending on the wavelength region, one speaks of the ultraviolet, the visible, and the infrared absorption spectrum of a substance (see Fig. 11-3 and Table 11-2). Measurement of the ultraviolet spectrum requires optical components and vessels made of quartz, which is transparent to the ultraviolet. For infrared radiation, windows and prisms are made of NaCl and other substances transparent to it and all lenses are usually replaced by mirrors. The wavelength dependence of the absorptivity is obtained by analyzing the transmitted radiation by means of prisms or diffraction gratings. If the substance of interest is in solution, the absorption spectrum of the solvent must be taken into account by some method. Often a solvent that does not absorb significantly in the region of interest is available.

Generally speaking, the ultraviolet and the visible spectra may furnish information concerning the electronic levels of the molecule or ion, and the infrared spectrum is determined by the vibrations of the atoms forming the molecule or ion, by the rotations of entire groups of atoms around bonds, and by the rotations of the molecule as a whole. The microwave spectrum of a substance,

TABLE 11-2   *Wavelength, Frequency, and Wave Numbers*

Definition and interrelations:

Wavelength λ	Distance between neighboring wave crests
Wave number v'	Number of waves per centimeter
Frequency v	Number of vibrations per second

$$\lambda \cdot v' = 1 \qquad \lambda \cdot v = c \qquad v/v' = c$$

where c is the velocity of light, $c = 3 \times 10^{10}$ cm/sec

Units:

λ 1 A (angstrom) $= 10^{-8}$ cm $= 10^{-4} \mu$ (micron)
$= 10^{-1}$ mμ (millimicron)

$1 \mu = 10^{-3}$ mm $= 10^{3}$ mμ $= 10^{4}$ A
1 m$\mu = 10^{-6}$ mm $= 10^{-3} \mu$ $= 10$ A

v' cm^{-1}

v sec^{-1}

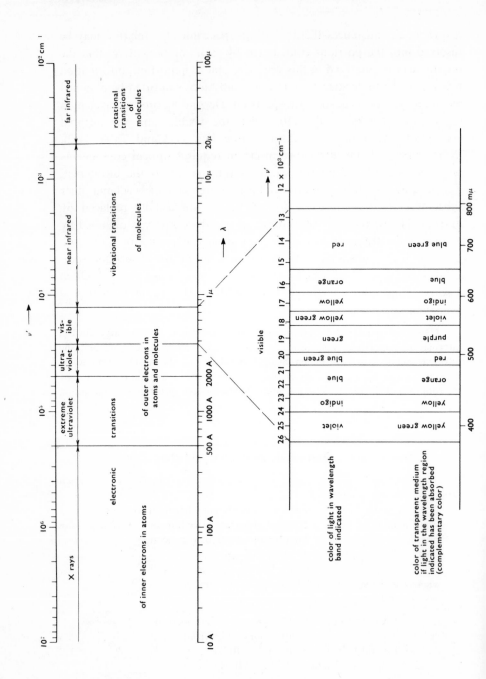

which is in the very far infrared (λ of the order of 1 cm), generally furnishes information about rotations.

In Figure 11-4 is shown the absorption spectrum of the MnO_4^- ion. Note that the main absorption band between 480 and 580 mμ is in the green region of the visible spectrum. This accounts for the magenta color of permanganate solutions.

Apparent deviations from Beer's law.   There are several reasons for apparent failures of Beer's law: The species absorbing the light may be involved in a chemical equilibrium, the radiation used may not be sufficiently monochromatic, or the instrument design may be faulty. A cause for actual failure will be discussed also.

An example of apparent failure due to chemical equilibrium is the transmittance of a solution containing the dark-blue copper ammonia complexes $Cu(NH_3)_i^{++}$ ($i = 1, 2, 3, 4$), which are in equilibrium with Cu^{++} and NH_3,

$$Cu(NH_3)_i^{++} = Cu(NH_3)_{i-1}^{++} + NH_3$$

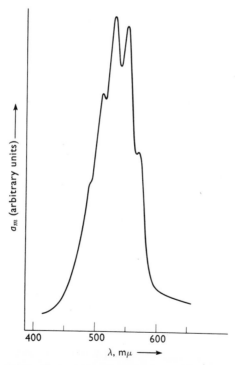

Figure 11-4 Absorption spectrum of MnO_4^- ion.

governed by the equation

$$\frac{[Cu(NH_3)_{i-1}^{++}][NH_3]}{[Cu(NH_3)_i^{++}]} = K_i$$

If an equilibrium mixture is diluted by a factor 2, the concentrations of the various complexes are not simply halved: there is a complex shift of the equilibria that may be computed from the above mass-action equations. The absorptivity is therefore not halved either, and relations (11-9) and (11-10) appear to be violated.

In effect, this is not a failure of Beer's law itself, and indeed information about the foregoing equilibria may be obtained from measurements of the absorbances of solutions of Cu^{++} and NH_3 at different wavelengths and concentrations.

A similar situation exists for the solution of an indicator system HIn and In⁻,

$$HIn = H^+ + In^-$$

where at least one of the two species, HIn or In⁻, is colored in the visible. Dilution will, in general, affect the pH so that the absorption spectrum of the solution again depends on the concentration in a more complicated way than corresponds to Beer's law.

Figure 11-5 shows, for example, the pH dependence of the molar absorptivity of methyl red, an indicator whose acid and basic forms are red and yellow, respectively, and whose interval of change is the pH range 4.2 to 6.1 (Table 8-2, page 166). The curve at pH 4 is very close to the absorption spectrum of the acid form, with an absorption band in the green so that the color in transmission is a red-purple. The curve at pH 6 is close to the spectrum of the basic form, with an absorption band centered in the indigo, which is responsible for the yellow color in transmission. The curve in between is due to a mixture of the two forms. Note the *isosbestic point* at 480 mμ, for which the absorption remains independent of the pH, since the molar absorptivities of both species are the same at this wavelength. For radiation of this wavelength there is not even an apparent failure of Beer's law.

The relation (11-8) is not obeyed unless the wavelength range of the radiation used is such that the absorptivity is constant in this range. If there is variation, the total intensity of radiation transmitted is the integral over the intensity distribution as a function of λ,

$$I_{total} = \int_{\text{wavelength range}} I_0(\lambda)10^{-a(\lambda)b}\, d\lambda$$

This equation cannot be reduced, in general, to a form equivalent to (11-8),

$$I_{total} \neq I_{0,\,total}\ 10^{-a_{av}b}$$

where $I_{0,total} = \int I_0(\lambda)\,d\lambda$ is the total incident radiation and a_{av} an average of the absorptivity in the wavelength range used. Note, however, that Equation (11-9) is not affected by these considerations, so that the concentration c and the thickness b of the layer occur only as their product in Beer's law. Therefore,

$$A_i = f(cb) \tag{11-13}$$

and when two solutions show the same absorbance and the absorbance

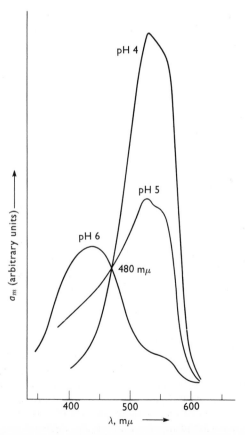

Figure 11-5 Absorption spectrum of methyl red at different pH values.

of the solvent can be neglected, the relation

$$c_1 b_1 = c_2 b_2 \qquad (11\text{-}14)$$

holds even though the absorptivity may not be constant in the range of wavelengths used.

It is of interest here to discuss briefly the term *monochromatic radiation*. Such radiation does not actually exist; by the very nature of waves any finite wave train must embrace a *range* of wavelengths. Since "monochromatic" has thus no absolute meaning, it is usually relevant to ask: "Monochromatic relative to what?" As far as Beer's law is concerned, monochromatic implies that the absorptivity does not vary significantly (another relative concept) over the wavelength range employed. It means one thing when the absorbing substance is mercury vapor, with very narrow atomic spectral lines, and another when the absorbing substance is the MnO_4^- ion, with its broad absorption band.

Other apparent deviations may be caused by faulty instrument design. Stray light may reach the eyes or the photoelectric device measuring the intensity of the radiation. The sample tubes in which the absorbances of two solutions are compared may not have been matched carefully; they may be scratched or may have fingerprints on them or air bubbles inside. If two photocells are used in the comparison, they also must be matched. These are only a few of many possible sources of instrument errors. It is also important that no solid particles that scatter light are suspended in the solutions to be examined. Errors may further occur through fluorescence, i.e., absorption of photons of a certain energy and wavelength and subsequent emission of photons of lower energy and longer wavelength.

The apparent validity of Beer's law may be tested for any given case by measuring and checking the constancy of the molar absorptivity at different concentrations, either by keeping b constant or by varying it independently. Colorimetric work is often based on the less stringent requirements (11-13) and (11-14) only, which can be tested by measuring the constancy of the absorbance when c and b are varied so that their product stays constant.

Actual deviations from Beer's law also occur, for the following reason: Absorption by a molecular or ionic system of a photon of frequency v raises this system from the energy level E_0 to the level E_1 (see Fig. 11-6). The total number of photons of frequency v that are removed from a beam traversing a medium is proportional to the number of molecules or ions at energy level E_0. The energy gained may be dissipated by transfer in collisions with surrounding molecules or by emission of one or more photons (fluorescence); emission of a photon of the original frequency does, of course, diminish over-all absorption. The number of particles at energy E_0 is depleted by absorption of photons and

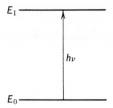

Figure 11-6 Absorption of radiation and energy levels.

replenished by all the processes that bring particles from other levels back to E_0, so that a steady state in which depletion and replenishment just balance is established. At ordinary levels of intensity the depletion in the number of particles at level E_0 is negligible, and the molar absorptivity is independent of the intensity of the radiation used to measure it. However, this is no longer the case at very high intensities or under special conditions that prevent efficient replenishment of particles at level E_0; Beer's law no longer holds, and the transmittance T_i depends also on I_0. These deviations are of no concern in colorimetric work, but the phenomenon of *optical pumping* of particles or crystalline systems to higher energy levels is the basis of recent techniques used to study spectra of molecules and crystals and to produce high-intensity beams of coherent light by the "optical maser" or "laser."

EXPERIMENTAL ASPECTS OF COLORIMETRY

As already mentioned, in colorimetric work the measured absorbance of a solution is used to determine the concentration of the dissolved colored substance or substances. In one method, a set of comparison solutions of various concentrations is prepared, in absorption cells of the same dimensions, until a color match between the solution of the unknown and a known solution is obtained. The comparison is usually visual. This method is cumbersome, but neither Beer's law nor even the relations (11-13) and (11-14) are required to find the result.

In another method two solutions are compared visually in two cells whose path lengths b can be varied individually. An instrument that operates in this way is the Duboscq colorimeter, shown diagrammatically in Figure 11-7. Light from a uniform source L passes through two absorption cells containing the solutions to be compared, through two transparent plungers, and finally through an arrangement of prisms and lenses into the eye. The two cells can be raised and lowered individually, thus changing the path lengths b_1 and b_2. When the absorbances of the two solutions match, $c_1 b_1 = c_2 b_2$.

Both these methods work well only when the two solutions contain the same single colored substance. When the solution of the unknown contains other colored substances, good results may often be obtained by using colored filters that pass a range of wavelengths in which the interfering substances do not absorb. Sometimes a sodium lamp or the suitably filtered radiation of a mercury arc is used as a monochromatic radiation source. If two or more substances in the same solution are to be determined by this method, visual comparisons in different wavelength regions have to be made. This can be expected to produce accurate results only in very favorable cases and is better done instrumentally, as briefly discussed later.

In instrumental methods the absorbances of the unknown and of a known solution are measured at the same path length b and in cells that are otherwise matched. Under these conditions

$$c_2/c_1 = A_2/A_1 = (-\log T_2)/(-\log T_1) \qquad (11\text{-}15)$$

The absorbances or transmittances are usually determined with a photoelectric device, and the radiation is made at least partially monochromatic by filters or, more completely, by a prism or grating and a system of slits.

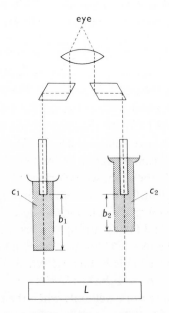

Figure 11-7 Duboscq colorimeter.

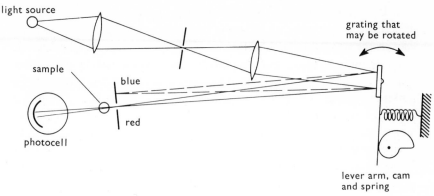

Figure 11-8   Simple photoelectric spectrometer.

A commercially available instrument is shown diagrammatically in Figure 11-8. A narrow range of wavelengths is selected from the incident white light by appropriate orientation of a diffraction grating. After passing the sample, the radiation falls on a photocell. Electronic amplification results in a needle deflection proportional to the intensity of the beam that falls on the photocell. The grating is turned by an attached lever arm that rides on a cam rotated by a knob. A wavelength scale is fastened to the same shaft as the cam. Whenever the sample tube is removed, an occluder falls into the light beam and prevents light from reaching the photocell. The needle of the meter goes to zero when the occluder is in place; if it does not, a zero adjustment knob must be turned until the needle is at zero. For reasons of electronic circuitry this adjustment must be changed from time to time to compensate for "zero drift." Still another knob controls the aperture of a diaphragm in front of the light source. This knob is usually so adjusted that the transmittance on the meter scale reads 100 per cent, or the absorbance zero, when the sample cell contains solvent. The absorbance scale is sometimes labeled "optical density."

More expensive instruments have two photocells, permitting direct comparison of the transmittances of two solutions or of a solution and of the solvent. The incident beam of radiation is split by a prism or other device, so that both solutions are exposed to the same parts of the light source. The two photocells are balanced against each other, which compensates for a number of sources of error, including intensity fluctuations of the light source.

239

It is best to measure the absorbances of the unknown sample and of a known standard with the same instrument setting, so that inaccuracies in the wavelength calibration or filters that are not standardized do not interfere and other instrumental error sources will also tend to cancel. Less accurate results are obtained by determining the absorbances of the unknown solution only and using a tabulated or previously determined value of the molar absorptivity to calculate the concentration. If the unknown sample contains colored contaminants that disturb the measurement of the component of interest, a wavelength where there is no interference may be chosen, or appropriate amounts of the same contaminants may be added to the cell containing solvent only and to the comparison standard, so that their influence is automatically taken into account. For high precision a set of standard solutions of concentrations and absorbances that bracket those of the unknown sample may be used.

If the solution contains several colored species of unknown concentration, it is possible, at least in principle, to determine their concentrations by measuring absorbances at different wavelengths. In a favorable case the absorption spectra of the different components differ widely; thus there is a wavelength region for each component where it absorbs and the others do not. More complex situations require the solution of a set of simultaneous linear equations of the type (11-12), with the concentrations of the different species as unknowns. In the petroleum industry instruments that permit the analysis of hydrocarbon mixtures by using infrared radiation at different wavelengths are used.

Transmittance range for highest precision in concentration measurement. The needle deflection of a colorimeter is proportional to the transmittance of the solution, and the question arises what the error of the solution concentration is if a certain error is made in the transmittance measurement. The concentration as a function of the transmittance is given by the equation

$$c(T) = -(\log T)/\varepsilon b = -(\ln T)/2.303\varepsilon b \qquad (11\text{-}16)$$

which follows from (11-11) and where the subscript i of T_i has been dropped. Let the actual concentration be c_0 and the corresponding transmittance be T_0, $c_0 = c(T_0)$, but suppose that the actual transmittance measured is $T_0 + \Delta T$, corresponding to the concentration $c_0 + \Delta c = c(T_0 + \Delta T)$. The error in the transmittance is ΔT; that of the concentration is Δc. A Taylor expansion yields

$$c_0 + \Delta c = c(T_0 + \Delta T) = c(T_0) + \frac{dc}{dT}\Delta T + \frac{1}{2}\frac{d^2c}{dT^2}\Delta T^2 + \cdots$$

where the derivatives are to be taken at $T = T_0$. All terms higher than linear in ΔT are neglected and the derivative remaining is found by differentiating (11-16), ε and b being kept constant, whence

$$\Delta c \approx \frac{dc}{dT}\Delta T = -\frac{\Delta T}{2.303\varepsilon bT}$$

Division by (11-16) results in the relative concentration error

$$\frac{\Delta c}{c} \approx \frac{\Delta T}{T \ln T} = \frac{\Delta T}{2.303T \log T}$$

Figure 11-9 is a plot of $-1/(T \ln T)$ versus T. The relative error for a given ΔT is smallest when $T = 1/e = 0.368$ or the absorbance

$$A = -\log T = 0.434.$$

The minimum is not sharp, and good results can be expected in a transmittance range from about 0.20 to 0.55 or an absorbance range from 0.7 to 0.2.

For absorbance values above 0.7 and below 0.2 the precision deteriorates rapidly. A possible source of error is connected with the

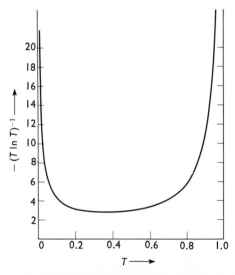

Figure 11-9   Graph of $-(T \ln T)^{-1}$ versus T.

use of a solution of high absorbance as blank for setting the instrument to zero absorbance or as a comparison solution in the split-beam instrument. The instrument readings will then be in a normal range, although the absorbance may actually be above a level favorable for accurate results.

*The manganese content of a steel sample
is to be determined by a colorimetric method.
The manganese in the dissolved sample
is oxidized to permanganate,
and the concentration of the resulting permanganate solution
is measured by quantitative comparison of
the transmittance of this solution
with that of a similar solution prepared
from a steel of known manganese content.
The transmittances are measured
by means of a photoelectric instrument.*

*Laboratory assignment 11
(2 periods)*

COLORIMETRIC DETERMINATION

OF MANGANESE IN STEEL

DISCUSSION

Steel is an iron alloy that usually contains small amounts of Mn, C, P, Si, and S. In addition, V, Cr, Co, Ni, Cu, Mo, and W are often used for alloying purposes in steels. Finally, small amounts of Al, Zn, As, Sb, and some other elements are used in the manufacture of steel as deoxidizers or for other purposes or are contained in the raw material and usually remain in the finished product.

In the analysis for Mn to be described, the sample is dissolved by treatment with nitric acid and ammonium peroxydisulfate and the manganese is oxidized to permanganate by potassium periodate. The permanganate is determined colorimetrically.

Upon treatment of the sample with $6\ F\ HNO_3$ most of it dissolves. Carbon may exist as graphite and as iron carbides, neither of which dissolves readily in HNO_3. The carbon is therefore oxidized to CO_2 by the addition of ammonium peroxydisulfate,

$$C + 2H_2O + 2HS_2O_8^- = 4HSO_4^- + CO_2 + 2H^+$$

The excess of peroxydisulfate is later destroyed by prolonged boiling,

$$2H_2O + 2HS_2O_8^- = 4HSO_4^- + O_2 + 2H^+$$

This treatment may leave undissolved the following products: silica $(SiO_2 \cdot xH_2O)$, tungstic acid (H_2WO_4), and antimonic acid (H_3SbO_4).

The main effects of the treatment with nitric acid and ammonium peroxydisulfate are summarized in Table 11-3. Although the oxidation potential of the couple $HSO_4^-/S_2O_8^=$ is high enough to oxidize Mn^{++} to permanganate, the rate is not favorable under the prevailing conditions and the oxidation is at best only partial. The peroxydisulfate may also convert part of the Mn^{++} to $MnO_2(s)$; this is undesirable, since in the later oxidation with periodate the rate of reaction of solid $MnO_2(s)$ is too slow for quantitative conversion to MnO_4^-, particularly if the precipitate of MnO_2 has been allowed to age. If any $MnO_2(s)$ or MnO_4^- appears to be present after the oxidation with peroxydisulfate, a small amount of $0.5\ F$ sodium sulfite solution is added to reduce either of them back to Mn^{++}. This has the additional effect of reducing any dichromic acid to Cr^{3+} and any vanadic acid to vanadyl ion (VO^{++}).

After any excess H_2SO_3 is boiled off, the Mn^{++} is oxidized to permanganate by the addition of KIO_4 to the acid solution,

$$2Mn^{++} + 5IO_4^- + 3H_2O = 2MnO_4^- + 5IO_3^- + 6H^+$$

TABLE 11-3 *Main Products of the Action of Nitric Acid and of Ammonium Peroxydisulfate on Steels*

$Fe \rightarrow Fe^{3+}$	$Ni \rightarrow Ni^{++}$
$Mn \rightarrow Mn^{++}, MnO_2\ (s), MnO_4^-$	$Cu \rightarrow Cu^{++}$
$C \rightarrow CO_2$	$Mo \rightarrow H_2MoO_4$
$P \rightarrow H_3PO_4$	$W \rightarrow H_2WO_4(s)$
$Si \rightarrow SiO_2 \cdot xH_2O\ (s)$	$Al \rightarrow Al^{3+}$
$S \rightarrow HSO_4^-$	$Zn \rightarrow Zn^{++}$
$V \rightarrow V(OH)_4^+$	$As \rightarrow H_3AsO_4$
$Cr \rightarrow HCr_2O_7^-$	$Sb \rightarrow H_3SbO_4(s)$
$Co \rightarrow Co^{++}$	

244

To prevent precipitation of what are believed to be iodates or periodates of Mn(III), phosphoric acid, which forms soluble complexes with Mn(III), is added. The treatment with periodate converts any Cr^{3+} or VO^{++} back to its higher oxidation state.

The MnO_4^- concentration is determined by comparison of its transmittance with that of a solution, prepared in exactly the same way, of a steel of known Mn content. The best wavelength for this comparison is that of the highest maximum of the MnO_4^- spectrum, at 525 mμ (see Fig. 11-4).

Some of the other components of the steels compared yield colored ions also, and they may interfere. They are the following:

Fe(III). When Fe(III) is used as indicator for SCN^- in the Volhard titration, HNO_3 is added to prevent the formation of colored ions like $FeOH^{++}$. Even so, Fe(III) in the presence of HNO_3 appreciably absorbs at 525 mμ. However, the phosphate complexes of Fe(III) are practically colorless, and the phosphoric acid added previously serves here also.

Ni^{++}, Co^{++}, Cu^{++}. All these ions are colored and interfere in the determination. Their influence can be compensated for by using as a comparison blank part of the solution that has not been oxidized with periodate.

$SiO_2 \cdot xH_2O$, H_2WO_4, H_3SbO_4, and C. A colloidal suspension of hydrated silica or a suspension of particles of any other matter causes errors due to the scattering of transmitted light. If the solution appears turbid, the solid material must be allowed to settle out; only clear supernatant must be used in the optical measurements. If necessary, hydrous silica can be dehydrated to SiO_2 by fuming with sulfuric acid, whereupon it will settle out rapidly or can be filtered off.

The ordinary dehydrating action of concentrated sulfuric acid is related to its strong acidity. The important reaction is the proton transfer

$$H_2SO_4 + H_2O = H_3O^+ + HSO_4^-$$

which is accompanied by the evolution of a large amount of heat. (Perchloric acid is a good dehydrating agent for the same reason.) The dehydrating action is considerably enhanced by the high temperatures reached when fuming (above 300°C for sulfuric acid).

$Cr_2O_7^=$. Presence of this colored ion interferes. One way of compensation is to determine the Cr content of the steel by another method of analysis and to add a corresponding amount of $K_2Cr_2O_7$ to the comparison standard. Another procedure is the following: Carefully

add drops of 0.1 F KNO_2 solution to a portion of the solution to be measured until the $KMnO_4$ color just disappears. The dichromate is not affected by this treatment, and the resulting solution can be used as a comparison standard.

$V(OH)_4{}^+$. Presence of this colored ion interferes but can be compensated for in a way similar to that described for $Cr_2O_7{}^=$.

All samples to be issued contain traces, at most, of interfering components. If any interfering substances appear to be present in your sample, consult with the laboratory instructor before embarking on special procedures.

PROCEDURES

11-1 Preparation of solutions. Obtain two samples of steel, one of known and the other of unknown Mn content. The Mn content of the known should be higher than that of the unknown.

Weigh out two portions of each sample that will correspond roughly to an (optimal) absorbance of about 0.43 for a final solution volume of 250 ml (0.3 g for a path length of 1.3 cm and an Mn content of 0.7 per cent). Dissolve the weighed samples in 25 ml of 6 F nitric acid. After solution is complete, boil for several minutes to remove oxides of nitrogen. Wait until boiling has ceased, and carefully and slowly sprinkle about 1 g of $(NH_4)_2S_2O_8$ into the hot solution. Avoid violent frothing. Boil gently for about 10 min to destroy any excess peroxydisulfate.

If a precipitate of MnO_2 has formed or the color of permanganate is apparent, add drops of 0.5 F Na_2SO_3 solution until all $MnO_4{}^-$ is reduced and all MnO_2 has dissolved. Boil for several minutes to expel the excess H_2SO_3.

Cool the solution so that it is not more than warm to the touch, and dilute to about 90 ml. Add 10 ml of concentrated (85 per cent) H_3PO_4, and follow with 0.5 g of KIO_4 added in small portions. Avoid violent frothing. Do not waste KIO_4 or any other chemicals containing iodine; they are expensive. Heat and boil for 3 min. Cool the solution, and dilute exactly to 250 ml (see procedure for preparing a solution of accurate volume, page 141). Permanganate solutions containing an excess of periodate are stable and can be kept until a succeeding laboratory period.

Aside from the undiluted solutions of the sample of *known* Mn content, dilutions with water in the ratios 3:1, 1:1, and 1:3 are needed. Prepare these dilutions by transferring 30, 10, and 10 ml of solution with the 10-ml pipet to three clean and dry conical flasks. Rinse the pipet with distilled water and add, respectively, 10, 10, and 30 ml of water.

11-2 Colorimetric comparison. Before you use the colorimeter, ask the laboratory instructor to explain its operation and care. The instrument should be turned on for at least 20 min to reach steady conditions before use.

Use the same colorimeter and colorimeter tube for all measurements. Orient the colorimeter tube exactly the same way each time and check for suspended particles, air bubbles, fingerprints, and scratches. Measure all absorbances at 525 mμ, where the absorbance of MnO_4^- has a maximum. It is wise to determine the location of this absorbance maximum (or transmittance minimum) experimentally for the instrument being used, because the wavelength calibration is often not reliable.

For each steel solution proceed as follows. Fill the colorimeter tube with distilled water and set the colorimeter for zero absorbance after insertion of this blank. Rinse the colorimeter tube several times with the steel solution and then fill the tube. Dry the outside of the tube carefully, insert it in the colorimeter, and read the absorbance.* Repeat this sequence of procedures twice and average the three absorbance readings.

Prepare a Beer's law diagram by plotting absorbances vs. concentrations for the undiluted and diluted solutions of the sample of known Mn content. Use the diagram to find the weight per cent of Mn in the unknown steel sample. The best accuracy is obtained if the absorbance of the unknown solution is bracketed by the absorbances of two dilutions of the solution of the sample with known Mn content.

PROBLEMS

11-1 Transmittance of cell containing MnO_4^- solution. The molar absorptivity of MnO_4^- at 525 mμ is 2360 (mole/liter)$^{-1}$ cm^{-1}. What is the transmittance of a cell of path length 1.3 cm containing a permanganate solution equivalent to 1 mg Mn in 100 ml of solution?

---

* If the absorbance of the solution of unknown Mn content is greater than 0.7, dilute a portion of the sample by a known factor to obtain an absorbance of about 0.4; if the absorbance is less than 0.2, prepare a new, more concentrated solution. Similarly, if the absorbance of the undiluted solutions of known Mn content is greater than 0.7, prepare dilutions in addition to those already made so that at least four well-spaced absorbance measurements can be obtained.

11-2 Mass-action constant from transmittance measurements. Two colorless species A and B form the colored compound AB,

$$A + B = AB \qquad [AB]/[A][B] = K_f$$

A solution that is 1.000 F in A and 0.010 F in B showed a transmittance of 79.8 per cent, and a solution 0.100 F in A and 0.100 F in B showed a transmittance of 28.8 per cent, both for the same value of b. Compute K_f. Discuss accuracy.

11-3 Check of Beer's law. A solution of a certain substance showed the following transmittance values as a function of the concentration and at $b = 10$ cm. Does the transmittance obey Beer's law? If so, what is the value of the molar absorptivity ε?

c, gfw/liter	T_i, per cent
0.001	70.5
0.002	49.5
0.003	34.2
0.004	24.5

11-4 Absorption of X rays. A lead foil, 1 mm thick, absorbs 5 per cent of X rays of a certain wavelength. What thickness will absorb 50 per cent of the same X rays?

11-5 Correction for colored contaminant. Two 25.00-ml portions of a solution containing both $KMnO_4$ and $K_2Cr_2O_7$ are treated as follows: The first portion is diluted to 100.00 ml (solution A). To the second portion drops of KNO_2 are added until all MnO_4^- has been reduced to Mn^{++}, and the resulting solution is diluted to 100.00 ml (solution B). The transmittances of the two solutions are measured in a photoelectric colorimeter, the instrument being set to show a transmittance of 1.000 for distilled water. Solutions A and B produce the respective readings of 0.353 and 0.857. Next, the colorimeter is readjusted to read 1.000 when solution B is used as a blank. (*a*) What reading for solution A is expected? (*b*) What is the permanganate concentration of the original solution? Path length $= 1.50$ cm; $\varepsilon MnO_4^- = 2360$ (mole/liter^{-1} cm^{-1}. Discuss accuracy.

11-6 Equilibrium involving a colored species. Two uncolored substances A and B form the colored compound A_2B. (*a*) Draw an approximate diagram of the absorbance of a solution containing A, B, and A_2B as a function of the concentration of A in a range of concentrations such that [B] is very much larger than [A]. Explain. (*b*) Show the dependence of the absorbance on [B] in a range of concentrations in which [B] is very much smaller than [A].

11-7 Optimum transmittance. At what value of T does $-(T \ln T)^{-1}$ have a minimum so that the relative precision of concentration measurements is optimal (see page 241)?

11-8 Error in colorimetric analysis. A solution that is $2 \times 10^{-4} M$ in MnO_4^- and $1 \times 10^{-2} F$ in $Fe_2(SO_4)_3$ is analyzed colorimetrically without correcting for the presence of the iron. (*a*) What is the error in the MnO_4^- concentration caused by this negligence? The path length is 1.5 cm, and the molar absorptivities are as follows: MnO_4^-, 2.36×10^3 $(mole/liter)^{-1}$ cm^{-1}; $Fe_2(SO_4)_3$, 20 $(gfw/liter)^{-1}$ cm^{-1}. (b) What would the error be if the path length were 2.0 cm?

11-9   Equilibrium constant from transmittance measurements.   In a certain solution a colored species AB_2 is at equilibrium with the two uncolored species A and B,

$$A + 2B = AB_2$$

Find the equilibrium constant from the following colorimetric data obtained with a path length of 1.00 cm. Assume that the foregoing equilibrium is the only one of importance.

solution concentrations, F		transmittance
of A	*of B*	
1.00×10^{-3}	1.00	0.327
1.00×10^{-3}	0.100	0.328
1.00×10^{-3}	0.0100	0.558

11-10   Error in colorimetric determination.   The usual reproducibility for a photoelectric colorimeter is 0.002 transmittance units. Calculate the possible relative error that may arise from this uncertainty when a concentration is determined from the following transmittance values: 0.10, 0.30, and 0.80.

REVIEW QUESTIONS

11-1.   Briefly explain and give the symbols for the following quantities: transmittance, internal transmittance, absorbance, absorptivity, molar absorptivity.

11-2.   Briefly discuss sources of apparent deviations from Beer's law.

11-3.   Sketch and briefly describe the operations of the Duboscq colorimeter.

11-4.   Briefly describe the purpose of the following steps in the colorimetric determination of Mn: (a) After dissolving the sample in HNO_3 the solution is boiled to expel oxides of nitrogen; (b) ammonium peroxydisulfate is slowly sprinkled into the hot solution; (c) phosphoric acid is added before oxidizing with potassium periodate.

11-5.   Several supposed deviations from the recommended procedures for the colorimetric determination of Mn are described; briefly describe the effect of each. (a) The periodic acid was not boiled off completely; (b) carbonaceous material was incompletely oxidized; (c) the steel contained 5 per cent Cr; (d) no phosphoric acid was used.

It is shown that simple complexing agents are generally unsuited for volumetric work, whereas satisfactory titrations may be based on reactions in which one particle of the complexing agent attaches itself in several places to one ion of the substance being determined. The usual pH dependence of such titrations is discussed, the reaction between Zn^{++} or Mg^{++} and EDTA being used as an example. The behavior of Erio T as an indicator for metal cations is explained. The reaction between EDTA and Zn^{++} or Mg^{++} forms the basis of a laboratory assignment.

twelve

COMPLEXOMETRIC
ANALYSIS

GENERAL PRINCIPLES

Titrations with simple complexing agents. The formation of stable complexes between metal cations such as Ag^+, Zn^{++}, or Cd^{++} and complex-forming species, or *ligands*, such as NH_3 or CN^- brings up the question whether it is feasible to titrate these cations with standard solutions of the complex-forming agent. There exist, indeed, volumetric methods based on this idea. One of them is the Liebig method of titrating CN^- with Ag^+. As long as there is an excess of CN^-, practically all Ag^+ added to the cyanide solution will form the complex $Ag(CN)_2^-$,

$$Ag^+ + 2CN^- = Ag(CN)_2^- \qquad K_I = 1 \times 10^{21} \qquad (12\text{-}1)$$

However, in the neighborhood of the equivalence point, addition of small increments of the standard $AgNO_3$ solution causes a rapid increase of $[Ag^+]$, which may be recognized by the appearance of a precipitate of $AgCN(s)$,

$$Ag(CN)_2^- + Ag^+ = 2AgCN(s) \qquad K_{II} = 2 \times 10^{11} \qquad (12\text{-}2)$$

or by other methods.* The large concentration change of Ag^+ near the equivalence point is similar to that in the Mohr titration of Cl^- with Ag^+ or that in the Volhard titration of Ag^+ with SCN^- (page 138). It is due here to the great stability of the complex $Ag(CN)_2^-$, analogous to the very small solubility of $AgSCN(s)$ in the Volhard method.

There are, however, very few other volumetric methods making use of the complex-forming properties of small ions and molecules like CN^- or NH_3, because it is in general not possible to devise a suitable scheme to determine a sharp end point. In the neighborhood of the equivalence point there usually is only a gradual change in metal-ion concentration upon the addition of small increments of titrant, and not the rapid change required for a satisfactory titration. The Liebig method and a few others are exceptions.

To understand the reason for this, consider the formation of the complex $Zn(NH_3)_4^{++}$. The over-all equilibrium for forming this complex is

$$Zn^{++} + 4NH_3 = Zn(NH_3)_4^{++} \qquad K_{total} = 1.1 \times 10^9 \qquad (12\text{-}3)$$

However, the following intermediary equilibria are involved also:

$$Zn^{++} + NH_3 = ZnNH_3^{++} \qquad K_1 = 1.8 \times 10^2 \qquad (12\text{-}4)$$

$$ZnNH_3^{++} + NH_3 = Zn(NH_3)_2^{++} \qquad K_2 = 2.2 \times 10^2 \qquad (12\text{-}5)$$

$$Zn(NH_3)_2^{++} + NH_3 = Zn(NH_3)_3^{++} \qquad K_3 = 2.5 \times 10^2 \qquad (12\text{-}6)$$

---

* In shaking $AgCN(s)$ with water the preponderant species going into solution are Ag^+ and $Ag(CN)_2^-$, because of the great stability of the complex $Ag(CN)_2^-$. The solution reaction is thus the reverse of reaction (12-2),

$$2AgCN(s) = Ag(CN)_2^- + Ag^+ \qquad K_{II}^{-1} = 5 \times 10^{-12}$$

For this reason $AgCN(s)$ is often formulated as $Ag \cdot Ag(CN)_2(s)$, even though all the silver atoms in the crystal are equivalent. The solubility product of silver cyanide is usually given the form

$$[Ag^+][Ag(CN)_2^-] = K_{SP} = 5 \times 10^{-12}$$

rather than

$$[Ag^+][CN^-] = const\,(= 7 \times 10^{-17})$$

251

$$\text{Zn(NH}_3)_3{}^{++} + \text{NH}_3 = \text{Zn(NH}_3)_4{}^{++} \qquad K_4 = 1.1 \times 10^2 \qquad (12\text{-}7)$$

$$K_{\text{total}} = K_1 K_2 K_3 K_4$$

The constants K_1, K_2, K_3, and K_4 are seen to be approximately equal. This is sometimes expressed qualitatively by saying that the NH_3 ligands go onto the Zn^{++} gradually, rather than all four in the same step. As the following more detailed discussion shows, the stability of $\text{Zn(NH}_3)_4{}^{++}$ is not sufficiently larger than that of the other zinc ammonia complexes to make reaction (12-3) the basis of a satisfactory volumetric method.

When a solution containing Zn^{++} is titrated with NH_3, all four complexes $\text{Zn(NH}_3)_i{}^{++}$ ($i = 1, 2, 3, 4$) are present in substantial amounts during most of the titration. To follow this quantitatively, it is well to write the four mass-action equations corresponding to (12-4) to (12-7) in the form

$$[\text{Zn(NH}_3)_i{}^{++}]/[\text{Zn(NH}_3)_{i-1}^{++}] = K_i[\text{NH}_3] \approx 200[\text{NH}_3] \qquad i = 1, 2, 3, 4 \qquad (12\text{-}8)$$

Inspection shows that as long as $[\text{NH}_3]$ remains small compared with 0.005 mole/liter, the right sides of Equations (12-8) are small compared with 1, so that the species present in the main is Zn^{++}. (The actual species is probably $\text{Zn(H}_2\text{O})_4{}^{++}$, and similarly for other cations. For simplicity's sake, we shall write Zn^{++}, since inclusion of the probable hydration of Zn^{++} and of other cations in this discussion adds nothing of importance.) When $[\text{NH}_3] \approx 0.005$, the right sides of Equations (12-8) are about 1, so that all four complexes are represented by similar concentrations. As $[\text{NH}_3]$ increases, so does the relative abundance of higher complexes, but even when $[\text{NH}_3] \approx 0.5$, conversion to $\text{Zn(NH}_3)_4{}^{++}$ is only about 99 per cent, and 1 per cent exists as $\text{Zn(NH}_3)_3{}^{++}$, 0.01 per cent as $\text{Zn(NH}_3)_2{}^{++}$, and so on down. The substantial excess of NH_3 needed in order that the solution contain a definite complex species defeats the stoichiometric aspects of the reaction. There is no stoichiometric relationship between Zn and NH_3 unless the concentration of $\text{Zn(NH}_3)_4{}^{++}$ is large compared with the concentrations of all other species containing Zn, but the additional NH_3 needed spoils the 1:4 ratio.

Figure 12-1 shows the dependence of the Zn^{++} concentration on the amount of NH_3 added, as computed by using Equations (12-8), and it is clear that there is no sharp change in $[\text{Zn}^{++}]$ near the equivalence point, as would be required for a quantitative titration.

The situation would be different if K_4 were much larger. Suppose for the moment that the titrant were $0.1 \, F$ in NH_3 and that the method should have an accuracy of at least 1 part per 1000. This would require that an ammonia concentration of the order of $10^{-5} \, M$ or less be able to hold better than 99.9 per cent of the Zn in the form of $\text{Zn(NH}_3)_4{}^{++}$. Thus, K_4 would need to be at least of the order of 10^8.

If K_4 were somehow raised to the value 10^8 at the expense of changing the other three constants to values near unity, the species $\text{Zn(NH}_3)_4{}^{++}$ would dominate

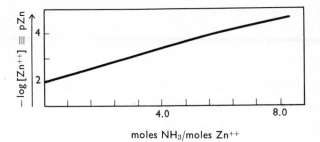

Figure 12-1 Titration curve of 10^{-2} M Zn^{++} with 4×10^{-2} F NH_3 (*after Schwarzenbach*).

at all but the lowest concentrations of NH_3; the four NH_3 ligands would be said to go on in one step. However, for the usual complexes the mass-action constants for the successive steps of adding ligands are all of the same order of magnitude; neighboring constants usually differ by less than a factor of 10 and rarely by as much as a factor of 100.

This is in marked contrast to the behavior of simple oxygen acids, which may be considered as complexes between their anions and H^+ ions. The mass-action constants corresponding to this complex formation are the reciprocals of the dissociation constants and are called association constants. Successive association constants are usually in the ratio of about 10^{-5} for simple oxygen acids.

The molecules tren and EDTA.   An elegant way to force four NH_3 ligands to combine all in one step with a metal cation like Zn^{++} is to tie them together by short chains of carbon atoms, as has been done in the molecule shown in Figure 12-2. In it all three H atoms of an NH_3 molecule have been replaced by aminoethyl groups,

$$-CH_2-CH_2-NH_2.$$

The resulting molecule has the name triaminotriethylamine, or tren for short.

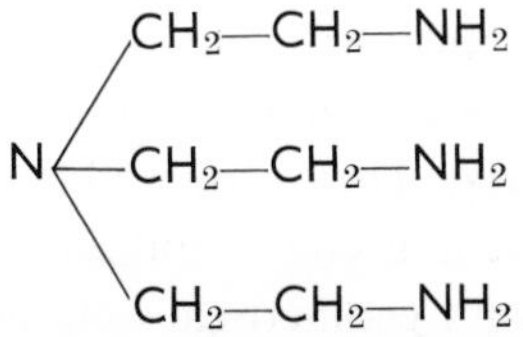

$$
N
\begin{cases}
CH_2-CH_2-NH_2 \\
CH_2-CH_2-NH_2 \\
CH_2-CH_2-NH_2
\end{cases}
$$

Figure 12-2 The structure of tren.

253

An amine is a molecule in which one or more of the H atoms of NH_3 have been replaced by organic groups. In the above example the substituents $(-CH_2-CH_2-NH_2)$ are amines in turn, called either ethylamine groups or aminoethyl groups, whichever is more convenient. The ethyl part of this group is derived from ethane (CH_3-CH_3). Any organic molecule can be given such a name descriptive of its structure. Another example follows shortly.

All four N atoms of tren are capable of linking up with, or of *coordinating* with, the same Zn^{++} ion, surrounding it tetrahedrally as the N atoms in the complex $Zn(NH_3)_4^{++}$ do. Complexing agents that have more than one coordinating atom, such as tren, are called *poly-dentate* (many-toothed) *ligands*, and a complex in which one such polydentate ligand is attached in several places to the same central atom is termed a *chelate* (Greek: *chele* = claw).

The formation constant for the complex between tren and Zn^{++}, given below, is over 400,000 times larger than that of the reaction between four NH_3 and Zn^{++}:

$$Zn^{++} + tren \quad = Zn(tren)^{++} \qquad K_9 = 4.5 \times 10^{14} \qquad (12\text{-}9)$$

$$Zn^{++} + 4NH_3 = Zn(NH_3)_4^{++} \qquad K_{total} = 1.1 \times 10^9 \qquad (12\text{-}3)$$

Thus, not only does complexing with tren proceed in one step, but the stability of the resulting complex is much greater than that of $Zn(NH_3)_4^{++}$.

This second effect, sometimes called the *chelate effect*, is due not to a chemical factor, related to the substitution of one or more H atoms of NH_3 by ethylene groups ($-CH_2-CH_2-$), but rather to the fact that, once an N atom has attached itself to a Zn^{++}, the other three N atoms that the Zn^{++} is ready to accept are almost in a position to form bonds with the Zn also, whereas in the formation of the $Zn(NH_3)_4^{++}$ complex all four NH_3 groups act independently of one another. Other things being equal, it is statistically more favorable to form the complex $Zn(tren)^{++}$ than $Zn(NH_3)_4^{++}$. The chelate effect has therefore also been called a *statistical effect* (or an entropy effect, to use a thermo-dynamic concept).

Tren forms stable chelates with many other metal ions. Also, many other molecules in which four substituted NH_3 groups are tied together have been synthesized. They form stable complexes with metal cations, provided that the carbon chains linking the nitrogens together are of a length compatible with geometrical requirements—long enough that the N atoms can reach, but not too long, since looseness and too

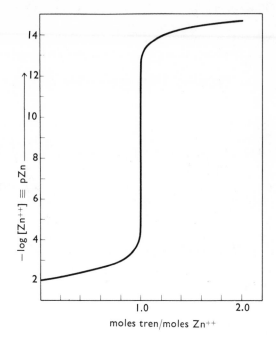

Figure 12-3   Titration curve of 10^{-2} M Zn^{++} with 10^{-2} F tren
(*after Schwarzenbach*).

much play in the resulting complex decrease its stability (again because of the statistical effect).

Tren can be used as a titrant for Zn^{++}, as is made plausible by Figure 12-3, which has been computed from Equation (12-9) and which shows the dependence of the Zn^{++} concentration on the amount of tren added to a zinc solution. However, the molecule known as EDTA, shown in Figure 12-4, forms an even more stable Zn complex and has the further advantage that it forms stable complexes with, and can be used as a titrant for, a large number of other cations also. EDTA contains oxygen atoms in addition to amine nitrogens; both are known to favor the formation of complexes. The name is an abbreviation of ethylenediamine tetraacetic acid, descriptive of the molecule because the substance derives from ethylenediamine ($H_2N-CH_2-CH_2-NH_2$), in which the four H atoms of the amine groups have been replaced by four acetic acid groups ($-CH_2-COOH$) (acetic acid, CH_3-COOH).

255

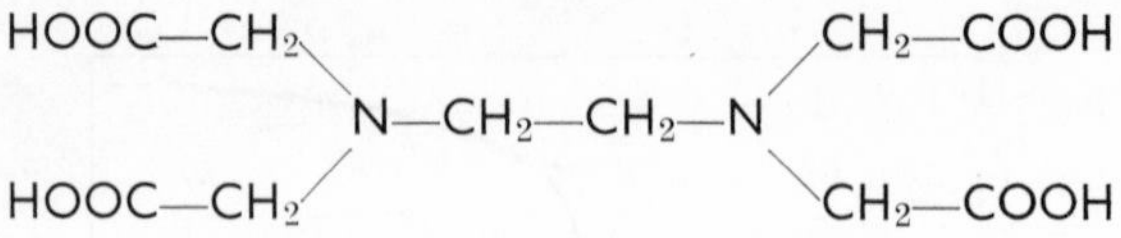

$$HOOC—CH_2$$
$$CH_2—COOH$$
$$N—CH_2—CH_2—N$$
$$HOOC—CH_2$$
$$CH_2—COOH$$

Figure 12-4   The structure of EDTA.

EDTA is a polyprotic acid, sometimes denoted by the abbreviated formula H_4Y. It is actually its anion Y^{4-} that is the powerful complexing agent. Both nitrogen atoms of this anion and one oxygen atom of each of its four acetate groups can coordinate with one and the same central metal atom. The EDTA anion Y^{4-} is thus a hexadentate complexing agent that forms stable complexes with many metal ions in which its two N atoms and four of its O atoms surround the central ion octahedrally. This is shown in Figure 12-5, which is a diagram of the structure of the complex CoY^- formed by Co^{3+} and Y^{4-}, as determined by X-ray crystallography. It is seen that the N and O atoms surrounding the Co atoms are at the corners of an octahedron. The figure also demonstrates that the geometry of the complex is such that the remaining O atoms of the four acetate groups are not in a position to form additional bonds with the central atom. The structures of other metal complexes of EDTA have not been worked out in detail by X-ray methods, but they can be presumed to be similar to that of CoY^-.

The complex-formation constants between Y^{4-} and Zn^{++} and Mg^{++} are respectively

$$Zn^{++} + Y^{4-} = ZnY^= \qquad K_{10} = 3.2 \times 10^{16} \qquad (12\text{-}10)$$

$$Mg^{++} + Y^{4-} = MgY^= \qquad K_{11} = 4.9 \times 10^{8} \qquad (12\text{-}11)$$

It is therefore possible to titrate both Zn^{++} and Mg^{++} with EDTA, and in one alternative of the laboratory assignment for this chapter.a solution of the salt $Na_2H_2Y \cdot 2H_2O$ is standardized with Zn and then used to titrate Mg. The disodium salt of H_4Y is ordinarily used in EDTA titrations because it is stable, easily purified, and not hygroscopic. It is sufficiently soluble, whereas H_4Y is quite insoluble in water.

Solutions of $Na_2H_2Y \cdot 2H_2O$ contain the species H_4Y, H_3Y^-, $H_2Y^=$, HY^{3-}, and Y^{4-} in different amounts, depending on the pH. The pK values corresponding to the successive dissociation constants of H_4Y are 2.0 for the first H, 2.67 for the second, 6.16 for the third, and 10.26 for the fourth. The more alkaline the solution, the larger the concentration of the higher dissociated species and, in particular, of Y^{4-}. The *effective* stability of the metal complexes of Y^{4-} therefore increases with the pH, and even though the complex-formation constants corresponding to Equations (12-10) and (12-11) are large, the great stability of EDTA complexes can be exploited only at a sufficiently high pH. A pH of 10 is favored for the titration of Mg, because in a less alkaline medium the concentration of Y^{4-} is too low and the complex $MgY^=$ not quite so stable as desired, and precipitation of $Mg(OH)_2$ may occur in a more alkaline medium. An additional reason for choosing a pH in this range is connected with the behavior of the end-point indicator; it will be discussed shortly. The Zn^{++} could be titrated satisfactorily in a more acid medium, and indeed Zn^{++} and Mg^{++} can be titrated separately in a solution containing both by first controlling the pH at 6.8, where only the Zn^{++} reacts. A separate titration at pH 10 would give the total of Mg^{++} and Zn^{++}. However, in the laboratory assignment of this chapter the same pH is used for both standardization of the EDTA solution with Zn^{++} and titration

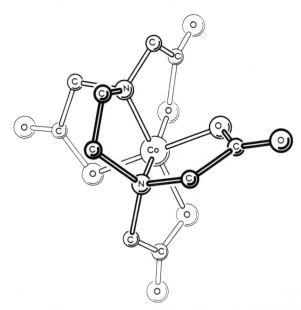

Figure 12-5 Structure of CoY^- as determined by X-ray crystallography (*Weakliem and Hoard*).

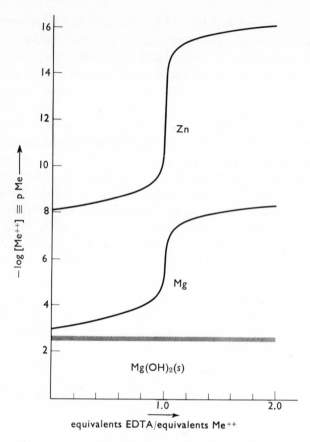

Figure 12-6   Titration curves for 10^{-3} M Mg^{++} and 10^{-3} M Zn^{++} with 10^{-3} F EDTA at pH 10 in NH$_3$/NH$_4$Cl buffer (*after Schwarzenbach*).

of Mg^{++}. Since the color change of the indicator depends to some extent on the pH, as will be evident later, the end points of the two titrations can be made strictly comparable only at the same pH.

At the pH of 10 used in the laboratory assignment the ratio

$$[Y^{4-}]/[HY^{3-}] = 10^{-10.26}/[H^+]$$

is close to unity, so that about half the EDTA present before complexing is in the form of HY^{3-} and the other half in the form of Y^{4-}. The concentrations of the other EDTA species are negligible at pH 10. The titration reaction for HY^{3-} is

$$HY^{3-} + Me^{++} \rightarrow MeY^= + H^+$$

where Me^{++} stands for Zn^{++} or Mg^{++}. During the titration, H^+ ions are thus liberated, and to maintain the pH, the solution has to be buffered. It is convenient to use a solution of ammonia and ammonium chloride for this purpose, with a concentration ratio of $[NH_3]/[NH_4^+]$ ≈ 5. Under those conditions

$$[OH^-] = 1.8 \times 10^{-5} \times [NH_3]/[NH_4^+] \approx 10^{-4}$$

The ammonia present will, of course, form the complex $Zn(NH_3)_4^{++}$ if Zn^{++} is present, but the stability of $ZnY^=$ is so much greater that this does not interfere with the titration. Indeed in the absence of NH_3 most of the Zn would be present as $Zn(OH)_4^=$ at pH 10. The loss of NH_3 by its complexing with Zn can be neglected, since the buffer has to be present in excess in any case. Mg^{++} does not form a stable ammonia complex. The changes of the concentrations of Zn^{++} and of Mg^{++} in separate titrations with EDTA at pH 10 are shown in Figure 12-6.

The concentration changes of metal ions near the equivalence point of the titration are large (see Figure 12-6), and concentrations of 10^{-3} F and even smaller lead to good end points. EDTA titrations are thus particularly favorable in the determination of small quantities of metals, a typical application being the titration of Ca and Mg in tap water. In the laboratory assignment, 0.01 F EDTA is used and the buffer concentrations are of the order of 0.5 F for NH_3 and 0.1 F for NH_4Cl.

METAL-ION INDICATORS

There exist colored organic compounds that are able to form complexes with metal cations and that change color during the process. The behavior of such metal-ion indicators is complicated by the fact that their color is also pH-dependent. They can react with H^+ ions just as with other cations and are thus pH indicators also. A typical metal-ion indicator is Erio T, which will be used in the titrations of the laboratory assignment of this chapter.

The structure of Erio T. The organic compound known commercially as Eriochrome T, or Erio T, forms chelates with many metal ions and in doing so undergoes a change in color. The structure of Erio T (Fig. 12-7) is more complicated than that of the two organic molecules discussed previously, but its important features can be

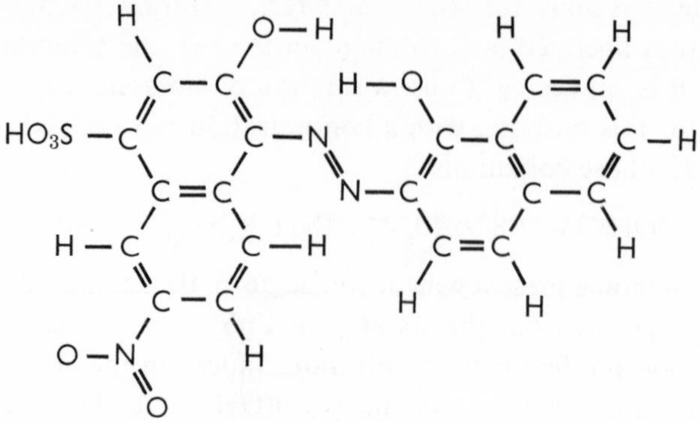

Figure 12-7 The structure of Erio T.

described readily. The compound is a triprotic acid which will be abbreviated as H_3E; the three protons involved are the hydrogen of the sulfonic acid group (HO_3S—) and the hydrogens of two hydroxyl groups attached to two of the rings of C atoms (hydrogen atoms directly attached to carbon atoms do not dissociate in an aqueous medium). The function of the sulfonic acid group is to increase the water solubility of the compound. Except in very acid solutions its H is dissociated, so that in a neutral-to-alkaline pH range Erio T exists as H_2E^-, $HE^=$, and E^{3-}.

The species involved in the formation of metal complexes is the completely ionized E^{3-}, and these complexes have the composition MeE^-. Chelate bonds are formed by both oxygens of the two original hydroxyl groups and by at least one of the two nitrogens of the bridge between the two double rings of C atoms. One of these N atoms may not be in a favorable geometrical position to form such a bond, but no detailed structural investigation proving this has been made.

The remaining portion of the Erio T molecule, particularly the regular sequence of single and double bonds, is responsible for its color. Changes in color may be caused by both complex formation and gain or loss of protons.

The color changes of Erio T.   The stability of the complexes of Erio T with Mg^{++} and Zn^{++} is such that during most of the titration of these ions with EDTA the metal-ion indicator is present as the metal complex ME^-. As the end point approaches, the concentration of this complex rapidly decreases in favor of uncomplexed Erio T. The situation is complicated by the pH-dependent equilibria between the different uncomplexed species of Erio T: H_2E^-, $HE^=$, and E^{3-}. The case of Mg^{++} will be discussed in detail, that for Zn^{++} being similar.

Figure 12-8 shows the stability regions and colors of the Mg complex and of the different uncomplexed species of Erio T as functions of the H^+-ion and Mg^{++}-ion concentrations. In the absence of metal ions the regions of stability of the species H_2E^-, $HE^=$, and E^{3-} are determined by the pK values of the second and third acid hydrogens of Erio T, which are 6.3 and 11.6, respectively. The metal complex is formed by the species E^{3-}, whose concentration is pH-dependent. For this reason the boundary of the stability field of MgE^- has a slope that depends on whether the adjoining field is that of E^{3-} (slope 0), $HE^=$ (slope 1), or H_2E^- (slope 2). The regions between the dashed lines are regions of transition between the species in adjoining fields. The field of stability of $Mg(OH)_2(s)$ is also shown. There is a tendency for $Mg(OH)_2$ to form supersaturated solutions, so that $Mg(OH)_2$ does not necessarily precipitate as long as its equilibrium solubility has not been exceeded greatly.

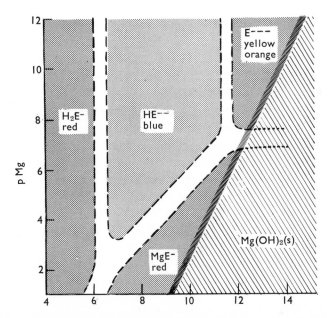

Figure 12-8 Colors of Erio T as function of pH and pMg $= -\log [Mg^{++}]$ (*after Schwarzenbach*).

The species H_2E^- and MgE^- have practically the same color, presumably because the hydroxyl oxygens of Erio T are similarly engaged in both. In H_2E^- hydrogen is bonded to them, whereas in MgE^- they are linked to the metal atom. It is clear from Figure 12-8 that Erio T may be used as metal indicator only in a pH range of about 7 to 11, the color change being from wine red to blue in going from the MgE^- complex to uncomplexed $HE^=$. At a pH much below 7 there is essentially no color change in the transition from uncomplexed H_2E^- to the metal complex. At a pH much above 11 the color difference between uncomplexed yellow-orange E^{3-} and red MgE^- is not distinctive.

The color change from red MgE^- to blue $HE^=$ at the end point of the titration is the more pronounced the higher the fraction of uncomplexed Erio T present as $HE^=$. Thus a pH range of about 8 to 10, in which at least 98 per cent of the uncomplexed dye exists as $HE^=$, is favored for the titration. The upper side of this range is preferred for the following reason: As already discussed and as is evident in Figure 12-8, the stability of MgE^- increases with the pH. For a satisfactory titration end point the stability of this complex must be large, so that prior to the end point all indicator exists as the metal complex. Its stability must be small compared with that of the Mg complex with EDTA, so that at the titration end point a small excess of EDTA suffices to liberate substantially all Erio T from its metal complex. These conditions are both satisfied at a pH of 10. At that pH the initial concentration of Mg^{++} should not be much in excess of 10^{-2} to 10^{-3} M, to prevent precipitation of $Mg(OH)_2$.

For Zn^{++} a diagram similar to Figure 12-8 can be drawn. The stability of the ZnE^- complex is, however, about 10^6 times larger than that of MgE^-, parallel to the much higher stability of $ZnY^=$ compared with that of $MgY^=$. The stability of ZnE^- is much larger than that of $Zn(NH_3)_4^{++}$, so that the presence of NH_3/NH_4Cl buffer does not interfere with the color change of the indicator. (There also exists a complex of lesser stability of formula ZnE_2^{3-}. Its color is blue, with a molar absorptivity about twice that of ZnE^-. Its presence does not interfere with a satisfactory titration end point.)

At pH 10 all but 2 per cent of the Erio T is in the form of $HE^=$. The indicator reaction is therefore

$$Me^{++} + HE^= = MeE^- + H^+ \qquad K = K_{12} \qquad (12\text{-}12)$$

It is useful to write the mass-action expression for this reaction as follows:

$$\frac{[\text{MeE}^-]}{[\text{HE}^=]} = \frac{K_{12}[\text{Me}^{++}]}{[\text{H}^+]} = \frac{[\text{Me}^{++}]}{K_{13}}$$

where $K_{13} = [\text{H}^+]/K_{12}$ depends on the pH. Its values for Mg^{++} and Zn^{++} at pH 10 are

$$\text{Me}^{++} = \text{Mg}^{++} \qquad K'_{13} = 4 \times 10^{-6} \qquad (12\text{-}13)$$

$$\text{Me}^{++} = \text{Zn}^{++} \qquad K''_{13} = 4 \times 10^{-12} \qquad (12\text{-}14)$$

The color dependence of this indicator on the concentration of Me^{++} at constant pH is comparable with the color dependence of an acid-base indicator on the concentration of H^+. Thus, when $[\text{Me}^{++}] = 10K_{13}$, the ratio of red-colored MeE^- ions to blue-colored $\text{HE}^=$ ions is 10. When $[\text{Me}^{++}] = K_{13}$, this ratio is 1. When $[\text{Me}^{++}] = K_{13}/10$, the ratio is 1/10. It is convenient to introduce the quantity $\text{pMe} = -\log[\text{Me}^{++}]$, analogous to pH. The color change of the metal indicator will then occur in the approximate pMe range $pK_{13} - 1$ to $pK_{13} + 1$, the midpoint of the change lying close to pK_{13}. Comparison of the values of pK_{13} for Mg^{++} and Zn^{++} with Figure 12-6 explains why Erio T is a satisfactory indicator for the EDTA titrations of these two cations.

The pH dependence of the color of Erio T makes it doubly important that the solution be well buffered. Since the Zn solution is prepared by dissolving pure Zn in HCl, sufficient excess of buffer must be added to neutralize the excess acid. No such neutralization is needed for the Mg samples, all of which are provided as neutral water-soluble salts.

The presence of traces of Cu^{++}, Ni^{++}, Co^{++}, and, particularly, of Fe^{3+} blocks the indicator by the formation of strong complexes. A simple test to establish the presence of such undesirable ions is to add 0.5 ml of pH 10 buffer and two drops of Erio T indicator to 100 ml of "distilled" water that is suspect. If a clear blue color results, the water is acceptable. A red color or a reddish tinge indicates the presence of ions that form complexes with Erio T. If the addition of a few drops of EDTA solution causes a color change to clear blue, the ions are Ca^{++}, Mg^{++}, and the like, and their presence may be taken into account by preparing a blank containing all but the substance being determined and titrating it with standard EDTA solution. If no clear blue color can be obtained in this way, heavy-metal ions like Cu^{++} and Fe^{3+} are present. Reaction with Erio T may be prevented by adding one drop of a $0.1 \, F$ Na_2S solution to the "distilled" water. This removes even minute amounts of heavy-metal ions because of the formation of sulfides of very low solubility. It does not, however, interfere with the titration.

Industrial applications of EDTA. Besides being of wide applicability in volumetric work EDTA, or *versene* as it is also called, is used in industry to reduce by complex formation the concentration of metal ions. In this function it is called a *sequestering agent*, because it almost completely complexes with, or sequesters, cations which may be of harm under the circumstances. An important application is as a water softener in the dyeing and the soap and detergent industries. It has been used as an antidote in heavy-metal poisoning. Traces of cations act as catalysts for undesirable reactions, but the complexed cations do not. An example is the catalytic decomposition of H_2O_2 by small amounts of ferric and cupric ions. Addition of EDTA reduces the concentration of these potential impurities to such an extent that the catalytic action is suppressed. There are many other applications, and the list is still growing.

A solution of the disodium salt
of ethylenediamine tetraacetic acid (EDTA),
which forms very stable complexes
with many metal cations, is prepared
and standardized by titration of known quantities of Zn.
This solution is then used to determine
either the percentage of Mg, in a mixture
of MgSO$_4$ and inert substances or the amount
of Zn in an unknown containing ZnO.
The indicator used in all these titrations is Erio T.

Laboratory assignment 12
(3 periods)

COMPLEXOMETRIC TITRATION

OF MAGNESIUM

PROCEDURES

12-1 Preparation of solutions.

1. Prepare a 0.01 F solution of EDTA by dissolving 1.8 to 2.0 g of disodium ethylenediamine tetraacetate dihydrate in 500 ml of water. EDTA dissolves slowly; heat to about 60°C if necessary. Shake vigorously to ensure complete solution.

2. Accurately weigh about 0.33 g of pure Zn (it should not be dried) and dissolve it in about 5 ml of 6 F HCl. Check scrupulously to see that all Zn is dissolved, and carefully transfer the solution to a 500-ml volumetric flask. Dilute to the mark, and mix well (see procedure for

preparing a solution of accurate volume, page 141). This 0.01 F solution serves to standardize the EDTA solution, and all results depend upon its accurate preparation. Use of a standard Zn solution prepared in this way is preferable to weighing out individual samples of Zn, because they would weigh on the order of 20 mg only.

3. Prepare 250 ml of a buffer solution that is 0.1 F in NH_4Cl and 0.5 F in NH_3.

12-2 Standardization of the EDTA solution. Pipet exactly 25.00 ml of the standard Zn solution into a 125-ml flask. Add 20 ml of the buffer solution and 15 ml of water, stir, and add one to two drops of Erio T indicator. The titration end point is sharpest when only enough indicator is used to impart discernible color to the solution. Titrate with the EDTA solution until the color changes to a clear blue; the last tinge of red must have disappeared. This end point is not easy to observe in fluorescent light, in which the red part of the spectrum is largely missing. Incandescent illumination or daylight is better, but the end point is seen best when viewed against the light of a yellow flame. EDTA reactions at room temperature are relatively slow, and the titration must be performed slowly near the equivalence point so that it is not overrun. It takes practice to detect the proper end point, and it may be wise to prepare a comparison solution containing distilled water, buffer, 1 ml of EDTA solution to mask impurities, and Erio T in the appropriate amounts.

Perform at least three satisfactory titrations, and compute the formality of the EDTA solution. Since the results of the subsequent titrations of the unknown rest on the precise weighing, dissolving, and diluting of just one sample of Zn, you should check your results by weighing, dissolving, and titrating an additional Zn sample of approximately 20-mg size. Of course this will uncover gross errors only, and it may be preferable to repeat the entire standardization procedure.

12-3a Titration of magnesium unknowns. (See 12-3b for an alternative procedure using zinc unknowns.) The magnesium unknowns contain $MgSO_4$, which is hygroscopic. The sample provided must be well dried and weighed out by difference. The weighing bottle must be well stopped and not opened longer than necessary for rapid removal of material.

Dry the sample provided at 160°C for 3 hr and let cool; weigh out three samples of such size that 25 to 40 ml of EDTA solution will be needed in the titration. Place each sample in a 125-ml flask, dissolve in about 40 ml of water, and add 10 ml of buffer. Add one to two drops of Erio T. Titrate as before, going slowly near the equivalence point. The color change is from wine red to clear blue; the last tinge of red must have disappeared at the end point.

12-3b   Titration of zinc unknowns   (Alternative for 12-3a).   Dry the sample provided for 1 hr at 110°C, let cool, and weigh three portions in the normal manner into 200-ml conical flasks. The amounts weighed out should be such as to require between 25 to 40 ml of EDTA solution. Rinse each sample to the bottom of the flask with 5 to 10 ml water. Add, in this sequence, the minimum amount of 6 F HCl to get a clear solution (4 to 6 drops), 40 ml of water, 20 ml of buffer, and one to two drops of Erio T indicator. Titrate with EDTA solution to a clear blue end point (disappearance of all red).

12-4   Computation of results.   Compute the weight percentage of Mg (12-3a) or of Zn (12-3b) found in your three samples, the average of these values, and the unbiased absolute and relative standard deviations of your results (see page 83).

PROBLEMS

12-1   Solubility of AgCl.   The following reaction constants are known:

$$Ag^+ + Cl^- = AgCl(aq) \qquad K_1 = 2 \times 10^3$$
$$AgCl(aq) + Cl^- = AgCl_2^- \qquad K_2 = 90$$

where AgCl(aq) refers to the undissociated molecular AgCl present in aqueous solutions of AgCl. When AgCl(s) is in excess, the equilibrium concentration of AgCl(aq) is [AgCl] = 3.6×10^{-7}. How many formula weights of AgCl(s) dissolve in 1 liter of 0.1 F NaCl?

12-2   Solution of precipitate by complex formation.   Ammonia gas is slowly passed into a suspension of 0.05 gfw of Zn(OH)$_2$ in 1 liter of water. (*a*) What is the concentration of NH$_3$ at the point where all Zn(OH)$_2$ has dissolved by forming Zn(NH$_3$)$_4^{++}$? Neglect any change in volume, and assume that the only equilibria of importance are those given below, with their respective mass-action constants:

$$Zn(OH)_2(s) = Zn^{++} + 2OH^- \qquad K_{SP} = 4.5 \times 10^{-17}$$
$$Zn^{++} + 4NH_3 = Zn(NH_3)_4^{++} \qquad K_{total} = 1.1 \times 10^9$$

(*b*) Consider whether taking the equilibria (12-4) to (12-7) into account will modify the result.

12-3   Solubility of amphoteric hydroxide.   Strong base is slowly added to a solution that is 0.1 F in Al$_2$(SO$_4$)$_3$ and 0.1 F in H$_2$SO$_4$. After a while, Al(OH)$_3$ precipitates, but upon further addition of base it dissolves again. (*a*) At what pH will Al(OH)$_3$ begin to precipitate? (*b*) At what pH will it have completely dissolved again in the form of Al(OH$_4$)$^-$? Neglect changes in volume.

$$Al(OH)_3(s) = 3OH^- + Al^{3+} \qquad K_{SP} = 2.0 \times 10^{-33}$$

$$Al(OH)_3(s) + OH^- = Al(OH_4)^- \qquad K_f = 40$$

12-4 Solubility product, complex formation, and hydrolysis. (*a*) How many formula weights of AgBr dissolve in 1 liter of a 0.1 F solution of NaCN? Neglect any reaction of CN^- with H_2O. (*b*) Show, by computing $[CN^-]$, [HCN], and $[OH^-]$, that any such hydrolysis of CN^- does not affect the result. Consider that $Ag(CN)_2^-$ acts as a pool furnishing CN^- and HCN.

$$AgBr(s) = Ag^+ + Br^- \qquad K_{SP} = 4.0 \times 10^{-13}$$

$$Ag(CN)_2^- = Ag^+ + 2CN^- \qquad K_d = 1 \times 10^{-21}$$

$$HCN = H^+ + CN^- \qquad K_a = 2 \times 10^{-9}$$

12-5 Solubility by formation of complex ion. Given are the following equilibrium constants:

$$HgCl_4^= = Hg^{++} + 4Cl^- \qquad K_d = 6 \times 10^{-17}$$

$$HgO(s) + H_2O = Hg^{++} + 2OH^- \qquad K_{SP} = 3 \times 10^{-26}$$

Compute the solubility (in formula weights per liter) of HgO(*s*) in 1 F NaCl buffered at pH 11, assuming that no other equilibria than those given are involved.

12-6 pH dependence of solubility.* Compute the solubility (gfw/liter) of CaF_2 in a solution buffered at pH 2.0.

12-7 Silverammine complexes.* Ammonia gas is passed into an aqueous suspension of finely divided AgCl(*s*), which reacts to form the complexes $Ag(NH_3)^+$ and $Ag(NH_3)_2^+$. What final molar concentration of NH_3 is required so that the total silver concentration is just 0.1 F? Assume first that only the equilibria $AgCl(s) = Ag^+ + Cl^-$ and $Ag^+ + 2NH_3 = Ag(NH_3)_2^+$ need be considered, but take other possible equilibria into account at a later stage and make suitable corrections if necessary.

12-8 Solubility and complex formation.* What is the solubility of AgI in 0.01 F NH_3? Consider the formation of both $Ag(NH_3)^+$ and $Ag(NH_3)_2^+$.

12-9 Precipitation of $Mg(OH)_2$.* Highly concentrated NH_3 solution is slowly added to a solution that is 0.020 F in $MgCl_2$ and 0.10 F in NH_4Cl. What is $[NH_3]$ at the point where $Mg(OH)_2$ just begins to precipitate? Neglect any change in volume.

12-10 Solubility and acid-base equilibria.* A saturated solution of $MgNH_4PO_4 \cdot 6H_2O$ in pure water has a pH of 9.71 and a Mg^{++} concentration of 5.6×10^{-4}. What is K_{SP} of magnesium ammonium phosphate? Consider the acid-base reactions of both NH_4^+ and PO_4^{3-} ions.

REVIEW QUESTIONS

12-1. Briefly explain the following terms: ligand, chelate, chelate effect, polydentate.

* For equilibrium constants, see pp. 399–401.

12-2. Briefly explain why it is not feasible to titrate Zn^{++} with NH_3, whereas Zn^{++} may be titrated with EDTA.

12-3. Why are titrations with EDTA affected by the pH? Why is the color change of metal indicators like Erio T pH-dependent?

12-4. What determines the pH range in which the titration of Mg^{++} with EDTA is satisfactory? Repeat for titration of Zn^{++} with EDTA.

12-5. Why is the presence of traces of ions like Fe^{3+} and Cu^{++} undesirable in the titrations of the laboratory assignment? What measures may be taken to carry out these titrations in spite of the presence of Fe^{3+}, etc.?

12-6. Why are NH_3 and NH_4Cl added to the solutions before the titration? Why does the NH_3 not interfere in the EDTA titration by the formation of ammine complexes?

12-7. Briefly discuss the effects of the following supposed deviations from the recommended procedures in the laboratory assignment: (*a*) The Zn^{++} was titrated at pH 8, the Mg^{++} at pH 10; (*b*) both Zn^{++} and Mg^{++} were titrated at pH 8; (*c*) traces of Ni^{++} were present in the Mg sample; (*d*) the Mg sample was dissolved in tap water rather than in distilled water.

REFERENCES

H. A. Laitinen, *Chemical Analysis*, Chap 13, McGraw-Hill, New York, 1960.

G. Schwarzenbach, *Complexometric Titrations*, Methuen, London, 1957.

F. J. Welcher, *The Analytical Uses of Ethylenediamine Tetraacetic Acid*, Van Nostrand, Princeton, N.J., 1958.

*The quantitative aspects of redox reactions
are summarized and oxidation numbers
and oxidation equivalents are discussed.
A general survey of coulometric
methods is followed by an exposition
of an example of the constant-current
method, the coulometric titration of As(III)
with iodine. Particular attention
is given to the buffering requirements
of the reactions involved. Simple coulometric
equipment for use with the constant-current
method is described. The coulometric titration
of As(III) with iodine also forms
the basis for a laboratory assignment.*

thirteen

COULOMETRIC
ANALYSIS

QUANTITATIVE ASPECTS OF REDOX REACTIONS

Oxidations and reductions, or redox reactions as they are called collectively, are reactions involving the transfer of electrons. A *reduction* is a gain of electrons, or an *electronation;* an *oxidation* is a loss of electrons, or a *deelectronation.* An oxidizing agent (ox) is a substance capable of gaining electrons in a reaction that converts it into a reducing agent (red):

$$ox + ne^- = red$$

A reducing agent behaves in exactly the opposite way, and reducing and oxidizing agents that are related by the above equation are called redox couples. There is close parallelism between redox reactions and acid-base reactions,

$$\text{base} + n \text{ protons} = \text{acid}$$

Simple redox couples are Fe^{3+}/Fe^{++}, $Zn^{++}/Zn(s)$, and I_2/I^-, with reaction equations like

$$Fe^{3+} + e^- = Fe^{++}$$

Species other than oxidizing and reducing agents may also participate in redox reactions, as they do in the couples MnO_4^-/Mn^{++} and $Cr_2O_7^-/Cr^{3+}$.

$$MnO_4^- + 8H^+ + 5e^- = Mn^{++} + 4H_2O$$

$$Cr_2O_7^= + 14H^+ + 6e^- = 2Cr^{3+} + 7H_2O$$

Note that charges as well as atoms are balanced. Equations like those shown are called half-reactions. Half-reactions may take place in the presence of electrodes able to furnish or to take up the electrons involved.

Chemists find it practical to label an electrical terminal by the type of electrode reaction associated with it. If the reaction is a reduction, the terminal is called the *cathode*; if an oxidation, the *anode*. The electrons therefore always enter a solution (or a melt or even a solid, as the case may be) through the cathode and leave through the anode. This direction of electron flow corresponds, of course, to a flow of (positive) current in the opposite direction.

Electrical terminals are also labeled *plus* and *minus*, but whether the electrons enter at the plus or minus terminal depends on the nature of the device of which the terminal is part. If the device produces a voltage, the minus terminal is the one in which the electrons accumulate to give it a negative charge. In a device that is driven by an external voltage the minus terminal is the one into which the electrons are forced by the external voltage, charging it negatively. Thus in a device that furnishes electricity, such as a battery, the negative pole is where the electrons leave (Fig. 13-1). In a device that uses electricity, like an electrolysis cell, the negative pole is where the electrons enter.

The plus and minus labels are convenient when connecting terminals of a d-c-generating to a d-c-utilizing device: minus goes to minus, plus to plus. Furthermore, it is possible to label the terminals of a storage battery permanently plus and minus, because the signs of the terminals remain the same whether the battery is being charged or discharged. However, the terms "anode" and "cathode" do not go hand in hand with "plus" and "minus." In an electrolysis cell the negative pole is

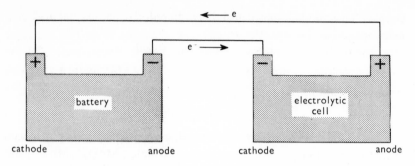

Figure 13-1   Anode, cathode, and positive and negative terminals.

the cathode; in a galvanic cell, the anode. The same plus terminal in a storage battery is the cathode when the battery is discharged and the anode when the battery is charged.

In any electrolytic process the number of electrons leaving through the anode equals the number of electrons entering through the cathode. This number of electrons also governs the stoichiometric aspects of the electrode reactions. If i is the number of electrons participating in the reaction of *one* particle, then the reaction of 1 mole of substance involves i faradays of electricity, where 1 faraday is the same as 1 mole or Avogadro's number of electrons. This essentially is Faraday's law of electrolysis. A convenient unit of electricity or electric charge is the coulomb, the electricity flowing through the cross section of a wire in 1 sec when the current is 1 amp. Thus 1 coulomb = 1 amp-sec and, conversely, 1 amp = 1 coulomb/sec. (The ampere is defined by the electromagnetic action of a current.) The two units of electric charge are related by the equation

$$1 \text{ faraday} = 96{,}485.8 \text{ coulombs/mole}$$

The value of the conversion factor is based on the C^{12} scale of atomic weights, and it is usually rounded to 96,500, correct to 0.01 per cent.

In the absence of electrodes half-reactions must always occur in such combination that no free electrons appear on either side of the reaction equation. For example, in the oxidation of Fe^{++} by MnO_4^-, the over-all reaction equation

$$8H^+ + MnO_4^- + 5Fe^{++} = Mn^{++} + 5Fe^{3+} + 4H_2O$$

combines the MnO_4^-/Mn^{++} half-reaction with 5 times the reversed

Fe^{3+}/Fe^{++} half-reaction given earlier. In the absence of electrodes all redox reactions involve the transfer of electrons from one or more oxidizing agents to one or more reducing agents. The reduction of the oxidizing agents is paralleled by the oxidation of the reducing agents. As already mentioned, there is close analogy between such redox reactions and acid-base reactions,

$$\text{red } 1 + \text{ox } 2 = \text{ox } 1 + \text{red } 2$$

$$\text{acid } 1 + \text{base } 2 = \text{base } 1 + \text{acid } 2$$

Oxidation numbers.   When an elemental particle like a Zn atom or a Fe^{3+} ion is oxidized or reduced, the result is simply described as a change in the charge of the particle. In more complex situations a generalization of the charge of an elemental particle, the oxidation number, is convenient for the same purpose. It is defined by the following rules:

1. The oxidation number of the atoms of an elemental substance is zero.

2. The oxidation number of a monoatomic ion is equal to the charge of the ion.

The oxidation numbers of the atoms of a more complex ion or molecule may be found by the following somewhat arbitrary rules:

3. When the structure of the particle is known, the oxidation number of each atom is the charge that would remain on it if the shared electrons were apportioned as follows: A shared pair is counted with the more electronegative of the two atoms bonded by it. Electron pairs shared by atoms of equal electronegativity are split evenly, unless structural reasons favor a different division (see, e.g., the discussion of the thiosulfate ion below).

It is an important rule that the *sum of the oxidation numbers* of all atoms of a particle *equals the charge* of the particle. The reason is that in the assignment of oxidation numbers each electron belonging to the particle is counted exactly once (explicitly or implicitly) and matched against the nuclear charge of one of the atomic nuclei.

The foregoing rules for dividing shared electrons cannot be used when the structure of the particle is unknown. The bonding may also be such that the electrons cannot be assigned simply, and thus again the rules cannot be applied. For example, this may be the case when the particle can be described by resonance between several structures. In such cases rule 4 can usually be applied:

4. When the structure of the particle is not known or is such that rule 3 leads to difficulties, it is often possible to assign reasonable oxidation numbers to all but one kind of the atoms, which are then given values so that the sum over all oxidation numbers equals the charge of the particle. Reasonable oxidation numbers are those which the atoms concerned exhibit in similar compounds when rule 3 applies. In particular, fluorine has the oxidation number -1 when combined with other elements, being the most electronegative element. Oxygen, when not combined with fluorine or in the elemental state, usually has oxidation number -2, except in peroxides, where some of the oxygen atoms are at -1. Hydrogen is at $+1$ when combined with nonmetallic atoms and at -1 in metal hydrides.

These rules lead, for example, to the oxidation states of $+6$ for S in $SO_4^=$, $+7$ for Mn in MnO_4^-, and $+6$ for Cr in $Cr_2O_7^=$. The reduction of MnO_4^- to Mn^{++}, which was discussed earlier and which means a gain of five electrons, is seen to involve a change in the oxidation number of Mn from $+7$ to $+2$.

When a particle contains several atoms of the same kind, rule 4 gives the average of the values that follow from rule 3.

The thiosulfate ion, $S_2O_3^=$, provides an example where rule 3 is not applied to the S atoms because of structural reasons. The structure of $S_2O_3^=$

$$\left[\begin{array}{c} :\ddot{O}: \\ | \\ :\ddot{S} - S - \ddot{O}: \\ | \\ :\ddot{O}: \end{array} \right]^=$$

is analogous to that of the $SO_4^=$ ion, and application of rule 3 would lead to oxidation numbers $+5$ for the central and -1 for the peripheral S atoms. However, because of the similarity of the $S_2O_3^=$ and the $SO_4^=$ ions, the oxidation number $+6$ is customarily assigned to the central S atom in thiosulfate. The O atoms and the peripheral S atom are given the oxidation number -2, emphasizing their structural near-equivalence; the thiosulfate ion may be obtained by replacing one of the oxide oxygens of the sulfate ion with sulfide sulfur. Rule 4 would give both S atoms the oxidation number $+2$, the average of $+6$ and -2 (or of $+5$ and -1). Even though incomplete, the information conveyed by knowledge of this average oxidation state is often all that is needed for stoichiometric considerations. For example, oxidation of one $S_2O_3^=$ to two $SO_4^=$ is seen to entail a change of two S atoms from the average state of $+2$ to the state $+6$, or a loss of 8 electrons. The same conclusion may be drawn from a more detailed consideration of the individual changes in oxidation states, or from an explicit balancing of the half-reaction concerned:

$$S_2O_3^= + 5H_2O = 2SO_4^= + 10H^+ + 8e^-$$

Oxidation numbers are useful for other reasons, in spite of the element of arbitrariness inherent in them. Aside from their convenience in describing oxidations and reductions, they are important in the classification of compounds. The examples given in Table 13-1 are characteristic of the connection between oxidation numbers and prefixes and endings. It is also customary to use a Roman number in parentheses, as in As(III), to indicate the oxidation states characteristic of a substance when its precise composition is irrelevant or not known. The latter is often the case in solution chemistry, when a symbol such as Sn(IV) refers to Sn in the $+4$ state in the form of complexes of unknown composition.

A knowledge of oxidation numbers is also useful for balancing redox equations. The changes of oxidation numbers on both sides of the equation must balance, and keeping track of these changes is a convenient way to account for the electrons that change hands. It should be realized that this method of bookkeeping of electrons

TABLE 13-1   *Oxidation Numbers and Nomenclature*

ionic species	oxidation number of central atom	name
Cl^-	-1	Chloride ion
ClO^-	$+1$	Hypochlorite ion
ClO_2^-	$+3$	Chlorite ion
ClO_3^-	$+5$	Chlorate ion
ClO_4^-	$+7$	Perchlorate ion
Mn^{++}	$+2$	Manganous ion
Mn^{3+}	$+3$	Manganic ion
$MnO_4^=$	$+6$	Manganate ion
MnO_4^-	$+7$	Permanganate ion

TABLE 13-2   *Examples of Gram Equivalents*

reaction		gram equivalents of reactants	
(1) $Na_2HAsO_3 + I_2$ + 2NaOH	$= Na_2HAsO_4 + 2NaI$ + H_2O	$Na_2HAsO_3/2$	$I_2/2$
(2) Na_2HAsO_3 + $3AgNO_3$	$= Ag_3AsO_3(s) + 2NaNO_3$ + HNO_3	$Na_2HAsO_3/3$	$AgNO_3$
(3) $2KMnO_4 + 10FeSO_4$ + $8H_2SO_4$	$= 2MnSO + 5Fe_2(SO_4)_3$ + $K_2SO_4 + 8H_2O$	$KMnO_4/5$	$FeSO_4/2$
(4) $2KMnO_4 + 3MnSO_4$ + $2H_2O$	$= 5MnO_2(s) + K_2SO_4$ + $2H_2SO_4$	$KMnO_4/3$	$MnSO_4/2$

works, no matter what rules have been used to assign oxidation numbers, as long as their sums equal the particle charges and all changes of oxidation numbers are considered.

Another important method of balancing redox equations is to separate them into half-reactions, which are balanced individually and finally combined so that no free electrons appear.

Oxidation equivalents.   In redox reactions the equivalent weight W_{eq} of a substance is that quantity that is equivalent to 1 mole of electrons, or 1 faraday. It thus depends on the number of electrons that are involved in the *reaction considered, per formula* of the substance. The equivalent index i is identical with this number, and the equivalent weight is related to the formula weight W_f of the substance by the equation

$$W_{eq} = W_f/i$$

TABLE 13-3   *Normalities of 0.1 F Solutions*

substance	reaction	normality
Na_2HAsO_3	(1)	0.2 N
Na_2HAsO_3	(2)	0.3 N
$KMnO_4$	(3)	0.5 N
$KMnO_4$	(4)	0.3 N

as it is for metathetical reactions (page 98). Examples involving redox reactions and metathetical reactions are given in Table 13-2. The reactions are written in terms of the substances involved rather than the ionic species, since the stress is on stoichiometry. The formulas in the two columns on the right stand for the formula weights. Reactions (1), (3), and (4) are of the redox type, and reaction (2) is metathetical.

The normality of a solution is its concentration in equivalents per liter and thus also depends on the reaction in which it is used. It is related to the formality by the equation

$$\text{normality} = i \times \text{formality}$$

Table 13-3 lists examples of normalities of 0.1 F solutions of some redox reagents in the reactions indicated.

THE COULOMETRIC METHOD

The coulometric method is an example of an analytical method that is based on the quantitative aspects of electrolysis. In electrogravimetric analysis the quantity of *substance* deposited at one or the other electrode is determined; in the coulometric method measurement is made of the quantity of *electricity* (or the number of coulombs) reacting directly or indirectly with the substance to be determined. The amount of substance then follows from Faraday's law. If the current remains constant during the electrolysis, the number of coulombs is the product of the amperage of the current and the total time of current flow. If, however, the current is not constant, the integral over the current as a function of time has to be taken. The term *coulometric titration* is often used, since an addition of titrant is made as in volumetric analysis even though this titrant is generated at an electrode.

Two distinct types of coulometric methods exist. In the first the substance to be determined reacts directly at one of the electrodes. This is called *direct*, or *primary*, coulometric analysis. For example, cupric ion in a nitric or sulfuric acid solution may be determined by reduction at the cathode. If such an electrolysis is carried out without special precautions, other metals will begin to plate out or hydrogen will be generated once the copper has been deposited. This can be prevented by applying a current source whose potential is controlled at a constant value that is too small for the evolution of H_2 or the plating out of other metals, yet large enough that at the end of the titration

277

the concentration of Cu^{++} is negligible. Near the end of such a *controlled-potential titration* the current will become small, and the titration is ended when the current has fallen below a certain amperage, the value of which depends mainly on the accuracy expected of the titration. The total amount of copper is proportional to $\int I\,dt$, where I is the current and t is the time. One may evaluate this integral graphically from a plot of I versus t or, more elegantly, by electronic means. However, its value is usually obtained by making the current pass in series through a so-called *chemical coulometer*, a device to measure amounts of electricity chemically by the principles already mentioned. An example of such a device is the hydrogen-oxygen coulometer in which water is electrolyzed. The total amount of hydrogen and oxygen gas is proportional to the amount of electricity passed.

Direct coulometric methods have their limitations, because only a few substances can be made to react directly at an electrode, and for those that do there often are difficulties in maintaining *100 per cent current efficiency*, or a stoichiometric correspondence between the number of coulombs involved and the quantities of substances reacted. Another disadvantage of the direct coulometric method is that it requires a long time, because the current decreases exponentially near the end of the titration.

The other method is the *secondary*, or *indirect*, coulometric titration, in which an intermediate reagent is generated electrolytically and then reacts stoichiometrically with the substance to be determined. It is more versatile than the primary method, since many substances can be determined even though they are incapable of quantitative direct electrode reaction. Furthermore, with the second method it is usually easier to obtain 100 per cent current efficiency by appropriate selection of the intermediate and by suitable control of its concentration.

Another advantage is that it is generally possible to maintain a constant current throughout the titration. The laboratory assignment for this chapter is an example of such a *constant-current* coulometric titration.

The end point of a coulometric titration can be determined by means similar to those used for volumetric titrations. It can be detected by chemical indicators, by *potentiometric methods*, in which the change in potential between two additional electrodes is measured during the titration, or by *amperometric methods*, which entail observation of the change in a small electric current established by applying a constant potential to a set of two auxiliary electrodes. Colorimetric and other methods for the observation of the end point also exist.

Coulometric methods have a number of unique advantages: (1) No standard solutions have to be prepared, since the reagent used is quantitatively generated by electrolysis within the titration cell. (2) Unstable reagents as well as stable ones can be used, since they are generated at the site of reaction. (3) There is no dilution during the titration. (4) Before the sample to be titrated is added, the generating solution may be "pretitrated" to the same end point as that of the actual titration. This eliminates any blank correction as well as errors that might be caused by reducing (or oxidizing) impurities in the generating solution. (5) Very small quantities can be determined with a relatively high accuracy, because it is possible to measure small amounts of electricity. For example, at the conditions prevailing in the laboratory assignment, 2 sec of generating time is equivalent to approximately 0.01 ml of a 0.01 F solution of I_2. (6) The method lends itself well to electronic automation as well as to operation by remote control for the handling of dangerous or radioactive substances.

As an example of the constant-current method, the coulometric titration of As(III) with I_2 will be discussed in detail.

COULOMETRIC DETERMINATION OF As(III)

In the analysis to be described a solution containing an unknown quantity of As(III) is mixed with a solution containing iodide. The iodide is oxidized to iodine at the anode, and the iodine in turn quantitatively oxidizes the As(III) to As(V).

Elementary iodine (I_2) is not very soluble in water and has an appreciable vapor pressure of 0.31 mm above a saturated ($1.34 \times 10^{-3} M$) solution at 25°C. Stable aqueous solutions of iodine are, however, possible when iodide is present also, owing to the formation of I_3^-, or tri-iodide ions,

$$I_2 + I^- = I_3^- \qquad K_1 = 7.1 \times 10^2 \qquad (13\text{-}1)$$

Tri-iodide solutions act in many respects like solutions of I_2 of the same molar concentration.

The sequence of reactions during the coulometric titration is the following:

Iodine or tri-iodide ion is generated at the anode from a KI solution that has been mixed with a solution of the sample containing As(III),

$$2I^- = I_2 + 2e^- \quad \text{or} \quad 3I^- = I_3^- + 2e^- \qquad (13\text{-}2)$$

The tri-iodide ions react quantitatively with the arsenious acid to be determined,

$$H_2O + I_3^- + H_3AsO_3 = H_2AsO_4^- + 3I^- + 3H^+$$

$$K_3 = 3.1 \times 10^{-4} \qquad (13\text{-}3)$$

[The As(V) exists mainly as a mixture of $H_2AsO_4^-$ and $HAsO_4^=$ under the optimal pH conditions to be discussed later, whereas H_3AsO_3 remains practically undissociated.] Once the As(III) is practically all oxidized, the tri-iodide ion concentration in the solution starts building up. This is conveniently observed by having present as indicator a suspension of starch, which forms an intense blue color with tri-iodide ions. For example, if the solution is about 10^{-5} F in iodine and at least 4×10^{-5} F in iodide, an easily visible blue color results. Iodine concentrations as low as 2×10^{-7} F have been detected by this reaction. The starch indicator is discussed further on page 338.

The cathode reaction is the evolution of hydrogen,

$$2H_2O + 2e^- = H_2 + 2OH^-$$

so that the over-all cell reaction is

$$H_2O + H_3AsO_3 = H_2 + H_2AsO_4^- + H^+$$

Any direct anodic oxidation of As(III) will not cause an error in the procedure.

The stoichiometric relations are the following:

$$\text{number of coulombs} = \int_0^t I \, dt = It = [\text{equivalents of As(III)}] \, \mathscr{F}$$

where I is the current, t is the titration time, and $\mathscr{F} = 96{,}500$ coulombs is the faraday.

The titration time t is measured by an electric clock that is switched on and off by the same switch that controls the current generating the iodine. The current I is measured by comparing its voltage drop (equal to IR) across a standard resistance R with a standard voltage and then so adjusting the current that the two voltages are equal. The standard voltage E_B is obtained from a mercury battery. From the known values of E_B and R the value of $I = E_B/R$ can be calculated. Alternatively, the voltage across the standard resistance can be measured by a precision voltmeter. The first method is preferred because of its more fundamental nature and its greater precision.

Buffering requirements. The conditions under which the procedure is expected to be quantitative will be discussed next. The mass-action expression for reaction (13-3) can be rewritten in the form

$$\frac{[H_2AsO_4^-][I^-]^3}{[H_3AsO_3][I_3^-]} = \frac{3.1 \times 10^{-4}}{[H^+]^3} \tag{13-4}$$

Inspection of (13-4) makes it apparent that this reaction can be forced either way by a change of the H^+-ion concentration. A detailed analysis, to be presented later, of Equation (13-4) and of the equilibria describing the dissociation of H_3AsO_4 shows that the reaction proceeds quantitatively in favor of As(V), provided that pH $\gtrsim$ 4.2 [Eq. (13-9)].

However, the pH may not be too alkaline, either, since in an alkaline solution I_3^- reacts with water to form I^- and HIO (hypoiodous acid),

$$I_3^- + H_2O = H^+ + HIO + 2I^- \qquad K_5 = 1.3 \times 10^{-12} \tag{13-5}$$

Clearly, this reaction must not be permitted to occur to any significant extent, because it delays the build-up of the I_3^- concentration needed for the iodine-starch end point. Since H^+ ions are involved in the reaction, equilibrium (13-5) can again be controlled by the pH. It will be shown in a later section that, as far as (13-5) and related equilibria are concerned, the titration will proceed quantitatively, provided that pH $\leqslant$ 7.9 [Eq. (13-13)].

It is important to realize that, in any discussion of pH limits that is based on mass-action equations, the assumption is made that all equilibria involved are actually attained. There is, however, no assurance that this is the case, and an experimental investigation is required in each new case to establish whether or not the predictions based on equilibrium considerations are valid in practice. For the present example it has been found that at a pH lower than 7 the reduction of iodine by arsenious acid becomes too slow to be acceptable and that the coulometric method yields excellent results at a pH between 7 and 9.

Detailed discussion of the pH requirements. The important equilibria affected by the pH are (13-3), the dissociation equilibria of H_3AsO_3 and H_3AsO_4, and some equilibria involving the tri-iodide ion.

As already intimated, the minimum pH is determined by the necessity of having the right side of the equilibrium (13-3) favored. There is the complication that As(V) exists not only in the form of $H_2AsO_4^-$ but also as other species related to it by the dissociation equilibria of H_3AsO_4, whose dissociation constants are as follows:

$$H_3AsO_4: \quad K_{a1} = 5.6 \times 10^{-3} \qquad K_{a2} = 1.7 \times 10^{-7} \qquad K_{a3} = 3 \times 10^{-12} \tag{13-6}$$

Coulometric analysis

The concentrations of H_3AsO_4 and its ions can be expressed in terms of $[H_2AsO_4^-]$ by the use of these constants, so that we obtain the following connection between $[H_2AsO_4^-]$ and $[As(V)]$, the total concentration of As(V):

$$[As(V)] \equiv [H_3AsO_4] + [H_2AsO_4^-] + [HAsO_4^=] + [AsO_4^{3-}]$$
$$= [H_2AsO_4^-]g(H^+)$$

where

$$g(H^+) = [H^+]/K_{a1} + 1 + K_{a2}/[H^+] + K_{a2}K_{a3}/[H^+]^2 \tag{13-7}$$

On the other hand, H_3AsO_3 is a weak acid, the values of the first two dissociation constants being $K_1 = 6 \times 10^{-10}$ and $K_2 = 3 \times 10^{-14}$, whereas K_3 is too small to be measured directly. Its dissociation is insignificant in the pH range of interest here, so that essentially all As(III) is present in the form of H_3AsO_3.

Since we wish to know the ratio of the concentrations of As(V) and of As(III), we combine (13-7) with (13-4) and solve for this ratio.

$$[As(V)]/[As(III)] = [H_2AsO_4^-]g(H^+)/[H_3AsO_3]$$

$$= 3.1 \times 10^{-4}[I_3^-]g(H^+)/[I^-]^3[H^+]^3 = [I_3^-]/[I^-]^3 f(H^+)$$

with

$$f(H^+) = 5.5 \times 10^{-2}/[H^+]^2 + 3.1 \times 10^{-4}/[H^+]^3$$
$$+ 5.3 \times 10^{-11}/[H^+]^4 + 1.6 \times 10^{-22}/[H^+]^5 \tag{13-8}$$

One of the curves of Figure 13-2 shows the dependence of $\log f(H^+)$ on the pH. Suppose now that a theoretical accuracy of 0.001 per cent is desired to provide for a reasonable factor of safety. This requires that $[As(V)]/[As(III)] \gtrsim 10^5$. Under the conditions of the laboratory assignment, $[I^-] \approx 0.133$, and we shall assume that at the starch-iodine end point $[I_3^-] \approx 2 \times 10^{-7}$. These values can be combined with (13-8) and the appropriate curve in Figure 13-2. They lead to the condition $\log f(H^+) \gtrsim 9.07$, so that

$$pH \gtrsim 4.2 \tag{13-9}$$

On the àlkaline side the pH range is limited by reaction (13-5) as well as the related reactions,

$$HIO = H^+ + IO^- \qquad K_{10} = 3 \times 10^{-11} \tag{13-10}$$

and

$$3HIO = 2I^- + IO_3^- + 3H^+ \qquad K_{11} = 1.2 \times 10^{-29} \tag{13-11}$$

This last equation may be combined with (13-5) to give

$$3I_3^- + 3H_2O = 8I^- + 6H^+ + IO_3^- \qquad K_{12} = 2.6 \times 10^{-65} \tag{13-12}$$

Reaction (13-11) [or (13-12)] is an example of a so-called auto-oxidation (more completely, auto-oxidation-reduction), or disproportionation, in which some of the HIO is oxidized and an equivalent amount is reduced. Reaction (13-5) is of this type also.

282

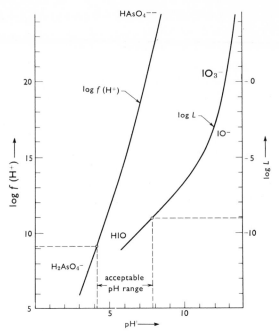

Figure 13-2 Dependence of log f (H$^+$) and of log L on pH. The ions listed along the curves indicate the species that are primarily involved, for the pH region given, in the equilibria discussed in the text.

In the solutions of interest here neither I$^-$ nor IO$_3^-$ ions are significantly converted to the acids, because the dissociation constant of HI is much larger than 1 and that of HIO$_3$ is 2×10^{-1}.

Let L be the total loss of I$_3^-$ ions by these reactions. It is given by

$$L \equiv [\text{HIO}] + [\text{IO}^-] + 3[\text{IO}_3^-]$$

and can be related to [I$_3^-$] by the appropriate mass-action constants,

$$L = \{K_5[\text{I}_3^-]/[\text{I}^-]^2[\text{H}^+]\}(1 + K_{10}/[\text{H}^+]) + 3K_{12}[\text{I}_3^-]^3/[\text{I}^-]^8[\text{H}^+]^6$$

Inserting numerical values for the constants and assuming the same values for [I$_3^-$] and [I$^-$] as above, the following dependence of L on [H$^+$] is obtained:

$$L = (1.47 \times 10^{-17}/[\text{H}^+]) + (4.41 \times 10^{-28}/[\text{H}^+]^2) + (6.4 \times 10^{-78}/[\text{H}^+]^6)$$

The second curve of Figure 13-2 is a plot of log L versus pH. In the laboratory assignment the original concentration of H$_3$AsO$_3$ is about 8×10^{-5} F. If again a theoretical error of not more than 0.001 per cent is sought, the condition $L \leq 8 \times 10^{-10}$ must be met, since there is a one-to-one correspondence between

283

H_3AsO_3 and $I_3{}^-$. From the appropriate curve in Figure 13-2 it is seen that this corresponds to

$$pH \lesssim 7.9 \tag{13-13}$$

As was pointed out earlier, these pH values are based on equilibrium considerations. It must be determined experimentally whether or not these equilibria are established with sufficient speed to make the procedure satisfactory. Such experiments show that the optimum pH value is in the neighborhood of 8.

Equilibrium considerations such as the ones given are of value because they indicate what is possible if the rates are fast enough. It may always prove possible to find catalysts that speed up slow reactions, or to achieve speed-up by a change in temperature. It is, however, impossible to shift an equilibrium by catalysts alone, so that equilibrium considerations establish under what conditions chemical reactions *may* proceed and under what conditions they *will not*, catalysts or no catalysts.

COULOMETRIC EQUIPMENT

Figure 13-3 is a circuit diagram of an apparatus for coulometric titrations. The direct current is provided by a constant-voltage power supply. It is passed through several resistors whose functions are as follows:

R_1 has a resistance that is very large compared with the resistance of the titration cell; thus small changes in the cell resistance during a titration will not cause a significant change in the total resistance and therefore in the current. R_2 is a variable resistor used to adjust the current exactly to the value desired. R_3 is a wire-wound precision resistor, 100.00 ohms; the voltage drop across this resistor is used to measure the current flowing in the circuit. R_4 is a dummy resistor, approximately of the same resistance as that of the coulometric cell. It is used when not generating I_2 to maintain a current flow in the circuit and thus keep the electrical components at a uniform operating temperature.

The meter M, battery B, and switch S_3 form the auxiliary circuit used to measure the current flowing in the generating circuit. In general, the voltage drop IR_3 caused by the passage of the generating current I through the precision resistor R_3 will not be equal to the voltage E_B of the mercury battery B. Momentarily closing the push-button micro-switch S_3 causes the null meter M to register current flow in one or the other direction, depending on whether IR_3 is larger or smaller than E_B. (For one direction of this current, B acts as a battery; for the other, as an electrolysis cell.) By changing the variable resistor R_2, the current may be adjusted until IR_3 is exactly equal to E_B; when that is true, the

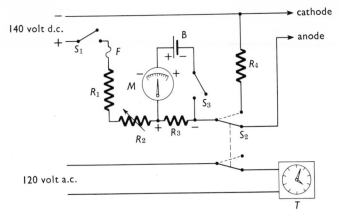

140 volt d.c.

120 volt a.c.

Figure 13-3   Circuit diagram of the coulometric apparatus. B, mercury battery, approximately 1.36 volt; F, $\frac{1}{8}$-amp 125-volt delayed fuse; M, null meter, e.g., d-c microammeter, zero-center type, range -100 to $+100$ or -500 to $+500$ μa; R_1, 10,000-ohm current-limiting resistor; R_2, variable resistor, 0–1000 ohms, for adjustment of generating current until current through null meter M is zero; R_3, wire-wound precision resistor of 100.00 ohms, accurate to 0.05 per cent, for measurement of IR drop by comparison with voltage of mercury battery B; R_4, 300-ohm dummy resistor; S_1, single-pole single-throw main power switch; S_2, double-pole double-throw generator switch shown in generating position (other position replaces coulometric cell by dummy resistor R_4 and stops timer T); S_3, push-button microswitch to permit check of generating current: and T, timer, 10 sec/revolution, total of 1000 sec.

meter will show no deflection when switch S_3 is closed. At that point

$$I = E_B/R_3$$

The null-meter reading is checked frequently during the coulometric titration, and R_2 is readjusted, if necessary, to keep the meter reading at zero and maintain the current at the original value.

    The electrode reactions of the mercury battery will be discussed in the next chapter. This battery is noted for maintaining constant voltage even during moderate current flow. Nevertheless, such current flow must be kept to a minimum and the null checks performed by operating the push button S_3 with reasonable dispatch. Testing at intervals of 30 to 45 sec is satisfactory. Any changes in the generating current are small and slow because of the constant voltage of the power supply and the large value of the resistor R_1. These changes are readily offset by adjusting R_2. The precise voltage E_B of the mercury battery is established by calibrating it with a standard cell using a potentiometer circuit, as discussed in the next section.

285

Coulometric analysis

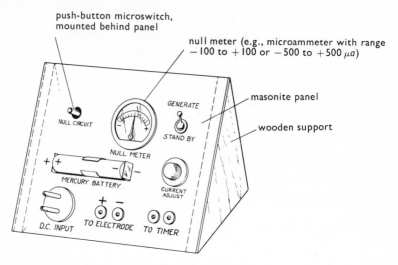

push-button microswitch,
mounted behind panel

null meter (e.g., microammeter with range
− 100 to + 100 or − 500 to + 500 μa)

GENERATE

masonite panel

NULL CIRCUIT

STAND BY

wooden support

NULL METER

+ +

−

MERCURY BATTERY

CURRENT
ADJUST

D.C. INPUT   TO ELECTRODE   TO TIMER

Figure 13-4   Control panel.

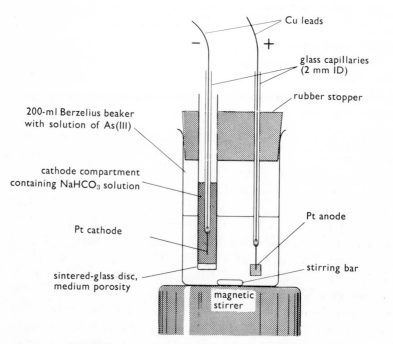

Cu leads

− +

glass capillaries
(2 mm ID)

rubber stopper

200-ml Berzelius beaker
with solution of As(III)

cathode compartment
containing NaHCO₃ solution

Pt anode

Pt cathode

sintered-glass disc,
medium porosity

stirring bar

magnetic
stirrer

Figure 13-5   Coulometric titration cell. (See page 408 for construction details of the
Pt electrodes.)

Figure 13-4 shows the control panel, and Figure 13-5 shows the coulometric titration cell. The anode consists of platinum foil of an area of about 3 cm^2. The cathode is a platinum wire placed inside a glass tube that is closed at the bottom by a disk of sintered glass to prevent any of the hydrogen evolved at the cathode from diffusing to the anode, where it would be oxidized and so give rise to errors. Both electrodes are carried by thin glass tubes, and the Pt is connected to copper leads with a drop of solder.

The two electrodes are immersed in the titration solution contained in a tall 200-ml beaker known as a Berzelius beaker. The cathode compartment has to be filled with a solution of $NaHCO_3$ prior to this immersion. The inside level of this solution should always be above the level of the surrounding liquid so that none of the As(III) can enter the cathode compartment and escape reaction. If the level in the cathode compartment is less than about 0.5 to 1 cm above the outside level, fresh $NaHCO_3$ solution should be added. Efficient agitation during the titration is achieved by magnetic stirring.

The equipment described, and shown assembled in Figure 13-6, has been constructed as simply as possible and should be capable of an accuracy of the order of 0.2 per cent. With some refinements the same equipment can be used for coulometric measurements of microgram quantities, with an accuracy of 0.1 per cent or better.

The slide-wire potentiometer. The voltage of the mercury cell is determined by comparing it with that of a standard cell of known voltage by means of a slide-wire potentiometer. The principles underlying this important instrument are as follows (Fig. 13-7).

The potentiometer has two internal voltage sources, the standard cell *St* and the working battery *W* that usually consists of several dry cells or of a storage battery. Standard cells are easily damaged by current flow, and the very precise voltage that is characteristic of a given cell exists only at zero current. The source *X* of unknown voltage is therefore not compared directly with the standard cell, but is instead compared with the voltage that is impressed onto a slide wire *ACB* of uniform resistance by the working battery *W*. The location *C* of the slide contact is indicated by a pointer on a uniformly graduated scale. The scale reading is thus proportional to the resistance R_{AC} between points *A* and *C*. It is also proportional to the voltage E_{AC} between *A* and *C*, because

$$E_{AC} = E_W \times R_{AC}/(R_{AB} + R)$$

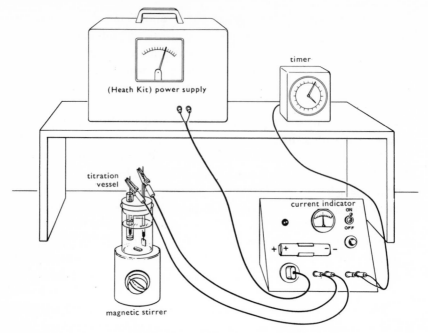

Figure 13-6   Coulometric equipment.

where E_W is the voltage of the working battery, R_{AB} is the resistance of the entire slide wire, and R is a variable resistor.

The slide-wire scale is divided into a convenient number of units, for example, 2000, and it is desirable to adjust R in such a way that the scale divisions correspond to millivolts (mv) for the voltage E_{AC}, whatever the location of C. To this end the contact C is adjusted to the scale mark that numerically equals the standard-cell voltage. This voltage is usually indicated on the cell. It is commonly between 1.0184 and 1.0194 volt for the unsaturated Weston cell. The standard cell is put into the circuit by means of switch S and the circuit is closed momentarily by tapping the key K while observing the galvanometer. The resistor R is adjusted until the needle deflection observed while tapping the key has vanished. Great care must be taken that only the minute currents necessary for a momentary needle deflection flow through the standard cell. Note the similarity between the potentiometer circuit and the null circuit used to adjust the titration current.

Once the voltage E_{AC} is adjusted to be equal to the scale reading at C all other scale markings indicate correct voltage also, because of the uniformity of the slide wire and the scale.

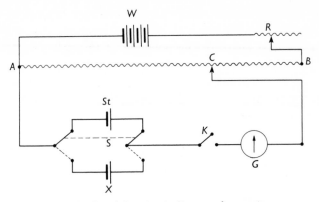

Figure 13-7 Simplified circuit diagram of potentiometer

ACB slide wire of uniform resistance (resistance proportional to length), with slide contact at C
G null meter, usually a galvanometer
K tapping key
R variable resistor
S double-pole double-throw switch
St standard cell
W "working" battery
X unknown potential

By changing the switch S to its other position, the unknown voltage source X is now introduced into the circuit. This time it is the position of the slide contact C that is changed until tapping of the key produces no galvanometer deflection. The unknown voltage is equal to the scale reading at this point.

In practice potentiometers are more elaborate, but the principles of operation remain unchanged. For example, there usually are additional resistors in series with the slide wire that can be switched in or out to make the adjustment of contact C easier. There are often two tapping keys, one with a large resistance in series to protect the standard cell during the initial rough adjustment of the resistor R. An additional precision resistor that is automatically switched into the circuit to replace the slide wire ACB at the time the standard cell is connected to the circuit is sometimes provided. This resistor is permanently adjusted to correspond to the exact voltage of the standard cell; it permits adjustment of the resistor R irrespective of the position of the slide contact C. For careful work the adjustment of R must be checked often, and the arrangement described obviates the tedious resetting of contact C to the standard-cell voltage each time.

The standard cell commonly used in ordinary laboratory work is the unsaturated Weston cell with electrode reactions that will be discussed in the next chapter. The potential of this cell is highly reproducible, remains constant over a long period of time, and has only a small temperature coefficient (-0.01 mv/°C near 20°C). However, any moderate current drain will cause concentration changes in the electrode compartments that will affect the cell potential. Thus, the tapping key should never be depressed for more than an instant.

The potentiometer circuit described is very fundamental because it permits the precise measurement of voltages without drawing a current at the actual time of measurement. A secondary application is the precise measurement of currents by determining the voltage drop associated with their passage through a known resistance. In many applications the slide-wire potentiometer has been replaced by the vacuum-tube voltmeter. However, even though its input resistance is very large, the vacuum-tube voltmeter still draws a small current. The slide-wire potentiometer requires no current flow and therefore has an input resistance approaching infinity. The accuracy afforded by potentiometers used in ordinary laboratory work is about 0.3 mv.

*The quantity of As(III) in a sample
is to be determined by measuring
the amperage and the total time
during which a current electrolytically generates
elementary iodine, which in turn
oxidizes As(III) to As(V). The end point
is recognized by the formation of
a starch-iodine complex of intense blue color
due to the combination of excess iodine
with starch present as indicator.*

*Laboratory assignment 13
(3 periods)*

COULOMETRIC DETERMINATION

OF ARSENIC

DISCUSSION

The As(III) in the original sample is in the form of As_2O_3, which is the anhydride of arsenious acid,

$$As_2O_3 + 3H_2O = 2H_3AsO_3$$

This reaction is very slow. It is speeded up greatly in an alkaline medium, and the procedures call for dissolving of the arsenious oxide in 1 F NaOH and for subsequent acidification with 0.5 F H_2SO_4. Alkaline solutions of As(III) are slowly oxidized by air, whereas neutral or acid solutions are quite stable.

To provide for a reasonably constant pH during the electrolysis, a 1 F NaHCO$_3$ solution is added to the As(III) solution to be titrated; the latter contains a small excess of H$_2$SO$_4$ to begin with. This acid, as well as the H$^+$ produced during the electrolysis, will change part of the HCO$_3^-$ present to H$_2$CO$_3$, of a concentration which cannot exceed about 3.4 × 10^{-2} mole/liter, the solubility of CO$_2$ at 20°C and 1 atm. The original concentration of NaHCO$_3$ is such that [HCO$_3^-$] remains considerably larger than [H$_2$CO$_3$] during the titration. Since the first dissociation constant of H$_2$CO$_3$ is 4.4 × 10^{-7}, the pH of the solution will thus be buffered in the neighborhood of 7 to 8.

The 1 F NaHCO$_3$ solution is also 1 F in KI to provide the iodide ions needed in the titration. It further contains a very small amount of As(III) to reduce any I$^-$ which might have become oxidized by air. It is necessary to perform blank runs on this *generating solution* in order to correct for the presence of the As(III).

The starch-indicator suspension contains a preservative to minimize bacterial action, which otherwise would decompose it in a few days. The decomposition products form reddish rather than blue addition products with iodine. The suspension should be discarded if it is found to react in this fashion.

PROCEDURES

13-1 Solution of the sample containing As(III). It is desirable to use small quantities of sample in the coulometric titrations. Rather than weighing out the small amounts needed directly, 20 times the amount desired is weighed out and dissolved, and *aliquots* (i.e., known portions) of one-twentieth are used in the titration. Note, however, that as long as only one sample is weighed out the accuracy may be low even when the precision turns out to be high.

Review the procedure for drying samples and weighing out by difference (page 82) and that for preparing a solution of accurate volume (page 141). Dry for 1 hr at 110°C* an amount of unknown that contains about 1 meq of As$_2$O$_3$ (about 0.8 g for a sample containing 6 weight per cent As$_2$O$_3$). Dissolve an accurately weighed quantity of this magnitude in the 500-ml volumetric flask, using 50 ml of 1 F NaOH. Particles of sample adhering to the upper part of the flask should be dissolved by carefully tipping the flask so that they are reached by the

* This temperature should not be greatly exceeded, because As$_2$O$_3$ (consisting of As$_4$O$_6$ molecules) tends to sublime.

NaOH solution. When all the substance appears to be in solution, carefully inspect to see that no tiny, undissolved particles of As_2O_3 remain. Add 300 ml of distilled water and 10 ml of 3 F H_2SO_4 and mix. Check to be sure the solution is acidic, and dilute to the mark. Do not wait overnight to add the acid, because air oxidation of As(III) in alkaline solution is relatively rapid.

13-2 Standardization of mercury battery. The mercury battery used in the coulometric experiment must be calibrated at the beginning of each period during which it is used. The calibration should be checked at the end of the period and should be within 1 mv of the original value. Follow the directions provided with the student potentiometer in the laboratory. Be sure the mercury battery is inserted with the proper polarity. Its voltage should be close to 1.35 volts. The battery should be discarded if the voltage is below 1.33 volts. Never hold down the tapping key of the potentiometer for more than an instant. Your final results depend upon the voltage of the standard cell remaining constant.

13-3 Blank titration of the KI solution. Ascertain that the switch S_2 is in the standby position, and turn on the power switch S_1. Before the actual titration is started, the power switch S_1 should have been on for at least 10 min. In general this switch should be left on at all times to keep the pertinent electrical components at operating temperatures.

Insert the calibrated mercury battery into the battery holder on the control panel and change the current adjust resistor R_2 until there is no meter deflection upon temporary closing of the pushbutton switch S_3. Do not let a current larger than about 0.1 ma flow through the battery.

Place the magnetic stirring bar in a tall 200-ml beaker, and add 10.00 ml of potassium iodide–sodium bicarbonate solution, 5 ml of starch solution, and 60 ml of distilled water. Rinse the electrodes thoroughly with distilled water, fill the cathode compartment with 0.2 F $NaHCO_3$ solution, and carefully insert the rubber stopper supporting the electrodes into the beaker. Take care that the electrode leads stay separated.

Check the standby current by closing the null-circuit switch S_3 for a moment, and readjust for zero meter reading if required. The current is approximately 14 ma, because the voltage of the mercury battery is about 1.35 volts and R_3 is 100.00 ohm.

When a steady current has been attained with the switch S_2 in the standby position, start the magnetic stirrer, zero the timer, and switch S_2 to the "generate" position. This also closes the timer circuit so that the time of iodine generation is recorded automatically. Immediately check the generating current for zero meter deflection and readjust the resistor R_2 if necessary.

Titrate until the blue-violet color that appears in the immediate vicinity of the anode begins to diffuse through the solution. Continue by generating small amounts of iodine, letting the current pass through the cell for periods of a few seconds or less. This corresponds to adding fractions of drops of standard solution in a volumetric titration. Continue until a pale blue-violet color persists throughout the solution for at least 30 sec.

Record the time, and either repeat the blank titration or continue with Procedure 13-4. Two consecutive blank runs should agree within about 0.5 to 1 sec. Check to see that S_2 is left in the standby position between runs.

13-4 Titrations of the As(III) solution. The following two alternatives exist: Either add 25.00 ml of the sample solution to the solution on which a blank run or a previous titration has just been completed or start fresh, adding to the titration vessel 35 ml of distilled water, 5 ml of starch solution, 10.00 ml of the potassium iodide–sodium bicarbonate solution, and 25.00 ml of the solution of the sample.

In either case, titrate as described under Procedure 13-3, checking the generating current at 30- to 45-sec intervals throughout the titration to ensure constancy of the current. However, do not get caught by the appearance of the end point while checking for a null-meter reading. Keep an eye on the titration beaker at all times. With a current of about 14 ma, 1 meq As_2O_3 in the original sample should take about 360 sec. Repeat the titration for a total of at least three 25.00-ml aliquots.

The starch-iodine complex may become adsorbed on the electrodes. As a precaution, it may be advisable to clean the electrodes with HCl before proceeding.

Since the entire determination depends on the weighing and complete dissolving of just one sample, it is advisable to repeat the procedure with a second sample.

13-5 Computation of results. The precision resistor R_3 has a size of 100.00 ohm, so that the generating current is $[E_B(mv)/100.00]$ ma. Compute the percentages of As_2O_3 of the original sample corresponding to the three or more titrations, making appropriate blank corrections. Compute the average of these values and the unbiased relative and absolute standard deviations (see page 83).

PROBLEMS

13-1 Normality of solutions. Consider separate solutions that are 0.200 F in the reagents shown in boldface type in the (unbalanced) reaction equations given below. What are the normalities of these solutions?

$$\textbf{K}_2\textbf{Cr}_2\textbf{O}_7 + Fe^{++} = Cr^{3+} + Fe^{3+}$$

$$\textbf{K}_2\textbf{Cr}_2\textbf{O}_7 + \textbf{BaCl}_2 = BaCrO_4 \;(s)$$

$$\textbf{H}_2\textbf{O}_2 + \textbf{KI} = I_3^- + H_2O$$

$$\textbf{KIO}_3 + \textbf{KI} + KCl = ICl$$

$$\textbf{CuSO}_4 + \textbf{KI} = CuI + I_2$$

$$\textbf{Na}_2\textbf{SO}_3 + \textbf{KMnO}_4 + H^+ = SO_4^= + Mn^{++}$$

13-2 Coulometry. The coulometric method was used to determine the quantity of As_2O_3 in a sample by oxidizing the As(III) in a solution of the sample with electrically generated iodine. The end point was reached in 557 sec and the current was measured by noting that it caused a voltage drop of 1.347 volts across a resistor of 100.0 ohms. How much As_2O_3 was contained in the sample?

13-3 Polarity of a current source. The polarity of a source of direct current may be found by the following test: The two wires coming from the source are connected by a piece of filter paper that has been moistened with KI solution containing soluble starch. It is found that a blue spot develops around one of the wires. (*a*) Explain this chemically. (*b*) Is the wire causing the blue spot positive or negative, and is the wire the anode or the cathode in the reaction considered?

13-4 Faraday's law. An electric current passes through a cell that is equipped with Pt electrodes and contains a solution of $CuCl_2$. The cathode reaction is deposition of Cu, whereas at the anode O_2 and Cl_2 are liberated. How many grams of Cu are deposited if 120 ml Cl_2 and 67 ml O_2 are evolved (measured at STP)?

13-5 Electrolysis. An electrolytic cell has separate anode and cathode compartments that are connected by a narrow tube filled with electrolyte. Each compartment contains originally 500 ml of a 0.100 F Na_2SO_4 solution. Both electrodes are made of Pt, and H_2 is evolved at the cathode, O_2 at the anode. A current of 75 ma flows for 20.0 min. How much O_2 at STP is produced? How many milliliters of 0.1 F HCl are needed to neutralize one of the electrode compartments? (Under the conditions of the problem practically the entire current through the cell is carried by Na^+ and $SO_4^=$ ions; H^+ and OH^- ions contribute less than 0.1 per cent.)

13-6 Electrolysis. Brass is an alloy of Cu and Zn that usually contains impurities such as Pb. A solution made by dissolving brass in HNO_3 was electrolyzed. The Cu was plated out on the cathode, and the Pb was deposited in the form of PbO_2 on the anode. Zn and impurities other than Pb stayed in solution. After completion of the electrolysis the cathode was found to have increased its weight by 0.263 g, the anode by 0.031 g. Assuming that no gas evolved at the cathode, how much gas at standard temperature and pressure must have evolved at the anode?

13-7 Electrolysis. In the electrolysis of a 50 per cent solution of H_2SO_4 2060 ml of H_2 are formed at the cathode and 537 ml of O_2 at the anode, both at 0°C and 1 atm. The only other product of the electrolysis is peroxydisulfuric acid, $H_2S_2O_8$. How many grams of $H_2S_2O_8$ are formed?

13-8 Conductance by electrolytes. An electrolytic cell with Pt electrodes was filled with 0.1 F NaCl solution and 20 volts of high-frequency alternating current was applied to the electrodes. Each pole changed its role as anode and cathode in quick succession so that no actual electrolysis occurred and the entire voltage was used to overcome the electrical resistance of the electrolyte. The experiment was repeated with 0.1 F Na_2SO_4 and 0.1 F K_2SO_4 and the following values of the current were observed: 1.087 amp (NaCl), 1.969 amp (K_2SO_4), 1.549 amp (Na_2SO_4). What current would you expect for a 0.1 F solution of KCl?

REVIEW QUESTIONS

13-1. Briefly explain the following terms: reduction, cathode, positive pole, faraday, current efficiency, constant-current titration, controlled-potential titration, generating solution.

13-2. Briefly state the rules for assigning oxidation numbers. What is the one rule that no system of oxidation numbers must violate?

13-3. Sketch and briefly explain the function of the potentiometer circuit.

13-4. Sketch and briefly explain the circuit used in the coulometric titration of the laboratory assignment.

13-5. The recommended procedure for obtaining a solution of H_3AsO_3 from As_2O_3 is to dissolve the arsenious oxide first in dilute NaOH and to acidify when solution is complete. Why is the As_2O_3 not dissolved directly in dilute acid? Why is it desirable to have an acid solution of As(III)?

13-6. Write balanced equations for the reactions, including the end-point reaction, in the coulometric titration of the laboratory assignment.

13-7. Briefly indicate why the pH of the solution containing As(III) in the coulometric titration must not vary greatly from the recommended value of 8 (*a*) toward a more acid solution; (*b*) toward a more alkaline solution.

13-8. What precautions are necessary in the preparation of solutions containing As(III), considering that As(III) is a reducing agent?

13-9. Why does the generating potassium iodide solution contain $NaHCO_3$? Why small amounts of As(III)?

13-10. Briefly discuss the effect of the following supposed deviations from the recommended procedures of the laboratory assignment. (*a*) The pH was too acid; (*b*) the pH was too alkaline; (*c*) the number of equivalents of KI present in the solution being titrated exceeded that of As(III); (*d*) this solution contained Cl^- ions in addition to I^- ions; (*e*) the dissolving of the As(III) sample in dilute NaOH was accelerated by vigorous shaking; (*f*) the generating solution had become depleted in As(III) and had assumed a slight yellowish tinge.

REFERENCES

J. J. Lingane, *Electroanalytical Chemistry*, 2nd ed, Interscience, New York, 1958.

W. J. Ramsey, P. S. Farrington, and E. S. Swift. "Coulometric titrations with iodine," *Anal. Chem.*, **22**, 332–335 (1950).

C. N. Reilly, "Coulometric titrations," *J. Chem. Educ.*, **31**, 543–545 (1954).

*A discussion of half-cell potentials
and their connection with the electromotive
force of cells and the mass-action constants
of cell reactions is followed
by an exposition of redox titrations,
the titration of Fe^{++} with $Cr_2O_7^=$
being used as an example. An account of
the reactions of a potential indicator,
diphenylamine sulfonate, is given. This indicator
is used in a laboratory assignment in which
iron is determined by titration with dichromate.
Instructions for a potentiometric titration
are also given.*

fourteen

REDOX

TITRATIONS

ELECTROMOTIVE FORCE OF GALVANIC CELLS AND HALF-CELL POTENTIALS

When a strip of Cu metal is placed in a beaker containing a solution with Cu^{++} ions, the half-reaction

$$Cu^{++} + 2e^- = Cu(s) \tag{14-1}$$

or its reverse, depending on the concentration of the Cu^{++} ions, takes place to a minute extent. The electrons liberated or used up generate a negative or positive electrical potential on the metal relative to the solution, which prevents continuation of the reaction.

Similarly, when a strip of Ag metal is immersed in a solution containing Ag^+ ions, the half-reaction

$$Ag^+ + e^- = Ag(s) \qquad (14\text{-}2)$$

or its reverse occurs to a minute extent and develops an electrical potential on the metal relative to the solution, which stops the reaction.

An idea of how small the extent of such reactions is may be gathered from the following example of the enormous electrical potential caused by free charges of the order of 1 faraday: One faraday of electricity placed at the center of the earth would lead to a potential of over 100 million volts at the earth surface; the same potential would result if the same electrical charge were distributed uniformly over the surface of the earth. A free charge of about 10^{-17} mole of electrons causes a potential of 1 volt at 1 cm distance.

There is no known way to measure potentials of metal electrodes relative to solutions, since the introduction of a second electrode into the solution needed to complete the electrical circuit creates another metal-to-solution potential. However, the existence of these potentials may be established by connecting the strips of Cu and Ag by a wire and the two solutions by a liquid junction (Fig. 14-1). A current begins to flow, its direction depending on the concentrations of the Ag^+ ions and Cu^{++} ions in the two solutions. If both concentrations are in the

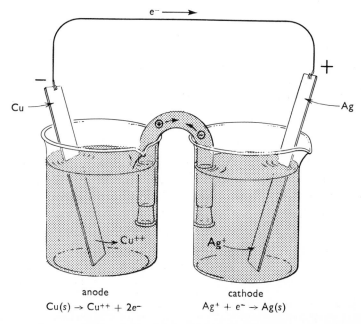

anode   cathode

$Cu(s) \rightarrow Cu^{++} + 2e^-$ $Ag^+ + e^- \rightarrow Ag(s)$

Figure 14-1   Combining two half-cells.

neighborhood of 1 M, Ag^+ ions plate out on the Ag electrode and the Cu electrode dissolves. Electrons flow through the wire from the Cu to the Ag, and the same current passes through the solution by the migration of positive and negative ions. This arrangement is an example of a galvanic cell.

The liquid junction usually consists of an inverted U tube filled with the solution of a salt, such as saturated NH_4NO_3 solution. This impedes mutual contamination of the solutions in the two beakers but provides for ionic conduction. The electrical potential between the two electrodes is used in part to overcome the electrical resistance offered by the solution to the flow of current.* It may decrease further during the flow of current, because of the depletion of Ag^+ ions in the neighborhood of the Ag electrode, the accumulation of Cu^{++} ions near the Cu electrode, or other transitory changes. The potential that establishes itself between the two electrodes in the absence of current flow is called the *electromotive force* (emf) of the cell. It represents an equilibrium situation and depends on the electrode material and the concentrations in the solutions, as will be discussed later. The cell emf must be measured with a voltmeter of high internal resistance so that there is virtually no current flow. Suitable for this purpose is the potentiometer discussed earlier, or a vacuum-tube voltmeter such as is used in a pH meter.

The advantage of using a solution of NH_4NO_3 rather than of another salt in the inverted U tube is that NH_4^+ and NO_3^- ions move at approximately the same speed in an electric field, although in opposite directions. This reduces the so-called liquid-junction potential caused by the difference in concentrations at the liquid-liquid interfaces to a very small value, so that its contribution to the total cell emf is negligible except in measurements of the highest accuracy. A saturated solution of KCl is also frequently used for the same reason, but the presence of Cl^- ions would interfere in the present situation by the precipitation of AgCl.

The beaker with the strip of Cu(s) immersed in the solution with Cu^{++} ions is called a *half-cell*; its over-all reaction is represented by the half-reaction (14-1). Similarly, the beaker with the strip of Ag(s) in contact with Ag^+ ions is a half-cell with the half-reaction (14-2). Half-cells are generally arrangements of liquid, solid, and sometimes gaseous phases, with an electrical connection, that represent, ideally, *one half-reaction*. In practice, the restriction to one half-reaction may not be possible; for example, the $Cu^{++}/Cu(s)$ half-cell just described contains,

---

* If this "internal resistance" is R_{int}, a potential IR_{int} is required to drive a current I through the cell and thus must be subtracted from the potential available at the terminals of a battery in the absence of current flow.

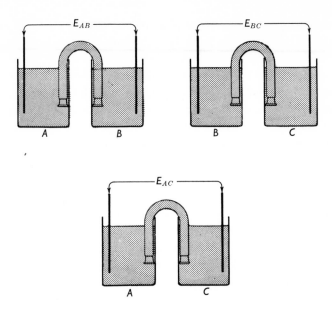

Figure 14-2   Addition of cell emf's.

at equilibrium, Cu^+ ions in very small concentrations and thus also involves the half-reaction $Cu^+ + e^- = Cu(s)$ and the related half-reaction $Cu^{++} + e^- = Cu^+$. Any two half-cells may be combined by a liquid junction into an *electrochemical cell*. If the electrons are permitted to proceed in the direction of spontaneous flow through an external electrical connection between the electrodes, such as in the arrangement of Figure 14-1, we shall speak of a *galvanic cell*. If there is an external voltage source that drives the electrons in the opposite direction, we shall speak of an *electrolytic cell*.

Electrode potentials.   The emf values of cells constructed by combining half-cells in this way have the following additive property: When three different half-cells A, B, and C are connected in the three possible ways into cells that will be called AB, BC, and AC, the resulting emf values are related by the equation (see Fig. 14-2)

$$E_{AC} = E_{AB} + E_{BC}$$

This makes it possible to assign to the three half-cells the three *electrode potentials* E_A, E_B, and E_C so that

$$E_{AB} = E_B - E_A$$

$$E_{BC} = E_C - E_B$$

$$E_{AC} = E_C - E_A$$

An arbitrary additive constant remains; it may be fixed by assigning the potential of zero volts to a standard reference half-cell, much as in choosing the ice point as the zero point of the centigrade temperature scale. By international agreement the standard hydrogen half-cell described below has been selected for this purpose. An electrode potential is thus the emf that develops when the half-cell involved is combined with the standard hydrogen half-cell. If the electrode considered is electrically negative relative to the standard hydrogen half-cell, its electrode potential will be given a minus sign; otherwise, a plus sign. (This sign convention is not universally adopted; it will be discussed further on page 316.) When any two half-cells are combined, the emf of the resulting cell is the difference between these electrode potentials, and the arbitrary choice of the potential zero has, of course, no effect on the emf thus found.

A parallel situation exists in acid-base dissociations, where no way is known to determine the mass-action constant for the reaction

$$\text{acid} = \text{base} + \text{proton}$$

The ratio of this constant to that of the reaction

$$H_3O^+ = H_2O + \text{proton}$$

is all that may be measured and constitutes the acid constant K_a of the acid considered.

The hydrogen half-cell represents the half-cell reaction

$$2H^+ + 2e^- = H_2(g) \tag{14-3}$$

Since hydrogen gas does not conduct electricity, a way to transfer electrons to it is needed. One way that has been found is to bubble the gas over a platinum electrode (Fig. 14-3) coated by a special process with finely divided platinum (called platinum black) and surrounded by a solution containing H^+ ions. (The design shown is one of the classical forms of the hydrogen electrode (J. H. Hildebrand). For high accuracy a more elaborate construction is required.) The Pt acts as catalyst for the reaction between H^+ ions and H_2 molecules and acquires a potential characteristic of reaction (14-3). This potential depends on the H^+-ion concentration in the solution and the partial pressure of the

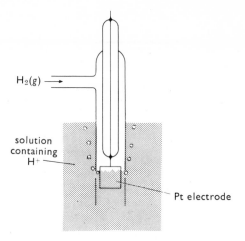

Figure 14-3   A hydrogen electrode.

H_2 gas. In the standard hydrogen half-cell or standard hydrogen electrode $[H^+]$ and p_{H_2} have their standard values, defined as $[H^+] = 1\ M$ and $p_{H_2} = 1$ atm. (More precisely, standard conditions refer to activities rather than concentrations.)

Other gas electrodes may be constructed along similar lines. Examples are the oxygen electrode with the half-reaction

$$4H^+ + O_2(g) + 4e^- = 2H_2O \qquad (14\text{-}4)$$

and the chlorine electrode with the half-reaction

$$Cl_2(g) + 2e^- = 2Cl^- \qquad (14\text{-}5)$$

In all half-cells discussed so far the concentration of the solution species that participate in the electrode reaction may be varied at will within a wide range. Such half-cells are called *half-cells* or *electrodes* of the *first kind*. (The term "electrode" is often applied not just to the metal part of the half-cell, but to the entire assembly; the latter is the case for the gas electrode just discussed.) In half-cells or electrodes of the *second kind* the concentration of the cations associated with the electrode metal is kept fixed through the common-ion effect by the presence of a salt of low solubility. An example of such an electrode is the AgCl/Ag half-cell, which consists of a silver wire in contact with AgCl(s) and a solution of a soluble chloride of a given concentration. The solution is saturated with silver chloride, and if any Ag^+ ions are reduced to Ag by the gain of electrons, they are replenished by the dissolving of AgCl(s), so that at all times $[Ag^+][Cl^-] = K_{SP}$. The dissolving of AgCl(s) also produces Cl^- ions, and the concurrent reactions may be described by the equations

$$Ag^+ + e^- = Ag(s)$$

$$AgCl(s) = Ag^+ + Cl^-$$

Inversely, if any Ag(s) is oxidized to Ag^+ by loss of electrons, AgCl(s) is precipitated to keep the product $[Ag^+][Cl^-]$ equal to K_{SP}. The half-reaction of this half-cell is thus most simply described as

$$AgCl(s) + e^- = Ag(s) + Cl^- \tag{14-6}$$

Another example of such an electrode is the calomel half-cell, in which liquid mercury (connected with the outside by a Pt wire) is in contact with solid calomel (Hg_2Cl_2) and a solution containing KCl of a given concentration. Its half-reaction is (l means liquid)

$$Hg_2Cl_2(s) + 2e^- = 2Hg(l) + 2Cl^- \tag{14-7}$$

The potentials of these two half-cells depend on the electrode material and on $[Cl^-]$.

Electrodes of this type behave well experimentally and furnish particularly reproducible potentials. They are often chosen as reference electrodes in preference to the standard hydrogen electrode, which is not convenient to use. Both half-cells mentioned are commonly used as part of the electrodes of a pH meter. The AgCl/Ag half-cell is used inside the glass electrode (Fig. 8-2a, page 169), and the calomel half-cell serves as reference electrode and is designed to include a KCl "salt bridge" (Fig. 8-2b).

Still other half-cells are those that represent couples in which both oxidized and reduced forms are ionic species in the solution. The electron transfer occurs at an inert electrode. An example is provided by a solution containing Fe^{++} and Fe^{3+} ions and a Au or a Pt electrode. The potential corresponds to the Fe^{3+}/Fe^{++} couple with the half-reaction:

$$Fe^{3+} + e^- = Fe^{++} \tag{14-8}$$

A platinum electrode immersed in a solution containing MnO_4^-, Mn^{++}, and H^+ ions may assume under favorable conditions the potential characteristic of the MnO_4^-/Mn^{++} couple with the half-reaction

$$MnO_4^- + 8H^+ + 5e^- = Mn^{++} + 4H_2O \tag{14-9}$$

It is often impossible to find a suitable inert electrode that permits experimental determination of such electrode potentials. However, their value may often be computed from other experimental quantities.

Standard electrode potentials.   When all the concentrations of the species participating in a half-reaction are at their standard values, the resulting electrode potential is called the standard electrode potential $E°$ of the half-cell. Standard concentrations (more precisely, standard activities) are defined as equal to $1\ M$. When the solubility of the substance concerned is too small to reach that value, the standard concentration is defined by the solubility of the substance, and an excess of the solid (or liquid, for example, Hg) form of the substance must be present to assure saturation. The standard partial pressure of gases is by definition 1 atm.

For example, the standard conditions are: for the Ag^+/Ag couple, $[Ag^+] = 1$; for the $AgCl/Ag$ couple, $[Cl^-] = 1$, presence of $AgCl(s)$; for the MnO_4^-/Mn^{++} couple, $[MnO_4^-] = [Mn^{++}] = [H^+] = 1$.

The sign and value of the standard electrode potential $E°$ are identical with the sign and value of the potential that the standard electrode concerned assumes or tends to assume when combined with the standard hydrogen electrode. The words *tends to assume* are used because it is often difficult and even impossible to realize experimentally a half-cell that corresponds to a redox couple of interest and permits the measurement of its standard potential directly.

Some values of standard electrode potentials are listed in Table 14-1. It should be noted that the more positive (or the less negative) the value of $E°$, the more powerful an oxidizing agent is the oxidized form of the couple and the weaker a reducing agent is the reduced form. (As already mentioned, the sign of $E°$ will be discussed further on page 316, because in many texts an opposite sign is given.) A more extensive list of standard electrode potentials is given on pages 402–404.

The Nernst equation.   When the concentrations in a half-cell are not at their standard values, the electrode potential E is given by the Nernst equation

$$E = E° - (0.0592/n) \log Q \qquad (14\text{-}10)$$

where $E°$ is the standard electrode potential, n is the number of electrons involved in the half-reaction, log is the decadic logarithm, and Q is the mass-action expression for the half-reaction, but omitting the electrons. To obtain the appropriate Q rather than its reciprocal, the

TABLE 14-1   *Standard Electrode Potentials*

reaction	$E°$, volts
$F_2(g) + 2e^- = 2F^-$	2.87
$H_2O_2 + 2H^+ + 2e^- = 2H_2O$	1.77
$Ce(IV) + e^- = Ce(III)$	1.7 (in 1 F HClO$_4$)
	1.61 (in 1 F HNO$_3$)
	1.44 (in 1 F H$_2$SO$_4$)
	1.23 (in 1 F HCl)
$PbO_2(s) + 4H^+ + 2e^- = Pb^{++} + 2H_2O$	1.47
$MnO_4^- + 8H^+ + 5e^- = Mn^{++} + 4H_2O$	1.51
$Cl_2(g) + 2e^- = 2Cl^-$	1.359
$Cr_2O_7^= + 14H^+ + 6e^- = 2Cr^{3+} + 7H_2O$	1.33
$O_2(g) + 4H^+ + 4e^- = 2H_2O$	1.229
$2IO_3^- + 12H^+ + 10e^- = I_2(s) + 3H_2O$	1.19
$Br_2(l) + 2e^- = 2Br^-$	1.0652
$Cu^{++} + I^- + e^- = CuI(s)$	0.85
$Ag^+ + e^- = Ag(s)$	0.7994
$Fe^{3+} + e^- = Fe^{++}$	0.771
	0.732 (in 1 F HClO$_4$)
	0.700 (in 1 F HCl)
	0.68 (in 1 F H$_2$SO$_4$)
	0.61 (in 1 F H$_2$SO$_4$ and 0.5 F H$_3$PO$_4$)
$O_2(g) + 2H^+ + 2e^- = H_2O_2$	0.69
$As(V) + 2e^- = As(III)$	0.577 (in 1 F HCl or 1 F HClO$_4$)
$I_3^- + 2e^- = 3I^-$	0.535
$I_2(s) + 2e^- = 2I^-$	0.534
$Cu^{++} + 2e^- = Cu(s)$	0.337
$Hg_2Cl_2(s) + 2e^- = 2Hg(l) + 2Cl^-$	0.2680
$AgCl(s) + e^- = Ag(s) + Cl^-$	0.2224
$Cu^{++} + e^- = Cu^+$	0.153
$S(s) + 2H^+ + 2e^- = H_2S$	0.14
$HSO_4^- + 3H^+ + 2e^- = SO_2(g) + 2H_2O$	0.14
$Sn(IV) + 2e^- = Sn(II)$	0.14 (in 1 F HCl)
$TiO^{++} + 2H^+ + e^- = Ti^{3+} + H_2O$	0.1
$S_4O_6^= + 2e^- = 2S_2O_3^=$	0.09
$2H^+ + 2e^- = H_2(g)$	0.000
$Pb^{++} + 2e^- = Pb(s)$	−0.126
$Ni^{++} + 2e^- = Ni(s)$	−0.23
$V^{3+} + e^- = V^{++}$	−0.255
$Cr(III) + e^- = Cr(II)$	−0.38 (in 1 F HCl)
$Fe^{++} + 2e^- = Fe(s)$	−0.440
$Zn^{++} + 2e^- = Zn(s)$	−0.7628
$Na^+ + e^- = Na(s)$	−2.698
$K^+ + e^- = K(s)$	−2.925
$Li^+ + e^- = Li(s)$	−3.03

Values accompanied by special conditions in parentheses are formal potentials, as explained on page 314. Most formal potentials given were measured by E. H. Swift, C. S. Garner, and collaborators. See pages 402–404 for a more extensive, alphabetical table.

half-reaction must be so written that the electrons are on the left,

$$ox + ne^- = red$$

The numerical factor 0.0592 actually contains the absolute temperature, and the value given is appropriate for 25°C, as are the $E°$ values listed in Table 14-1.

The same conventions apply to Q as were stated earlier for the mass-action equilibrium expression (Chap. 7). For example, for the half-reaction

$$Zn^{++} + 2e^- = Zn(s)$$

the potential might have been written

$$E = E^{°\prime} - (0.0592/2) \log \{[Zn]/[Zn^{++}]\}$$

However, the value of [Zn], the concentration of Zn at zero oxidation state, is constant in the presence of metallic Zn. Thus, if the contributions of [Zn] and [Zn^{++}] to the logarithmic term are separated

$$E = E^{°\prime} - (0.0592/2) \log [Zn] - (0.0592/2) \log \{1/[Zn^{++}]\}$$

the term with [Zn] may be combined with $E^{°\prime}$ to give

$$E° = E^{°\prime} - (0.0592/2) \log [Zn]$$

This is *the* standard potential of the Zn electrode, with the value of -0.7628 volt, as given in Table 14-1. Thus

$$E = 0.7628 - (0.0592/2) \log Q$$

where $Q = 1/[Zn^{++}]$, does not contain [Zn].

The other conventions concerning the participation of gases or of water in the electrode reaction are handled in a similar way, so that Q contains the partial pressures of such gases rather than their concentrations and does not contain [H$_2$O].

In terms of red and ox the general form of Q is

$$Q = [red]/[ox] \tag{14-11}$$

although it is somewhat more complex when the half-reaction involves several reactants, products, or both; two examples are provided by Eqs. (14-14) and (14-15). When all concentrations are at unit values, Q equals 1 and $E = E°$, as indeed it should. When the concentrations in the half-cell are such that [ox] > [red], inspection of (14-10) and (14-11) shows that E is positive relative to $E°$ (on the presumption that, if there are reactants and products other than red and ox, their concentrations are at unity). As the half-reaction proceeds from left to right, the electrode potential becomes more and more negative. The more positive or the less negative the potential E, the stronger the inherent oxidizing power of the redox couple considered, at the concentrations specified in Q. It must be noted that all considerations based on potentials, the Nernst equation, and the mass-action law presuppose that the reactions involved occur at rates such that equilibrium is actually attained.

Two examples of Nernst equations give the potentials of the Fe^{3+}/Fe^{++} couple and of the $Cr_2O_7^=/Cr^{3+}$ couple. The half-reactions are

$$Fe^{3+} + e^- = Fe^{++} \tag{14-12}$$

and

$$Cr_2O_7^= + 14H^+ + 6e^- = 2Cr^{3+} + 7H_2O \tag{14-13}$$

which lead to the potentials

$$E_{Fe} = E_{Fe}^\circ - 0.0592 \log \{[Fe^{++}]/[Fe^{3+}]\} \tag{14-14}$$

$$E_{Cr} = E_{Cr}^\circ - (0.0592/6) \log \{[Cr^{3+}]^2/[Cr_2O_7^=][H^+]^{14}\} \tag{14-15}$$

The subscripts of these electrode potentials should actually be Fe^{3+}/Fe^{++} and $Cr_2O_7^=/Cr^{3+}$, respectively; for simplicity's sake these have been abbreviated here to Fe and Cr.

The values, at 25°C, of the two standard potentials are

$$E_{Fe}^\circ = +0.771 \text{ volt} \qquad E_{Cr}^\circ = +1.33 \text{ volts} \tag{14-16}$$

The $Cr_2O_7^=/Cr^{3+}$ couple thus has a stronger oxidizing tendency, under standard conditions, than the Fe^{3+}/Fe^{++} couple has. Note that a change of the concentration ratio of Fe^{++} to Fe^{3+} by a factor of 10 corresponds to a change of 0.0592 volt in E_{Fe}; a change in the concentration of $Cr_2O_7^=$ by a factor of 10 corresponds to a change in E_{Cr} of 0.0592/6, or about 0.01 volt only, there being six electrons involved per $Cr_2O_7^=$; finally, a tenfold change in the Cr^{3+} concentration is seen to correspond to a change of E_{Cr} by 0.0592/3, or about 0.02 volt.

The Nernst equation may be derived by the use of thermodynamics. Its structure is closely analogous to that of the mass-action law, as will be demonstrated by using the $Cr_2O_7^=/Cr^{3+}$ couple as an example. Consider the complete mass-action expression that corresponds to the half-reaction (14-15), including, at least formally, the electron concentration $[e^-]$.

$$[Cr^{3+}]^2/[Cr_2O_7^=][H^+]^{14}[e^-]^6 = K_{Cr} \tag{14-17}$$

To compare this equation with (14-15), it is convenient to form the decadic logarithms of both sides, multiplied by 0.0592/6, and to rearrange the result as follows:

$$- (0.0592/6) \log [e^-]^6 = (0.0592/6) \log K_{Cr}$$
$$- (0.0592/6) \log \{[Cr^{3+}]^2/[Cr_2O_7^=][H^+]^{14}\} \qquad (14\text{-}18)$$

Term-by-term comparison of Equations (14-18) and (14-15) shows them to express the same relationship, provided the following identifications are made:

$$- E_{Cr} = (0.0592/6) \log [e^-]^6 = 0.0592 \log [e^-] \qquad (14\text{-}19)$$

and
$$E_{Cr}^\circ = (0.0592/6) \log K_{Cr} \qquad (14\text{-}20)$$

or
$$K_{Cr} = 10^{6E_{Cr}^\circ/0.0592} \qquad (14\text{-}21)$$

The negative of the electrode potential E_{Cr} is thus seen to be proportional to the logarithm of the electron concentration, except for the proviso to follow; the negative sign reflects the negative charge of the electrons. The proviso is that all potentials are known up to an additive constant only, since only potential differences between half-cells are accessible to measurement. The convenient but arbitrary disposition of this constant by assigning the potential zero to the standard hydrogen cell does not, of course, remove it from existence. The unknown additive constant of the potential corresponds to a multiplicative factor in $[e^-]$ so that the actual relation between E and $[e^-]$ is

$$- E = 0.0592 \log (k[e^-]) \qquad (14\text{-}22)$$

the factor k being unknown.

The constant K_{Cr} measures the tendency of the half-reaction (14-13), at standard conditions, to go to the right. The larger the corresponding K for any other half-reaction, the larger this tendency. This parallels the statement that, the more positive the E° of a half-reaction, the stronger the oxidizing power of the redox couple involved, at standard conditions. Constants like K_{Cr} have no absolute meaning, and indeed the unknown factor k that appears in (14-22) also occurs in (14-20), its minus sixth power multiplying K_{Cr}. However, as will be seen later, when half-reactions are so combined that no free electrons occur on either side of the result, the corresponding mass-action constant is given by a ratio of constants like K_{Cr}, in which the unknown factor k cancels.

At concentrations other than standard the tendency of a half-reaction to go to the right, compared with that of the standard hydrogen half-reaction, is measured by E, the electrode potential at the prevailing concentrations. It is important to note that this electrode potential, as computed from the Nernst equation, is not changed—as indeed it should not be—if the half-reaction is multiplied by a factor f. In detail, this factor changes the number n of electrons appearing in (14-10) to nf, and Q is changed to Q^f; the two changes just cancel in (14-10).

Cell potentials. When two half-cells are combined into an electrochemical cell, the half-cell with the more positive electrode potential provides the positive terminal and the other, the negative terminal. The voltage of the cell is the difference between the two potentials.

If the combination is permitted to run as a *galvanic cell*, the half-reaction with the more positive electrode potential proceeds spontaneously from left to right; it represents a reduction, and the corresponding terminal is the cathode. The half-reaction with the less positive electrode potential runs from the right to left, as an oxidation, and the terminal is the anode.

Suppose that an external voltage that is opposite and equal to the voltage developed by the cell is applied. The cell reaction is kept exactly in balance, and the cell is just on the point of being run as an *electrolytic cell*, reversing the electrode reactions and interchanging the roles of anode and cathode. The voltage required to bring the cell to this point is called the *equilibrium decomposition potential*.

To make electrolysis proceed at a finite rate, additional voltage is needed to compensate for the IR drop in the entire circuit. Sometimes further voltage, called *overvoltage*, is required because of irreversible phenomena that occur when a gas is evolved or a solid substance is deposited at an electrode.

When considering an electrochemical cell, it is usually convenient to begin with an *arbitrary* choice of the half-reaction to be reversed and written as an oxidation, without considering whether this choice makes the cell galvanic or electrolytic. The cell reaction is obtained next by multiplying the two half-reactions with suitable factors so the electrons cancel after adding the reaction equations. The half-reaction that was reversed represents the anode reaction, and its potential must be subtracted from the potential of the other half-reaction that represents the reduction at the cathode:

$$E_{\text{total}} = E_{\text{cathode}} - E_{\text{anode}}$$

It follows from the earlier discussion that if E_{total} is positive, the cell reaction has the tendency to go from left to right spontaneously, so that the cell acts as a galvanic cell with the cell reaction as written. The same cell may be run as an electrolytic cell by forcing the reaction from right to left. This interchanges the roles of cathode and anode. The equilibrium decomposition potential is E_{total}.

If E_{total} is negative, the reverse of each statement in the preceding paragraph is true. The cell reaction has the inherent tendency to occur from right to left with the galvanic cell potential equal to $|E_{total}|$. To run the cell as an electrolytic cell requires an opposed external voltage of $|E_{total}|$ and additional voltage for the actual passage of current and for overcoming possible overvoltage.

To furnish an example, the half-cells represented by (14-12) and (14-13) are combined into a cell with the over-all reaction

$$Cr_2O_7^= + 14H^+ + 6Fe^{++} = 2Cr^{3+} + 7H_2O + 6Fe^{3+} \quad (14\text{-}23)$$

To obtain this equation, the Fe^{3+}/Fe^{++} half-reaction had to be reversed and multiplied by 6 so that the six electrons of the $Cr_2O_7^=/Cr^{+++}$ of Equation (14-13) would be matched. It is convenient to rewrite the anode potential (14-14) to correspond to these six electrons

$$E_{anode} = E_{Fe} = E_{Fe}^\circ - (0.0592/6) \log \{[Fe^{++}]^6/[Fe^{3+}]^6\} \quad (14\text{-}24)$$

so that the factor multiplying the logarithmic term is identical with the corresponding factor for the cathode potential

$$E_{cathode} = E_{Cr} = E_{Cr}^\circ - (0.0592/6) \log \{[Cr^{3+}]^2/[Cr_2O_7^=][H^+]^{14}\}$$

$$(14\text{-}25)$$

By subtracting (14-24) from (14-25) and combining the two logarithmic terms

$$E_{total} = E_{Cr}^\circ - E_{Fe}^\circ - (0.0592/6)$$

$$\times \log \{[Fe^{3+}]^6[Cr^{3+}]^2/[Fe^{++}]^6[Cr_2O_7^=][H^+]^{14}\} \quad (14\text{-}26)$$

The value and sign of E_{total} depend not only on the E° values but also on the concentrations of the species participating in the cell reaction. Whether the cell reaction proceeds in the direction it was written or in the opposite direction therefore depends on these concentrations.

Equilibrium constants of cell reactions.　　When the potential of the completed cell is zero, equilibrium exists between the two half-cells. This fact permits the computation of equilibrium constants for reactions such as (14-23) as follows. Consider a solution with equilibrium concentrations of the species that participate in reaction (14-23). Make up two half-cells, one representing the $Cr_2O_7^=/Cr^{3+}$ couple, with $[Cr_2O_7^=]$, $[Cr^{+++}]$, and $[H^+]$ as they exist in the equilibrium mixture, the other representing the Fe^{3+}/Fe^{++} couple, again with equilibrium concentrations $[Fe^{3+}]$ and $[Fe^{++}]$. The potential E_{total} of this combination must be zero; and by setting the left side of Equation (14-26) equal to zero and rearranging it, the equilibrium constant K_{23} of reaction (14-23) may be computed:

$$E_{total} = 0 \qquad E_{Cr}^\circ - E_{Fe}^\circ$$
$$= (0.0592/6) \log \{[Fe^{3+}]^6[Cr^{3+}]^2/[Fe^{++}]^6[Cr_2O_7^=][H^+]^{14}\}$$

and $K_{23} = [Fe^{3+}]^6[Cr^{3+}]^2/[Fe^{++}]^6[Cr_2O_7^=][H^+]^{14}$

$$= 10^{6(E_{Cr}^\circ - E_{Fe}^\circ)/0.0592} \tag{14-27}$$

An instructive way of obtaining the equilibrium constant for reaction (14-23) is to combine the equation for K_{Cr},

$$[Cr^{3+}]^2/[Cr_2O_7^=][H^+]^{14}[e^-]^6 = K_{Cr} = 10^{6E_{Cr}^\circ/0.0592} \tag{14-28}$$

with the corresponding equation for K_{Fe},

$$[Fe^{++}]/[Fe^{3+}][e^-] = K_{Fe} = 10^{E_{Fe}^\circ/0.0592} \tag{14-29}$$

so that $[e^-]$ cancels. As might be expected, the proper combination is $K_{Cr}/(K_{Fe})^6$, so that

$$K_{23} = K_{Cr}/(K_{Fe})^6 = 10^{6(E_{Cr}^\circ - E_{Fe}^\circ)/0.0592} \tag{14-30}$$

which is the result obtained earlier.

The unknown factor k discussed in connection with Equation (14-22) would occur in (14-28) as factor k^{-6} and in (14-32) as factor k^{-1}, so that it would cancel in (14-30). Once again the analogy to the acid constants K_a should be remembered.

Using the standard potentials given in (14-16),

$$K_{23} = 10^{6(1.33 - 0.77)/0.0592} = 5 \times 10^{56} \tag{14-31}$$

This indicates a strong tendency in reaction (14-23) to go to the right, as long as $[H^+]$ is sufficiently large.

Another important argument leads to the same result. In a solution containing $Cr_2O_7^=$, Cr^{3+}, and H^+, as well as Fe^{++} and Fe^{3+}, there will be equilibrium only when the potential of the $Cr_2O_7^=/Cr^{3+}$ couple equals that of the Fe^{3+}/Fe^{++} couple. If these potentials are not equal, suitable oxidation and reduction reactions will tend to take place until they are. At equilibrium the concentrations of the various ions will be such that the left sides and thus also the right sides of Equations (14-14) and (14-15) are equal to each other and equal to the *potential of the solution* (relative to the standard hydrogen electrode),

$$E = E_{Fe} = E_{Cr} = E^\circ_{Fe} - 0.0592 \log \{[Fe^{++}]/[Fe^{3+}]\}$$
$$= E^\circ_{Cr} - (0.0592/6) \log \{[Cr^{3+}]^2/[Cr_2O_7^=][H^+]^{14}\} \quad (14\text{-}32)$$

Suitable rearrangement again leads to Equation (14-27). The potential of the solution E may be measured under favorable circumstances by the use of an inert electrode and a reference electrode connected to the solution by a liquid-liquid junction.

To generalize, if a solution contains any number of redox couples, oxidations and reductions will occur until the potentials of all couples are equal (it always being assumed that rates are sufficiently large that equilibrium is attained). This potential is called the potential of the solution. A particularly important case involves the presence of a *redox indicator*, consisting of a redox couple in which the oxidized or the reduced species, or both, have intense colors so that a change from one form to the other may be recognized. If the total indicator concentration is small, the indicator couple assumes the potential of the solution without significantly changing it. The indicator color then permits determining the solution potential by observation, at least in a certain range of potentials, as will be discussed on page 321.

Standard potential of an electrode of the second kind. This potential is related to the standard potential of the metal involved and the pertinent solubility product, as shown by considering the AgCl/Ag electrode as an example. The half-reaction

$$AgCl(s) + e^- = Ag(s) + Cl^- \qquad E^\circ_{AgCl} \; E^\circ_{AgCl/Ag} = 0.2224 \text{ volt}$$

corresponds to the Nernst equation

$$E = 0.2224 - 0.0592 \log [Cl^-] \qquad (14\text{-}33)$$

It is, however, equally permissible to consider the half-reaction of this half-cell to be

$$Ag^+ + e^- = Ag(s) \qquad E^\circ_{Ag^+/Ag} = 0.7994 \text{ volt}$$

as long as cognizance is taken of the fact that $[Ag^+]$ is related to $[Cl^-]$ by the solubility product of AgCl, so that the Nernst equation may be written

$$E = 0.7994 - 0.0592 \log [Ag^+]^{-1}$$
$$= 0.7994 - 0.0592 \log \{[Cl^-]/K_{SP}\}$$
$$E = 0.7994 - 0.0592 \log [Cl^-] + 0.0592 \log K_{SP} \qquad (14\text{-}34)$$

Since the silver wire can assume only one potential E, the right sides of

(14-33) and (14-34) must be equal. Rearrangement leads to

$$K_{SP} = 10^{(0.2224 - 0.7994)/0.0592} = 1.8 \times 10^{-10}$$

This example illustrates how $E°$ values for redox reactions that involve different species but the same change in oxidation state [here, oxidation of Ag(0) to Ag(I)] may be used to calculate equilibrium constants. Further examples are given on pages 336 and 340.

Formal potentials. The precise definition of standard potentials $E°$ refers to standard *activities* rather than standard *concentrations* of the species concerned. Since a concentration of 1 mole/liter does not accurately correspond to an activity of 1 mole/liter, measured and calculated potentials differ, unless all concentrations and gas pressures that appear in the Nernst equation have been converted into activities. This is a cumbersome procedure and often not possible because of lack of sufficient data. Fortunately, conversion to activities is usually not necessary when the results are used to investigate the feasibility of analytical methods and the like. A more serious situation exists when the species participating in a half-reaction are largely present as complexes. If the mass-action constants for the formation of these complexes are known, the concentrations in the Nernst equation can be calculated. However, this is unwieldy and in many cases impossible, since the constants and even the precise nature of the complexes may not be known. In all such situations the concept of the *formal potential $E_f°$* is useful. This is the potential of the electrode when the concentrations of the species involved are 1 F. Certain other conditions may be specified, such as the presence of 1 F HCl. For example, the standard potential of the couple Fe^{3+}/Fe^{++} is 0.771 volt, and a number of formal potentials for the same couple are as follows: 0.732 volt in 1 F $HClO_4$, 0.700 volt in 1 F HCl, 0.68 volt in 1 F H_2SO_4, and 0.61 volt in a solution that is 1 F in H_2SO_4 and 0.5 F in H_3PO_4. All these potentials are less positive than $E°$. Aside from activity effects, this is due to the fact that the ions Cl^-, $SO_4^=$, and $HPO_4^=$ form stronger complexes with Fe^{3+} than Fe^{++}, thus increasing the ratio $[Fe^{++}]/[Fe_3^+]$ that appears in (14-14). Other formal potentials are listed in Table 14-1. Formal potentials may be used in the Nernst equation and for the evaluation of "formal" mass-action constants with results that approximate those actually observed even at conditions that are not exactly those specified.

As mentioned, formal potentials may be computed if the mass-action constants of all reactions involving the species appearing in the Nernst equation are known. Conversely, potential measurements at various concentrations of complexing agents provide an important method of evaluating complex formation and similar mass-action constants.

Measurement of pH. Another important application of potential measurement is the determination of the pH of a solution. This determination may be made by using a hydrogen electrode, since its potential

$$E = 0.000 - (0.0592/2) \log \{p_{H_2}/[H^+]^2\}$$

depends on $[H^+]$. In fact, when $p_{H_2} = 1$ atm,

$$pH = -E/0.0592 \qquad (14\text{-}35)$$

Aside from the cumbersome hydrogen electrode, any other half-cell representing a half-reaction that includes H^+ as a reactant or product may be used to measure the pH of a solution. The concentrations of all other species involved in the half-reaction must, of course, be kept constant. Electrodes of this kind have been used in the past, but all (including the hydrogen electrode) suffer from the disadvantage that, besides responding to the pH, their potential is changed by the presence of redox couples. They may thus be used to measure the pH only when there is no interference from oxidizing or reducing agents. This disadvantage is overcome by the glass electrode described on page 167, which responds only to the pH.

The mercury battery and the Weston standard cell. The Ruben Mallory mercury battery used in the coulometric experiment has an anode made of amalgamated Zn in an electrolyte of about 8 F KOH saturated with ZnO(s), which exists in the solution mainly in the form of potassium zincate, $K_2Zn(OH)_4$. The anode reaction ($-$terminal) is therefore

$$Zn\,(amalgam) + 2OH^- = ZnO(s) + H_2O + 2e^-$$

The cathode is in the same electrolyte, and it consists of mercuric oxide mixed with graphite to improve the electric conductivity; it further contains liquid mercury produced by the cathode reaction ($+$terminal)

$$HgO(s) + H_2O + 2e^- = Hg(l) + 2OH^-$$

The cell reaction is thus

$$Zn\,(amalgam) + HgO(s) = ZnO(s) + Hg(l)$$

The over-all cell reaction involves only substances of constant concentrations or activities; the electrolyte acts only as intermediary. This is undoubtedly part of the reason for the excellent voltage characteristic of this battery. The Ruben Mallory battery was developed mainly during World War II when a self-contained source of sustained voltage despite current drain was badly needed. It has since found numerous applications in the electronic industry and elsewhere.

The *unsaturated* Weston cell that is often used to furnish the reference voltage in ordinary potentiometers has an anode of a 12.5 weight per cent Cd amalgam and a cathode of mercury covered with solid mercurous sulfate. The electrolyte is a solution saturated with cadmium sulfate at 4°C and therefore not saturated with this substance at room temperature. The electrolyte is, however, saturated with the very slightly soluble mercurous sulfate that forms part of the cathode.

The anode reaction ($-$terminal) is

$$Cd\,(amalgam) = Cd^{++} + 2e^-$$

A Cd amalgam containing between 5 and 15 per cent of Cd exists at ordinary temperatures as a mixture of a liquid and a solid phase, both of fixed but different compositions that depend on temperature and pressure only. Since these two phases are at equilibrium, they both develop the same equilibrium potential. Removal of Cd in the form of Cd^{++} or the reverse does not change the compositions of the two phases, but changes only their relative amounts; the anode potential thus remains unchanged.

The cathode reaction ($+$terminal) is

$$Hg_2SO_4(s) + 2e^- = Hg(l) + SO_4^=$$

and the over-all reaction

$$Cd\,(amalgam) + Hg_2SO_4(s) = 2Hg(l) + Cd^{++} + SO_4^=$$

It is seen that the voltage of the unsaturated Weston cell depends on the concentrations of Cd^{++} and $SO_4^=$ and stays constant only if those concentrations remain unchanged. Thus, passage of only the smallest currents may be tolerated.

In the *saturated* Weston cell the concentrations of Cd^{++} and $SO_4^=$ are kept constant by the presence of an excess of crystals of $CdSO_4 \cdot \frac{8}{3}H_2O$, so that at equilibrium the solution is saturated with this substance. Even so, passage of moderate currents may cause noticeable concentration changes, and restoration of equilibrium may take considerable time.

The saturated Weston cell is the most reliable standard cell known, and it is therefore invariably used as a primary voltage standard. The U.S. National Bureau of Standards maintains a group of saturated Weston cells made with chemicals of the highest purity and kept continually at 25°C. The maximum variation per year that has been reported for these cells is 0.6 μv, or 6 parts in 10 million.

The unsaturated Weston cell has a smaller temperature coefficient than the saturated type, and this is one reason for its preference in applications that do not require extreme accuracy. A related reason is that when the temperature of the saturated cell is raised, there is a time lag during which the cell voltage changes until the solution becomes saturated again. Unsaturated Weston cells need to be checked periodically against a primary standard.

The sign of $E°$.   Special attention has to be given to the sign of electrode potentials, because there is no universal agreement on this subject, as was mentioned earlier. The reasons are as follows.

On the one hand the potential of an electrode is a physical quantity: the potential the electrode assumes relative to the hydrogen electrode when the half-cell considered is combined with the standard hydrogen half-cell. This electrode potential, including the sign, does not depend, of course, on which way the half-cell reaction is written.

On the other hand, $E°$ is a quantitative measure of the tendency of the half-reaction considered to go to the right, as is most clearly seen from the relationship

$$E° = (0.0592/n) \log K \tag{14-36}$$

where K is the equilibrium constant for the half-reaction including the electrons. When the half-reaction is written in the reverse direction, K changes to K^{-1} and therefore $E°$ changes to $-E°$. The sign of $E°$ in this view thus depends on whether the half-reaction is written as reduction or as oxidation. The relationship between $E°$ and K has firm foundations in thermodynamics (see Appendix IV), and if $E°$ is viewed as a thermodynamic quantity rather than as a physical potential, the sign change upon reversal of the half-reaction is mandatory. [It should be noted that while changing sign upon reversing the half-reaction, $E°$, as related to K by Equation (14-36), remains unchanged when the half-reaction is multiplied by a positive factor f, because n changes to nf and K to K^f].

The first point of view has many adherents, particularly in Europe, whereas the second point of view is strongly represented in America. It was recommended in 1953 at the Seventeenth Conference of the International Union of Pure and Applied Chemistry that the sign-invariant quantity be called the *electrode potential* and the sign bivariant quantity the *half-cell emf*.

When a half-cell is written as a reduction, with the electrons on the left, the half-cell emf is equal to the electrode potential in sign and value. This is the reason why in Table 14-1, which contains a selection of standard electrode potentials, the half-reactions are all written as reductions, so that the $E°$ values represent electrode potentials and half-cell emf's at the same time. When a half-reaction is written as an oxidation, with the electrons on the right, the signs of half-cell emf and electrode potential are opposite. Half-cell emf values that correspond to such half-reactions *must not be called electrode potentials*.

To consider an example, the redox couple $Cu^{++}/Cu(s)$ can be said to have half-reactions and half-cell emf's

$$Cu^{++} + 2e^- = Cu(s) \qquad E°_{Cu^{++}/Cu} = 0.337 \text{ volt (electrode potential)} \tag{14-37}$$

or $\quad Cu(s) = Cu^{++} + 2e^- \qquad E°_{Cu^{++}/Cu} = -0.337 \text{ volt} \tag{14-38}$

Equation (14-37) is that used in Table 14-1, and the $E°$ given is the standard electrode potential; the Cu electrode in a standard $Cu^{++}/Cu(s)$ half-cell assumes a potential of $+0.337$ volt when this half-cell is combined with the standard hydrogen half-cell. Equation (14-38) leads to the opposite sign for $E°$. In many tables of standard half-cell emf's the sign corresponds to this way of writing the half-reaction, as oxidations, with the electrons on the right. Although these $E°$ values are now opposite in sign to the standard electrode potentials, there is merit in such a listing also: the more electropositive a metal, the more positive the $E°$ associated with it. For example, Cu is less electropositive, or more noble, than hydrogen; this is reflected by the half-cell emf of -0.337 volt that goes with (14-38). When looking up $E°$ values, it is important to find out whether they correspond to a reduction or an oxidation. If this is not stated explicitly, it can be found easily by looking at the alkali metals, for which a negative $E°$ implies a reduction (so that the half-cell emf is also the electrode potential), whereas a positive $E°$ implies an oxidation.

REDOX TITRATIONS

General requirements

1. Titrations based on redox reactions depend on the *potentials involved for the completeness of the reaction.* Favorable potentials are, however, not a sufficient basis for a successful redox method, since the rates of the reactions concerned are often slow.

2. The oxidizing and reducing agents involved must also be *stable in the solvent used,* which frequently is water. Slow rates of the oxidation or reduction of water sometimes permit the use of reagents that are actually unstable on an equilibrium basis. Examples are solutions of MnO_4^- and of Ce(IV), in both of which water would be oxidized if equilibrium were established. The rates, however, are slow enough to permit the preparation of standard solutions of either reagent.

Oxidizing agents that are often used in redox titrations are MnO_4^-, $Cr_2O_7^=$, Ce(IV), I_2 in the form of I_3^- (tri-iodide ion), IO_3^-, and ClO^-. Common reducing agents are Fe^{++}, Sn^{++}, $S_2O_3^=$ (in conjunction with I_3^-), and to a lesser extent Ti^{3+} and Cr^{++}, since an oxygen-free atmosphere is required for quantitative work with these last two strong reducing agents. Thiosulfate ($S_2O_3^=$) is a very important volumetric reagent but is used in conjunction with iodine only, as will be discussed in detail in the next chapter.

3. Another important requirement for an acceptable redox method is the availability of reagents that permit *placing the substance to be determined into a definite oxidation state* before the titration is performed. These reagents have to be added in excess, because the quantity of substance to be reduced or oxidized by them is at best known only roughly. The nature of these reagents must therefore be such that either they do not interfere with the titration or an excess can be destroyed prior to the titration. Commonly used oxidizing agents are Cl_2 and Br_2. The excess may be removed by boiling. Others are H_2O_2 and $K_2S_2O_8$, where the excess is destroyed by heating so that oxidation of H_2O to O_2 occurs; this was discussed for $K_2S_2O_8$ on page 244. For reducing purposes metals and metal amalgams are often convenient, because an excess may be removed by filtration. Another reducing agent is Sn^{++}, which is employed to reduce iron from the $+3$ to the $+2$ state in the laboratory assignment for this chapter, the titration of iron with dichromate. Excess Sn^{++} is oxidized to Sn(IV) by the addition of $HgCl_2$ solution,

$$Sn^{++} + 2HgCl_2 = Hg_2Cl_2(s) + Sn(IV) + 2Cl^-$$

The products of this reaction do not interfere with the titration of Fe^{++} with $Cr_2O_7^=$. This will be discussed further on page 325.

4. As mentioned in the general discussion of volumetric methods, suitable means for the preparation of a standard solution must be available. Reducing agents often used as primary standards are As_2O_3, $Na_2C_2O_4$ (sodium oxalate, oxidized to $2Na^+ + 2CO_2$), and $Fe(NH_4)_2(SO_4)_2 \cdot 6H_2O$. Similarly used oxidizing agents are $K_2Cr_2O_7$, KIO_3, and $KBrO_3$.

5. A final requirement is that a *suitable means to recognize the titration end point must exist*. Sometimes the color of one of the reagents is very intense; the appearance or disappearance of such a characteristic color serves the purpose. One example is strongly purple MnO_4^- changed to colorless Mn^{++} when reduced in acid solutions and to a brown precipitate of MnO_2 when reduced in neutral or alkaline solutions. A less specific example is I_3^- in the presence of a starch suspension, which forms a compound of intense blue color, as discussed on page 338. Potential indicators also are available, as mentioned earlier; some examples are given in Table 14-2. One of these, diphenylamine sulfonic acid, will be discussed in detail on page 322. The end point may also be determined in favorable cases by measuring the solution potential during the titration with an inert electrode, as discussed on page 327.

TABLE 14-2 *Some Potential Indicators*

indicator	potential at change of color, volts	indicator color	
		oxidized form	*reduced form*
Nitroferroin	1.31	Red	Greenish blue
Ferroin	1.12	Red	Pale blue
Dimethyl ferroin	0.97	Yellowish green	Red
Diphenylamine sulfonic acid	0.83	Reddish violet	Colorless
Diphenylamine	0.76	Violet	Colorless

For a successful redox titration the solution potential must change rapidly upon addition of small increments of titrant near the equivalence point. This behavior is illustrated by the potential curve for the titration of Fe^{++} with $Cr_2O_7^=$ considered below. An account of the operation of a typical potential indicator follows.

Potential curve for the titration of Fe^{++} with $Cr_2O_7^=$. Assume that 100.0 ml of a 0.1000 F solution of Fe^{++} is titrated with a 0.01667 F (or 0.1000 N) solution of $Cr_2O_7^=$. For simplicity of computation the pH is to be kept at zero during the titration. The potential throughout the titration is given by the double relation (14-32).

At the equivalence point the sum of the iron concentrations in both forms is 0.0500 mole/liter, which takes the dilution by a factor of 2 into account. Thus, if we set the concentration of unreacted Fe^{++} equal to x, it follows that

$$[Fe^{++}] = x \qquad [Fe^{3+}] = 0.05 - x$$

Since electrons are conserved,

$$[Cr_2O_7^=] = x/6 \qquad [Cr^{3+}] = (0.05 - x)/3$$

Inserting these values and $[H^+] = 1$ into (14-32) yields

$$E = E_{Fe} = 0.771 - 0.0592 \log [x/(0.05 - x)] \qquad (14\text{-}39)$$

$$E = E_{Cr} = 1.33 - (0.0592/6) \log [6(0.05 - x)^2/9x] \qquad (14\text{-}40)$$

When x is neglected in the combination $0.05 - x$, it is apparent that combining the two equal quantities E_{Fe} and E_{Cr} in the proportions $E_{Fe}/7 + 6E_{Cr}/7$ will cause the remaining two x's to cancel:

$$E = E_{Fe}/7 + 6E_{Cr}/7$$
$$= 1.25 - (0.0592/7) \log [0.05(6x)/9x]$$
$$E = 1.26 \text{ volts}$$

Inserting this value into (14-39) or (14-40) and solving for x is equivalent to satisfying the mass-action expression (14-27). The result is

$$x = [Fe^{++}] = 2 \times 10^{-10}$$

so that at the equivalence point the oxidation of Fe^{++} is seen to be quantitative and the neglecting of x in the combination $0.05 - x$ is justified.

Suppose, next, that 99.99 ml of titrant has been added to 100.00 ml of the original Fe^{++} solution. It is assumed that all but y ml of the $Cr_2O_7^=$ has reacted with Fe^{++}, so that

$$[Fe^{3+}] = (99.99 - y)0.1/199.99 \qquad [Fe^{++}] = (0.01 + y)0.1/199.99$$

$$[Cr_2O_7^=] = (0.1)y/6(199.99) \qquad [Cr^{3+}] = (99.99 - y)0.1/3(199.99)$$

$$[H^+] = 1$$

Notice that y, which is probably a very small quantity, occurs in conjunction with other terms in the expression for $[Fe^{++}]$, $[Fe^{3+}]$, and $[Cr^{3+}]$, where it will be ignored, but not in the expression for $[Cr_2O_7^=]$. Accordingly, the Fe^{3+}/Fe^{++} half-cell is used to compute the potential, neglecting y, and the $Cr_2O_7^=/Cr^{3+}$ half-cell to compute y,

$$E = 0.771 - 0.0592 \log [(0.01 + y)/(99.99 - y)] \approx 0.771 - 0.0592 \log 10^{-4}$$

$$= 1.008 \text{ volts}$$

$$1.008 = 1.33 - (0.592/6) \log [(99.99 - y)0.1/3(199.99)]^2 [6(199.99)/(0.1)y]$$

The solution of the equation for y is

$$y = 8 \times 10^{-32}$$

so that 8×10^{-32} ml of the original dichromate solution remains unreacted. The assumption in the computation of E that y is negligible compared with 0.01 is thus well satisfied. Other points of the titration potential curve may be computed similarly.

Figure 14-4 shows the potential as a function of the milliliters of $Cr_2O_7^=$ solution added. It will be noted that the limiting slope of the near-horizontal part of this curve on the left is six times the slope of the near-horizontal part on the right, which is a consequence of there being six electrons involved in the half-reaction of one $Cr_2O_7^=$ ion and only one in the half-reaction of one Fe^{3+} ion. For the same reason the equivalence point occurs, not halfway between the $E°$ values of the two half-cells, but at approximately one-seventh the difference of these values, on the side of $E_{Cr}°$. The slope of the potential near the equivalence point is very steep, so that the asymmetrical nature of the curve is not detrimental to the volumetric titration method for which the reaction is used.

Potential indicators.   As mentioned earlier, a potential indicator is a substance that may exist in a reduced form I_{red} and an oxidized

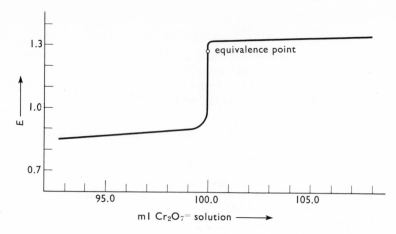

Figure 14-4   The solution potential as function of the quantity of $Cr_2O_7^=$ added.

form I_{ox}, at least one of which must be intensely colored. The indicator reaction is a half-reaction of the type

$$I_{ox} + ne^- = I_{red} \tag{14-41}$$

and the ratio of reduced to oxidized form is related to the potential of the solution by an equation of the form

$$E = E_I^\circ - (0.0592/n) \log [I_{red}]/[I_{ox}] \tag{14-42}$$

Both (14-41) and (14-42) may involve other ions, such as H^+, as well.

The color dependence of the indicator on the potential can be discussed qualitatively in a way patterned after the customary discussion of the color dependence of an acid-base indicator on the pH of a solution. As the potential E changes from the value $E_I^\circ - (0.0592/n)$ to E_I° and finally to $E_I^\circ + (0.0592/n)$, the ratio $[I_{red}]/[I_{ox}]$ changes from 10 to 1 and finally to 1/10, corresponding to a color change of the solution from that of the reduced form of the indicator to that of the oxidized form. The indicator thus changes color in a potential range of $2(0.0592)/n$ $\approx 0.12/n$ volt, approximately centered at E_I°. The color change of redox indicators is, in general, independent of the specific chemical nature of the other ions involved, as is that of pH indicators.

An example of a potential indicator is the sodium salt of diphenylamine sulfonic acid used in the laboratory assignment to follow. It is colorless in the reduced form, and its reaction with an oxidizing agent is somewhat involved, as described in the following: Diphenylamine sulfonate ion (DAS) has the structure

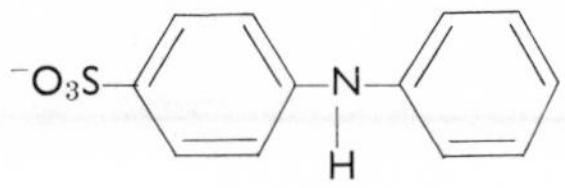

(colorless)

Figure 14-5   Structure of diphenylamine sulfonate ion (DAS).

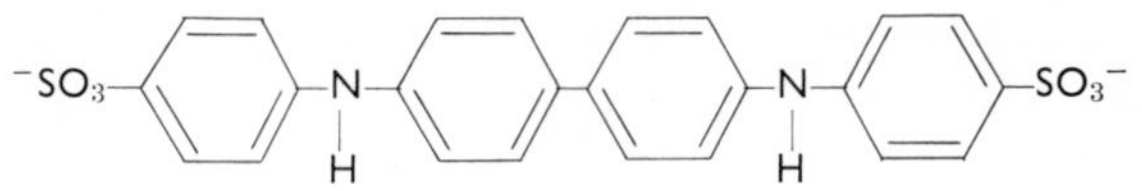

(colorless)

Figure 14-6   Structure of diphenylbenzidine sulfonate ion (DBS).

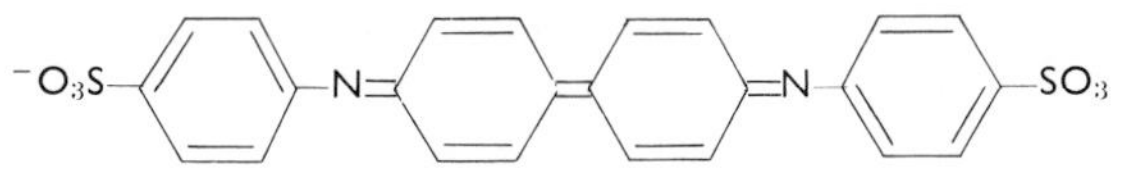

(reddish violet)

Figure 14-7   Structure of diphenylbenzyl violet (DBV).

shown in Figure 14-5, where the hexagons indicate phenyl groups ($-C_6H_4-$ and $-C_6H_5-$), substituted here on one or both sides. The substance is an amine, as implied by its name, and the sulfonic acid group ($-SO_3{}^-$) serves to increase the water solubility of the substance.

The production of a colored substance by the oxidation of DAS occurs in two steps. The first is oxidation in an irreversible reaction in which two molecules of DAS are combined, with the loss of two electrons and two H^+ ions, to the equally colorless diphenylbenzidine sulfonate ion (DBS)

$$2DAS \rightarrow DBS + 2H^+ + 2e^-$$

The structure of diphenylbenzidine sulfonate ion (DBS) is shown in Figure 14-6. The middle part of this molecule is closely related to benzidine

$$(H_2N-C_6H_5-C_6H_5-NH_2)$$

the relationship being one of substitution of a hydrogen atom of each of the amine groups of benzidine by a phenylsulfonate group ($-C_6H_4SO_3{}^-$), as implied by the name.

Upon further oxidation two more H^+ ions and two electrons are lost in a reversible reaction, and diphenylbenzyl violet (DBV) of reddish-violet color is produced,

$$DBS = DBV + 2H^+ + 2e^-$$

This occurs in the neighborhood of $E_1^\circ = 0.83$ volt. The structure of DBV is shown in Figure 14-7. Its color is due to the regular sequence of single and double bonds throughout the molecule or, as it is called, a system of *conjugated double bonds*.

323

*A standard solution of potassium dichromate
is to be prepared and used
to determine the quantity of iron
in an ore sample. The indicator used
is diphenylamine sulfonate.
Optional instructions for potentiometric
titration are also given.*

*Laboratory assignment 14
(3 to 4 periods, in part optional)*

REDOX TITRATION OF IRON

WITH DICHROMATE

DISCUSSION

The preparation of the solution of iron. The samples to be analyzed are iron ores, which first have to be dissolved. The iron is then quantitatively reduced to the bipositive state and finally titrated with the standard dichromate solution.

The common iron ores are magnetite (Fe_3O_4), hematite (Fe_2O_3), limonite ($Fe_2O_3 \cdot xH_2O$), and siderite ($FeCO_3$). Although FeS_2 (iron pyrite) is an iron mineral, it is counted among the sulfur ores. (An ore of a given element is a mineral that is commercially mined and worked as a source of that element.)

324

Hydrochloric acid is more effective in dissolving the oxide ores of iron than is nitric or sulfuric acid. This is probably due to the formation of stable chloride complexes. The reaction is speeded up considerably by the presence of reducing agents such as $SnCl_2$. The reason is believed to be surface reduction of the ferric iron. A residue of silica may remain undissolved, and it may be ignored if it is light in color. If a significant reddish or dark residue remains, it can be brought into solution by treatment with HF or by fusion with Na_2CO_3. The samples to be dispensed are of such nature, however, that even a small darkish residue or one that contains specks of carbonaceous or other black material may be disregarded. The resulting solution contains Fe(III) and possibly some Fe(II).

The reduction of the Fe(III) to Fe(II) is performed by the addition of $SnCl_2$ solution, the Sn(II) being oxidized to Sn(IV). This reaction is performed in a hot solution, since it is rather sluggish in the cold. It is important to remove any excess of Sn(II), because it would react with the dichromate solution added, as well as with the Fe(III) produced in the titration. Removal is achieved by reaction with $HgCl_2$ solution, any surplus of which is of no concern here, since it does not oxidize Fe(II). The reaction products are Sn(IV) and a precipitate of Hg_2Cl_2, which will not reduce significant amounts of Fe(III) or dichromate, particularly if permitted to age for a few minutes,

$$2Fe(III) + Sn(II) = 2Fe(II) + Sn(IV)$$

$$Sn(II)\,(excess) + 2HgCl_2 = Sn(IV) + Hg_2Cl_2(s) + 2Cl^-$$

Unfortunately, the reaction between $HgCl_2$ and $SnCl_2$ may produce metallic Hg, which is capable of rapid reduction of the Fe(III) produced in the titration.

$$Sn(II)\,(excess) + HgCl_2 = Sn(IV) + Hg(l) + 2Cl^-$$

This can be avoided by rapidly adding a sizable excess of mercuric chloride to a cold solution in which the concentration of Sn(II) is low. For this reason the reduction of ferric iron by stannous chloride has to be performed in such a way that only a small excess of Sn(II) results. This is done by proceeding in two steps.

The solution is first concentrated to a small volume so that the presence of any significant amount of tripositive iron is apparent from the yellow color characteristic of the chloride complexes $FeCl^{++}$, $FeCl_2^+$, and $FeCl_4^-$. If the concentrated solution is not yellow to start with, an excess of Sn(II) from the preparation of the solution is still present and 0.2 F KMnO$_4$ solution is added until the first yellow color appears. This is followed by the addition of SnCl$_2$, in drops, until the yellow color changes to a colorless condition or to a pale greenish-yellow tinge due to Fe(II). Two further drops of SnCl$_2$ are added, and the solution is ready for the second step, the reduction of the small excess of Sn(II) with mercuric chloride.

The oxidation of the Sn(II) is performed with KMnO$_4$ rather than, say, K$_2$Cr$_2$O$_7$ because reduction in acid solution produces colorless Mn(II) from KMnO$_4$, whereas K$_2$Cr$_2$O$_7$ results in green Cr(III), which might mask the appearance of the yellow color of the chloride complexes of Fe(III). The 0.5 F solution of SnCl$_2$ used in the assignment is, incidentally, also 3 F in HCl. The HCl is present because slow air oxidation of solutions of Sn(II) produces Sn(IV), which tends to form hydrated oxides of various composition with water:

$$Sn(IV) + (x + 2)H_2O = SnO_2 \cdot xH_2O + 4H^+$$

In strong HCl solutions no precipitation of hydrated Sn(IV) oxides occurs, chiefly because the tin exists in the form of complexes such as SnCl$_6^=$ which are soluble. Sometimes mossy tin (metallic tin) is added to the supply bottles of Sn(II) solutions to keep practically all dissolved Sn at the $+2$ state.

Once the mercuric chloride solution has been added and the precipitate of Hg$_2$Cl$_2$(s) left to age for a few minutes, the solution must be titrated forthwith, because otherwise there is danger of oxidation of Fe(II) by air.

The standard dichromate solution. Potassium dichromate (K$_2$Cr$_2$O$_7$) can be purified to a high degree, is stable, is not hygroscopic, and can be dried without decomposition. It can therefore be used as a primary standard, and it is employed in this assignment to prepare directly a solution of known concentration by accurately weighing the desired amount, dissolving it, and diluting it to volume.

The resulting solution is very stable. It has the desirable property of oxidizing Cl$^-$ to Cl$_2$ only very slowly, if at all, which is due in part to the fact that Cl$_2$ is comparable in oxidizing power with dichromate and in part to a low rate of oxidation of Cl$^-$ by Cr$_2$O$_7^=$, in the case that the concentrations of the species involved should favor such a reaction. Thus, dichromate solution can be used for volumetric titrations even in 2 F HCl solutions. (Another oxidizing agent frequently used in titrations is KMnO$_4$, which is a stronger oxidizing agent than either Cr$_2$O$_7^=$ or Cl$_2$. Titrations in a medium containing HCl and which involve $KMnO_4$ require special precautions to prevent oxidation of Cl^- to Cl_2.) The color of the $Cr_2O_7^=$ ion is not sufficiently intense to be used in recognizing the end point of the titration, particularly not in the presence of the green Cr(III) species that result from its reduction. The titration end point has to be established, therefore, by means of a suitable potential indicator or by measurement of the potential during the titration (potentiometric titration).

The use of diphenylamine sulfonate indicator. As explained earlier, the indicator change from colorless to reddish violet occurs at about 0.83 volt. This is, unfortunately, not as high as is needed for the titration, and inspection of Figure 14-4 shows that at this potential the oxidation of Fe(II) is by no means stoichiometric. This situation is rectified by the addition of sulfuric and phosphoric acids to the solution being titrated, which substantially reduces the concentration of Fe^{3+} by the formation of stable ferric phosphate and sulfate complexes. The reduction in $[Fe^{3+}]$ favors the left side of the half-reaction $Fe^{3+} + e^- = Fe^{++}$, as shown by the substantial lowering of the formal potential E_f° by the presence of 1.0 F H_2SO_4 and 0.5 F H_3PO_4 (see Table 14-1 and discussion on page 314). Thus the nearly horizontal part on the left of the potential curve of Figure 14-4 is moved to a less positive potential and the steep portion substantially lengthened. As a consequence, Fe(II) is quantitatively oxidized to Fe(III) at the indicator end point (see also Prob. 14-7). A large H^+-ion concentration is also required to drive titration reaction (14-23) sufficiently to the right.

The oxidation of the colorless DAS to DBS and to the reddish-violet DBV is slow, but both reactions are catalyzed by the presence of Fe(II) so that the indicator reaction is fast enough to be satisfactory. Further oxidation of DBV to products that are not colored causes a fading of the end point, but at the end point the concentration of Fe(II) is too small to cause any significant increase in the rate of this oxidation. The color remains unbleached long enough to provide a satisfactory end point.

Because of the sluggishness of the indicator oxidation in the absence of Fe(II) it is not possible to run a blank to establish the quantity of $Cr_2O_7^=$ necessary to oxidize the indicator. For this reason the titration gives the best results when the $Cr_2O_7^=$ solution has been standardized against a Fe(II) solution prepared by dissolving a known quantity of pure iron wire.

Potentiometric titration. The solution potential during the titration may be followed by an indicator electrode consisting of a Pt

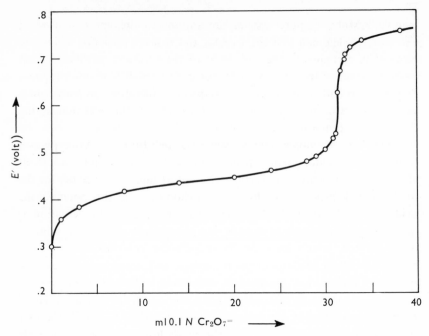

Figure 14-8   Solution potential E' during titration of Fe(II). The potential E' is measured against a saturated calomel electrode with a potential of 0.246 volt.

wire. The saturated calomel electrode that is used in conjunction with the glass electrode for pH measurements is well suited to being the reference electrode. The saturated calomel electrode is designed to include a KCl "salt bridge," as shown in Figure 8-2b (page 169). It has a potential of $E = 0.246$ volt relative to the standard hydrogen half-cell. The pH meter may be used to measure the voltage between the Pt and the calomel electrodes. An experimental titration curve is shown in Figure 14-8.

When several redox couples of markedly different standard potentials are present, the titration curve shows a steep portion for each of them. Thus, the titration curve for a solution containing Sn(II) and Fe(II) has two steep portions, one for the oxidation of the Sn(II), the other for the Fe(II). It should therefore be possible in the present assignment to forego the addition of the $HgCl_2$ and to allow the excess Sn(II) to remain unoxidized; the quantity of iron present would then be obtained from the difference between the volumes of dichromate solution needed to reach the two steep parts of the potential curve.

However, this turns out to be impractical, because the solution contains substantial quantities of Sn(IV) even at the start, and the first steep part of the potential curve never fully develops. The excess Sn(II) must therefore be oxidized with $HgCl_2$ in the potentiometric titration also.

It should be noted that a platinum electrode generally does not assume the potential of the $Cr_2O_7^=/Cr^{3+}$ couple. However, the Fe^{3+}/Fe^{++} couple is reversible, and a Pt wire readily assumes the potential corresponding to the ratio of Fe^{++} to Fe^{3+}, unless Fe^{++} or Fe^{3+} is extremely small. Since at equilibrium the potentials of both couples are equal, the potential measured generally corresponds to the solution potential, except when the equivalence point has been passed and Fe^{++} has become exceedingly small.

PROCEDURES

14-1 Preparation of standard dichromate solution. Review, if necessary, the general procedure for drying samples and weighing out by difference (page 82). Dry between 2.3 and 2.6 g of $K_2Cr_2O_7$ for 1 hr at 110°C. Weigh the weighing bottle to an accuracy commensurate with that for determining volumes with volumetric flasks. Insert a funnel with a long stem into the neck of a clean 500-ml volumetric flask, and carefully transfer most of the potassium dichromate to the funnel. Leave dichromate particles clinging to the weighing bottle undisturbed and weigh the weighing bottle again. Wash the dichromate on the funnel into the flask by small amounts of water and proceed as indicated in the procedure for preparing a solution of accurate volume (page 141), finally diluting the solution to the mark. The resulting solution is approximately 0.1 N. Mix the solution carefully and transfer it to a clean, dry, well-stoppered bottle. Compute the formality and normality of the solution at the standard laboratory temperature of 20°C and label the bottle. Dichromate solutions are very stable.

14-2 Standard iron solution (optional). It may be advisable to check the standardization of the dichromate solution and to practice the dichromate titration as follows. Accurately weigh several samples of about 0.17 g of pure iron wire. Dissolve as directed in Procedure 14-3 and follow the directions of Procedures 14-4 and 14-5. Some pieces of iron wire may dissolve very slowly and leave considerable black residue (probably carbon). Samples containing such residue should be discarded.

14-3 Solution of the iron ore sample. Dry the finely ground ore sample for 1 hr at 110°C, and weigh three portions into 500-ml conical flasks with an accuracy appropriate to this volumetric determination (1 part in 1000). The size of these portions should be such as to be equivalent to about 35 ml of titrant. To each add 20 ml of 6 F HCl and 1 ml of 0.5 F SnCl$_2$ solution, cover each with a small watch glass, and cautiously heat so that there is no boiling or bumping. It is wise not to swirl the mixture until most of the sample has dissolved, so as to minimize deposition of the powdered ore on the walls of the flask. If the solution becomes yellow, add further drops of SnCl$_2$ to keep all the dissolved iron in the reduced form, a procedure that increases the rate of solution. The sample should dissolve in about 15 to 30 min.

For use in Procedure 14-5 mix 800 ml of distilled water, 160 ml of 9 F H$_2$SO$_4$, and 80 ml of 85 per cent phosphoric acid in a 1500-ml beaker or conical flask and let cool to room temperature; this is sufficient for four titrations.

14-4   Reduction of the dissolved iron.   Check the time before proceeding. Once the iron is in the reduced form and the mercuric chloride solution has been added, the solution must be titrated almost immediately; it cannot be stored. A fairly rapid worker should be able to complete the reduction and titration in about 10 min; slower workers may spend as much as $\frac{1}{2}$ hr.

Obtain for each sample about 10 ml of a saturated solution of HgCl$_2$ in a 10-ml graduate. Never use a pipet without a pipet bulb to transfer mercuric chloride, because of the very poisonous nature of mercuric salts. Solutions of 0.5 F SnCl$_2$ and of 0.2 per cent diphenylamine sulfonate are ordinarily available in dropper bottles. Make certain that these items are obtainable before proceeding.

Carefully wash any solution from the cover glass and from the walls of the flask into the main body of the solution, using as little water as possible, and evaporate the solution to about 15 ml. Add drops of 0.2 F KMnO$_4$ solution until the first yellow color appears. Heat to near boiling, and add 0.5 F SnCl$_2$ drop by drop, keeping the solution hot and swirling the flask, until the yellow color turns colorless or to the pale greenish-yellow tinge characteristic of dipositive iron. Add an excess of two drops of SnCl$_2$ solution.

If appreciably more than two drops of SnCl$_2$ solution is added by accident, this should be followed by drops of KMnO$_4$ solution until the first appearance of yellow color and then again by drops of SnCl$_2$ solution.

Cool to room temperature by running tap water over the outside of the flask, and rapidly add the 10 ml of HgCl$_2$ solution from the graduate while swirling the flask. Any local excess of Sn(II) must be quickly overcome so that no metallic mercury is formed.

The precipitate of Hg_2Cl_2 should preferably look silky and light. For unknown reasons, the precipitate may turn out to be gray, without this being harmful to the titration. The sample must, however, be discarded when the precipitate is black. If only a small excess of Sn(II) is present to react with the $HgCl_2$ solution added, the resulting precipitate of Hg_2Cl_2 may be so small as to be hardly noticeable, particularly because of its colloidal nature. If it thus appears as if no precipitate had formed, the procedure should, nevertheless, be continued. The important criterion for the completeness of the reduction to Fe(II) is the change of the color of the solution from yellow to colorless or to a pale greenish-yellow tinge while $SnCl_2$ solution is added. This change in color is quite sharp because of the high concentrations involved.

14-5   Titration of iron with standard dichromate solution.   If necessary, review the procedure for titration, page 141. Permit the reduced solution to stand for 2 min so that the precipitate of mercurous chloride can change from a colloidal to a more crystalline form, which will not appreciably reduce the $Cr_2O_7^=$ added or the Fe(III) formed. Do not wait much longer, since oxidation of Fe(II) by air will become significant. Add 250 ml of the mixture of H_2SO_4, H_3PO_4, and H_2O prepared in Procedure 14-3 and six drops of the indicator. Immediately titrate with the dichromate solution, but perform the titration unhurriedly and carefully while swirling the flask and avoiding large local excesses of $Cr_2O_7^=$. The reaction produces green chromic ions from the orange dichromate solution. When the solution turns from clear green to blue green, the titration is near the end and should be continued by adding fractions of a drop. The end point is a sharp change to a purple or violet-blue color.

14-6 Computation of the results.   Compute the weight percentage of Fe for each of the ore samples titrated. Calculate the average and the absolute and relative unbiased standard deviations (page 83).

14-7 Potentiometric titration (*optional*).   Accurately weigh out a sample of about 170 mg of pure iron wire, and treat it as indicated in Procedures 14-2 to 14-4.

Titrate with an arrangement similar to that used in Procedure 8-4 (the measurement of the pH during an acid-base titration, Figure 8-4) but use a Pt electrode rather than a glass electrode. The pH meter must be zeroed so that 0 mv corresponds to a pH of 14 [note the minus sign in Equation (14-35)]. The instrument should be switched into the mode of operation that permits direct reading of millivolts. The range in which a full-scale reading corresponds to 1400 mv or a similar range should be used. Use small increments of titrant at the end of the titration, when the slope of the potential curve is large. At each point it may take $\frac{1}{2}$ min or more until the potential indicated has stopped drifting, particularly after the end point of the oxidation of iron has been passed. Prepare a graph of the titration potential, with the milliliters of $Cr_2O_7^=$ solution added along the abscissa and the potential along the ordinate. Note that the potential of the saturated calomel half-cell is 0.246 volt. Compare the volume of titrant needed to reach the end point and the quantity of the Fe known to be present.

PROBLEMS

14-1 Galvanic cell. (*a*) Compute the potential of a cell made by combining two half-cells, one consisting of a Zn electrode dipping into a solution in which $[Zn^{++}] = 0.1$, the other of a Pb electrode dipping into a solution in which $[Pb^{++}] = 0.02$. (*b*) What chemical reaction would proceed spontaneously if the two electrodes were connected through an external wire? Which electrode would be positive? Which would be the cathode?

14-2 Reaction constants. Find the equilibrium constant for the reaction

$$2Ag(s) + H_2S(g) = H_2(g) + Ag_2S(s)$$

from the data below and the $E°$ values of the Ag^+/Ag and H^+/H_2 couples given in Table 14-1:

$$H_2S(g) = 2H^+ + S^= \qquad K_{diss} = 1.1 \times 10^{-22}$$

$$Ag_2S(s) = 2Ag^+ + S^= \qquad K_{SP} = 2 \times 10^{-50}$$

14-3 Nernst equation. The potential of an Ag electrode in a solution that is 0.100 *F* in $AgNO_3$ and 1 *F* in NH_3 is found to be 0.319 volt. What is the value of the complex-formation constant of $Ag(NH_3)_2^+$, on the assumption that this is the only complex formed in significant amounts?

14-4 Redox equilibrium. Ferric iron may be quantitatively titrated with a titanous salt. (*a*) Calculate the value of the equilibrium constant of the reaction involved in the titration,

$$Ti^{3+} + Fe^{3+} + H_2O = TiO^{++} + Fe^{++} + 2H^+$$

(*b*) Calculate the ratio $[Fe^{++}]/[Fe^{3+}]$ at the equivalence point, assuming that $[H^+] = 1$.

14-5 Stability of $Cr_2O_7^=$ in water. Consider aqueous solutions which are 1 *M* in Cr^{3+} as well as in $Cr_2O_7^=$ but which are at different pH. Disregarding questions of reaction rates, would the $Cr_2O_7^=$ oxidize water, furnishing $O_2(g)$ at 1 atm, (*a*) at pH 0? (*b*) at pH 4? (*c*) Is there a pH value at which the solution specified above is just at equilibrium with $O_2(g)$ of 1 atm. If so, what is the pH value?

Note: The species $HCr_2O_7^-$, H_2CrO_4, $HCrO_4^-$, and $CrO_4^=$ are also present in these solutions, in quantities that depend on the pH and the equilibrium constants involved (see Table V-5 page 400). The existence of these equilibria does not affect the problem, because of the explicit condition $[Cr_2O_7^=] = 1$. The formal concentration of $K_2Cr_2O_7$ required to achieve unit molarity in $Cr_2O_7^=$ depends, however, on the concentration of the other species also, because it is their source. When the pH is increased above 4, $Cr(OH)_3$ ($K_{SP} = 10^{-30}$) begins to precipitate.

14-6 Equilibrium between metals and their ions.   A piece of metallic Cu is placed in a 0.1 F $AgNO_3$ solution. What is the composition of the solution when equilibrium has been reached?

14-7 Titration curve.   Compute and plot the solution potential as well as $[Fe^{++}]$ for the situation underlying Figure 14-4 for the following quantities of $Cr_2O_7^=$ solution added: 90.00 ml, 99.90 ml, 99.99 ml, 100.0 ml, 100.01 ml, 100.10 ml, 101.00 ml. Use, however, the formal potential for the Fe^{3+}/Fe^{++} couple,

$$Fe^{3+} + e^- = Fe^{++} \qquad E^\circ_f = 0.61 \text{ volt (in 1 } F \text{ } H_2SO_4 \text{ and 0.5 } F \text{ } H_3PO_4)$$

14-8 Completeness of oxidation of Fe(II) at titration end point.   Assume that the DAS end point occurs at 0.83 volt, and compute the ratio $[Fe(III)]/[Fe(II)]$ for the following two cases: (*a*) In the absence of H_2SO_4 and H_3PO_4 ($E^\circ = 0.771$ volt). (*b*) In the presence of 1 F H_2SO_4 and 0.5 F H_3PO_4 ($E^\circ_f = 0.61$ volt).

14-9 Standard potentials and solubility products.   Given are the standard potentials for the following three electrodes: $Pb^{++}/Pb(s)$, $PbSO_4(s)/Pb(s)$, $PbO_2(s)/Pb^{++}$ (see page 403). Calculate (*a*) the solubility product of $PbSO_4$; (*b*) the standard potential of the electrode $PbO_2(s)/PbSO_4(s)$.

14-10 Equilibrium pressure of oxygen for solution of H_2O_2.   Given are the standard potentials for the two couples $O_2(g)/H_2O_2$ and $O_2(g)/H_2O$ (see page 403). Find the partial pressure of oxygen gas that would be at equilibrium with a 0.1 M solution of H_2O_2.

14-11 Dependence of electrode potential on the pH.   Express the potential E of an electrode at equilibrium with a solution containing equal molar concentrations of Mn^{++} and MnO_4^- as a function of the solution pH.

14-12 Dichromate titration of iron.   An iron-ore sample weighing 1.6763 g requires 34.69 ml of 0.0983 N dichromate solution for complete titration. How much iron, in weight per cent, does the ore contain?

REVIEW QUESTIONS

14-1.   Briefly explain the following terms: electrolytic cell, half-cell, galvanic cell, electrode potential, half-cell emf, electrode of second kind, standard potential, equilibrium decomposition potential, formal potential.

14-2.   Recapitulate Nernst's equation and enumerate the conventions that apply to the quantity Q.

14-3.   Recapitulate the connection between standard potentials and equilibrium constants.

Redox titration of iron with dichromate

14-4. Why are electrodes of the second kind favored for establishing voltage standards?

14-5. Briefly list several requirements a redox reaction must satisfy to form the basis of a quantitative method.

14-6. Give balanced equations for the steps involved in the laboratory assignment: solution of the ore (assumed to consist of Fe_2O_3), reduction of the iron, titration reaction.

14-7. Briefly discuss the effects of the following supposed deviations from the procedures recommended in the laboratory assignment. (*a*) No $HgCl_2$ solution was added; (*b*) no $SnCl_2$ solution was added; (*c*) the precipitate of Hg_2Cl_2 was black; (*d*) no phosphoric acid was added; (*e*) the solution being titrated was vigorously shaken during the titration; (*f*) the $K_2Cr_2O_7$ used in the preparation of the standard solution had not been dried prior to being weighed out.

REFERENCES

General electrochemistry

H. A. Laitinen, *Chemical Analysis*, Chaps. 15 to 17, McGraw-Hill, New York, 1960.

J. J. Lingane, *Electroanalytical Chemistry*, 2nd ed., Interscience, New York, 1958.

Reference electrodes

G. J. Janz, *Reference Electrodes, Theory and Practice*, Academic, New York, 1961.

Values of standard electrode potentials

G. Charlot, *Selected Constants: Oxydo-Reduction Potentials*, Pergamon, New York, 1958.

W. M. Latimer, *Oxidation Potentials*, 2nd ed., Prentice-Hall, Englewood Cliffs, N.J., 1952.

Electrode sign convention

T. S. Licht and A. J. deBéthune, "Recent developments concerning the signs of electrode potentials," *J. Chem. Educ.*, **34**, 433–440 (1957).

F. C. Anson, "Electrode sign conventions," *J. Chem. Educ.*, **36**, 394–395 (1959).

*Solutions of iodine and thiosulfate,
their stability and standardization,
the starch-iodine end point, and sources of error
are discussed. A laboratory assignment
provides instructions for the standardization
of a thiosulfate solution
with potassium iodate and for the iodometric
determination of copper.*

fifteen

IODOMETRIC
METHODS

GENERAL PRINCIPLES

Solutions of iodine. Iodometric titrations are based on the half-reaction

$$I_2(s) + 2e^- = 2I^- \qquad E^\circ_{I_2/I^-} = 0.534 \text{ volt} \qquad (15\text{-}1)$$

This potential is intermediate to that of many other couples. Iodide may thus be oxidized quantitatively by many oxidizing agents (for example, IO_3^-, $Cr_2O_7^=$, MnO_4^-, and H_2O_2); and many reducing agents quantitatively reduce iodine [for example, As(III) in neutral or alkaline solutions, HSO_3^-, H_2S, and Sn(II)].

As mentioned in Chapter 13 (page 279) the solubility of I_2 in water is low (1.34×10^{-3} F at 25°C) and its vapor pressure relatively high

335

Iodometric methods

(0.31 mm at 25°C). Both the low solubility and the high vapor pressure would be a serious obstacle to the use of the I_2/I^- couple in volumetric work, were it not for the reaction

$$I_2 + I^- = I_3^- \qquad K_2 = 710 \qquad (15\text{-}2)$$

which makes it possible to achieve iodine concentrations of practical magnitude. For example, in a solution that contains 2.5 per cent KI (0.15 F in KI) and is also 0.05 F (0.1 N) in I_2, $[I_2] = 7 \times 10^{-4}$, which is at about half of saturation in the species I_2. Such a solution is stable experimentally, provided that it is kept in a well-stoppered bottle that is not left open any longer than necessary. Contact with reducing gases and dust must also be avoided.

The half-reaction appropriate to a solution of I_3^- is

$$I_3^- + 2e^- = 3I^- \qquad E^\circ_{I_3^-/I^-} = 0.535 \text{ volt} \qquad (15\text{-}3)$$

It is related to the potential of (15-1) by the solubility of $I_2(s)$ in water and the equilibrium constant K_2 of reaction (15-2) in the following way. In (15-1) an excess of $I_2(s)$ is specified, which is equivalent to saturation of the solution with I_2. Under these conditions the concentration of I_3^- depends on that of I^- only,

$$[I_3^-] = K_2[I^-][I_2]^\circ$$

where $[I_2]^\circ$ is the saturation value of the concentration of I_2. Inserting the values of K_2 and $[I_2]^\circ$,

$$[I_3^-] = 710[I^-]134 \times 10^{-3} = 0.95[I^-]$$

Under these conditions the Nernst equation appropriate to (15-3) is

$$E = E^\circ_{I_3^-/I^-} - (0.0592/2) \log [I^-]^3/[I_3^-]_{\text{satd with } I_2}$$
$$= 0.535 + (0.0592/2) \log 0.95 - (0.0592/2) \log [I^-]^2$$
$$E = 0.534 - (0.0592/2) \log [I^-]^2$$

The last expression is the Nernst equation for the half-reaction (15-1), with $E^\circ_{I_2/I^-} = 0.534$ volt. It is fortuitous that the two E° values are almost equal, based on the fact that, when $[I^-] = 1$ in a saturated solution of I_2, $[I_3^-]$ is 0.95 M, which is close to the standard concentration.

Reducing agents may be titrated with a standard tri-iodide solution. This is sometimes called the iodimetric method. Examples are

$$HSO_3^- + I_3^- + H_2O = SO_4^= + 3I^- + 3H^+$$
$$Sn(II) + I_3^- = Sn(IV) + 3I^-$$

Oxidizing agents may be determined by adding an excess of I^- and titrating the I_3^- generated with a standard solution of a reducing agent. This is sometimes called the iod*o*metric method. Examples are

$$2MnO_4^- + 15I^- + 16H^+ = 2Mn^{++} + 5I_3^- + 8H_2O$$

$$2Ce(IV) + 3I^- = 2Ce(III) + I_3^-$$

Thiosulfate Solutions. The ideal reducing agent for the titration of I_3^- is usually thiosulfate ($S_2O_3^=$), which is oxidized to tetrathionate ($S_4O_6^=$). The half-reaction of the $S_4O_6^=/S_2O_3^=$ couple is

$$S_4O_6^= + 2e^- = 2S_2O_3^= \qquad E° = 0.17 \text{ volt} \qquad (15\text{-}4)$$

The thiosulfate ion was discussed briefly on page 274. The structure of the tetrathionate ion is

$$\left[\begin{array}{ccc} \overset{\displaystyle :\ddot{O}:}{\underset{\displaystyle :\ddot{O}:}{\overset{|}{\underset{|}{}}}} & & \overset{\displaystyle :\ddot{O}:}{\underset{\displaystyle :\ddot{O}:}{\overset{|}{\underset{|}{}}}} \\ :\ddot{O} - S - \ddot{S} - \ddot{S} - S - \ddot{O}: & & \end{array} \right]^=$$

It contains two S atoms at an oxidation state of -1 and two at $+6$.

In a neutral or slightly acid solution the titration reaction between I_3^- and $S_2O_3^=$,

$$I_3^- + 2S_2O_3^= = 3I^- + S_4O_6^= \qquad (15\text{-}5)$$

proceeds rapidly and stoichiometrically.

This reaction of thiosulfate is unique because other oxidizing agents convert thiosulfate at least in part to sulfate. Indeed, in a weakly basic solution I_3^- itself oxidizes some of the $S_2O_3^=$ to $SO_4^=$,

$$4I_3^- + S_2O_3^= + 10OH^- = 2SO_4^= + 12I^- + 5H_2O \qquad (15\text{-}6)$$

which is, of course, different in stoichiometry from (15-5). This reaction probably involves hypoiodous acid (HIO) formed in basic solutions that contain I_3^-,

$$I_3^- + OH^- = HIO + 2I^- \qquad (15\text{-}7)$$

as discussed below. Hypoiodous acid is known to oxidize $S_2O_3^=$ to $SO_4^=$,

$$4HIO + S_2O_3^= + 6OH^- = 2SO_4^= + 4I^- + 5H_2O$$

It is found experimentally that for 0.05 *F* solutions of I_3^- that are acid or even neutral the titration reaction with thiosulfate solution is quantitative, irrespective of which of the two solutions is used as the titrant. When more dilute or slightly alkaline solutions of I_3^- are titrated with $S_2O_3^=$, the amount of titrant consumed is low because the HIO formed by reaction (15-7) oxidizes some of the $S_2O_3^=$ to $SO_4^=$. However, a solution of I_3^- in which the concentration of HIO is kept at an insignificant level by a suitably low pH may be used as a titrant for a slightly alkaline solution of $S_2O_3^=$. The desired titration reaction (15-5) is so rapid that all I_3^- is consumed before any HIO can form, so that there is no oxidation of $S_2O_3^=$ to $SO_4^=$. The pH during the titration should, however, not exceed 9.

Thiosulfate solution must not be acidified, because even dilute acid causes decomposition to sulfurous acid and sulfur, which precipitates,

$$S_2O_3^= + 2H^+ = H_2SO_3 + S(s) \qquad (15\text{-}8)$$

The reaction of H_2SO_3 with I_3^-,

$$H_2SO_3 + I_3^- + H_2O = SO_4^= + 3I^- + 4H^+$$

reduces more I_3^- per original thiosulfate than does the main titration reaction (15-5), so that (15-8) increases the *titer* (the effective concentration) of the thiosulfate solution. Loss of SO_2 gas may counteract and even overbalance this increase in titer. Fortunately, reaction (15-8) is much slower than the titration reaction (15-5), and experiments have shown that thiosulfate solution may be used as *titrant* with tri-iodide solutions as strongly acid as 3 to 4 M in H^+, provided that there is *effective stirring* to avoid local depletion of I_3^-. In fact, standard thiosulfate solution usually contains small amounts of sodium carbonate for reasons of stability (page 342) and should therefore be titrated into an at least slightly acid solution of tri-iodide.

End-point indicator. The customary end-point indicator is a suspension of starch as used in the coulometric determination of As(III) (page 280). In titrations with I_3^- the end point is recognized by the appearance of the blue color of the starch-iodine complex. In titrations with thiosulfate the end point is marked by the disappearance of this color. Addition of the starch suspension is delayed, however, until the brown color of the tri-iodide solution has changed to a faint yellow, because the approach of the end point is easier to observe in this way. At high concentrations of I_3^- there is also some coagulation and decomposition of the starch, and the color change is therefore more sensitive and reversible at low concentrations of I_3^-.

Starch may be separated into two fractions, amylose and amylopectin, the proportions of which depend on the plant source of the starch. Amylose, or "soluble starch," is abundant in potatoes, and one of its forms has the structure of a long helical chain able to accommodate in its center iodine molecules with their axes along the chain axis. This is the intensely blue complex used as indicator for iodine. Amylopectin does not form colloidal solutions and interacts only loosely with iodine, forming reddish adsorption compounds. In the preparation of a starch suspension appropriate for indicator purposes the amylopectin is separated by decantation from the colloidal solution of amylose and discarded.

Starch suspensions usually contain a preservative to prevent or delay decomposition by bacterial action. The decomposition products are harmful, since they adsorb appreciable amounts of iodine with the appearance of a red color. Indicator preparations that give a reddish color with iodine must be discarded.

The starch-iodine end point is most sensitive in slightly acid solutions and is about ten times less pronounced at 50°C than at 25°C. Starch indicator cannot be used in highly acid solutions in which $[H^+]$ exceeds 3 or 4. When $[H^+]$ is near 1 or above, the titration must be performed with reasonable dispatch. Otherwise, undesirable decomposition products that act like those mentioned above are formed.

STANDARDIZATION

Solutions of tri-iodide are usually standardized against arsenious oxide of primary-standard grade. The reaction involved is the same as that used in the coulometric titration of As(III) and has been discussed extensively in Chapter 13 (page 280 ff).

Thiosulfate may be standardized against a weighed quantity of I_2, which is dissolved in a solution of KI. In other methods, known quantities of oxidizing agents are added to a solution of KI and the tri-iodide formed is titrated with the thiosulfate solution to be standardized. Primary standards so used are $K_2Cr_2O_7$ and KIO_3. Solutions of $KMnO_4$ of known concentration may also be used.

Standardization with iodate.   The laboratory assignment for this chapter calls for the standardization of a thiosulfate solution against KIO_3. This substance may be purified easily by recrystallization and is available commercially in a state of high purity. It reacts rapidly and quantitatively with I^- to produce I_3^-,

$$IO_3^- + 8I^- + 6H^+ = 3I_3^- + 3H_2O \qquad (15\text{-}9)$$

as long as the pH is appreciably below 7. It is seen that one KIO_3 is equivalent to three I_3^-, so that the equivalent weight of KIO_3 is $KIO_3/6 = 35.67$, which is small and thus a disadvantage.* For example, 0.14 g of KIO_3 is equivalent to 40 ml of 0.1 F thiosulfate solution. For this reason it is better to use a larger quantity of KIO_3 to prepare a standard solution and to use *aliquot portions* (i.e., known fractions) for the standardization of the thiosulfate solution.

The pH dependence of reaction (15-9) is so critical that the reaction stops at a pH near 7 when the supply of acid is less than needed for all the IO_3^- to react. The reaction may thus be used for the standardization of strong acids by adding an excess of IO_3^- and I^- and titrating the I_3^- formed with thiosulfate. It also is the basis of a test for the presence of iodide in iodate or of iodate in iodide.

Standardization with copper. Metallic copper may also be used as primary standard for thiosulfate by using the same reaction employed in the laboratory assignment to determine copper in a copper alloy. In this method Cu^{++} is used to oxidize I^- to I_3^-, being reduced to $Cu(I)$; the I_3^- produced is titrated with standard thiosulfate solution. On the face of it oxidation of I^- to I_3^- requires a potential substantially above that of the standard potential of the I_3^-/I^- couple (0.535 volt), whereas $E°$ for the Cu^{++}/Cu^+ couple is only 0.17 volt,

$$Cu^{++} + e^- = Cu^+ \qquad E°_{Cu^{++}/Cu^+} = 0.17 \text{ volt} \qquad (15\text{-}10)$$

This situation, however, is radically changed by the low solubility of $CuI(K_{SP} = 3 \times 10^{-12})$, because of which the products of the reaction

$$2Cu^{++} + 5I^- = 2CuI(s) + I_3^- \qquad K_{11} = 5 \times 10^6 \qquad (15\text{-}11)$$

are favored. The same situation is expressed by the standard potential of the half-reaction

$$Cu^{++} + I^- + e^- = CuI(s) \qquad E°_{Cu^{++}/CuI} = 0.85 \text{ volt} \qquad (15\text{-}12)$$

The values of $E°_{Cu^{++}/Cu^+}$ and $E°_{Cu^{++}/CuI}$ are, of course, related by the solubility product of $CuI(s)$, as follows: To use an argument somewhat different from that given on page 313, the solution potential equals $E°_{Cu^{++}/CuI}$ when $[Cu^{++}] = [I^-] = 1$. At these conditions

$$[Cu^+] = K_{SP}/[I^-] = K_{SP}$$

Inserting these concentrations into the Nernst equation for (15-10),

---

* This is, of course, not the equivalent weight of KIO_3 in reaction (15-9), but that corresponding to the subsequent reaction (15-5) of the tri-iodide produced.

$$E^\circ_{Cu^{++}/CuI} = E^\circ_{Cu^{++}/Cu^+} - 0.0592 \log K_{SP}$$

The value of K_{11} indicates that reaction (15-11) is sufficiently quantitative to form the basis of an analytical method. An excess of I^- and reduction of the I_3^- concentration by the subsequent titration with thiosulfate are additional factors to make reaction (15-11) stoichiometric. This is substantiated by experimental investigations. These experiments show, however, that at a pH above 4 the formation of $Cu(OH)^+$,

$$Cu^{++} + H_2O = Cu(OH)^+ + H^+$$

causes the reaction to become sluggish. High concentrations of acetate and other complexing agents are equally undesirable, because they also decrease the concentration of Cu^{++} ions. An upper limit of $[H^+]$ is about 0.3, above which air oxidation of iodide becomes appreciable. In the laboratory an $HSO_4^-/SO_4^=$ buffer system is used to maintain the pH near 2. Another buffer system often used involves the conjugate acid-base pair HF and F^-, with a pH between 3 and 4.

SOURCES OF ERROR

Solutions of iodide and tri-iodide. The two major sources of error inherent in the use of the I_3^-/I^- couple are (1) loss of iodine because of its relatively high vapor pressure and (2) partial oxidation of iodide by air.

The first of these may be minimized by having a sufficiently high concentration of I^- and by working in cold solutions. In addition, no reactions that produce gases may be used, because iodine vapor would be carried away by such gases.

The second error source, the oxidation of iodide by air, follows the equation

$$6I^- + O_2(g) + 4H^+ = 2I_3^- + 2H_2O \qquad K_{13} = 10^{47} \qquad (15\text{-}13)$$

Examination of the mass-action expression and the equilibrium constant shows that even at pH 7 the products of this reaction are highly favored. Fortunately, the reaction rate is small, and it has been found that there is no appreciable *oxygen error*, as it is called, when iodide solutions with a H^+-ion concentration as high as 0.4 M are left in contact with air. The rate is increased, however, by the presence of metal ions, such as Cu^{++}, and by the reaction of I^- with other oxidizing agents. For example, when iodide is oxidized with $Cr_2O_7^=$ at a H^+-ion concentration above 0.4 M, an appreciable oxygen error is *induced*. Such reactions must therefore be performed with reasonable speed, and titration of an acid tri-iodide solution with thiosulfate must not be delayed. Reaction (15-13) is also induced by light, and thus standard solutions of I_3^- must be stored in the dark or in dark bottles.

Thiosulfate solutions. Error sources that involve thiosulfate standard solutions are the following: It has been found that microorganisms may change the titer of thiosulfate solutions by conversion of thiosulfate to sulfite and sulfur. Their action is largely inhibited at a pH between 8 and 9. It has been found that 0.1 F thiosulfate solutions are stable provided that they have been prepared with freshly boiled water, contain 0.01 per cent of Na_2CO_3 (to provide the proper pH), and are so handled as to minimize bacterial infections.

Although the potential of the $O_2(g)/H_2O$ couple is sufficient to oxidize $S_2O_3^=$ to $S_4O_6^=$, it is found that saturation with O_2 does not appreciably affect the titer of thiosulfate solutions. This, however, is no longer true in the presence of traces of certain metal ions such as Cu^{++}, which catalyze air oxidation of thiosulfate. The reaction presumably involves the steps

$$2Cu^{++} + 2S_2O_3^= = 2Cu^+ + S_4O_6^=$$

and

$$4Cu^+ + O_2(g) + 2H_2O = 4Cu^{++} + 4OH^-$$

The presence of such metal ions is therefore undesirable. As mentioned earlier, thiosulfate solutions must never be acidified before being used in a titration.

Error sources specific to the iodometric determination of copper are discussed in conjunction with the laboratory assignment.

*A thiosulfate solution is to be prepared
and standardized against an iodate solution
of known concentration.
The copper content of an alloy sample
is determined by dissolving a weighed quantity
in acid, reacting the Cu^{++} in the resulting
solution with excess iodide,
and titrating the tri-iodide produced
with the standard thiosulfate solution.*

*Laboratory assignment 15
(4 periods)*

IODOMETRIC DETERMINATION

OF COPPER

DISCUSSION

The iodometric method is commonly used to determine the copper content of alloys such as brasses and bronzes. In the following pages the possible interference of other alloy constituents is discussed, and error sources specific to this determination are considered.

Interference by other alloy constituents.   Common constituents of copper alloys are Zn, Ni, Sn, Pb, Al, and small amounts of Fe. The iodometric determination of Cu is not affected by the presence of Zn, Ni, and Al. Iron would interfere if present in its higher oxidation state, because the couple Fe^{3+}/Fe^{++} is capable of oxidizing I^- to I_3^-, and

343

indeed this oxidation is the basis for an iodometric method to determine iron. This interference may be avoided effectively by the addition of fluoride ions, which form complexes of high stability with Fe(III), like FeF_6^{3-}. The concentration of Fe^{3+} is thus reduced to such a low level that its presence no longer affects the determination of Cu^{++}. Fluoride is usually added together with hydrofluoric acid in the form of an acid fluoride. It then serves the double purpose of masking Fe(III) and of participating in the buffer system HF/F^- that was mentioned on page 341. The presence of HF causes some etching of the glass container. When only small amounts of iron are present, the Fe(III) may be sufficiently masked by the addition of H_3PO_4. The alloy samples used in the laboratory assignment contain at most traces of iron, so that the use of fluoride or phosphoric acid is not necessary.

The presence of tin may interfere in the following way: The sample is dissolved in nitric acid, which converts tin to the $+4$ state. In this oxidation state tin is noted for the formation of colloidal precipitates of $SnO_2 \cdot xH_2O$,

$$Sn(IV) + (x + 2)H_2O = SnO_2 \cdot xH_2O + 4H^+$$

which adsorb appreciable quantities of Cu^{++}. This may be prevented by the presence of complexing agents such as Cl^- (forming $SnCl_6^=$, etc.) and $SO_4^=$ (forming complexes of unknown composition). The procedure used in the assignment calls for fuming with sulfuric acid, which dissolves any hydrated SnO_2 that has formed earlier. Some SnO_2 may precipitate later when the sulfuric acid solution is diluted, but the amount of Cu^{++} adsorbed under these circumstances is negligible.

The presence of Pb(II) in the determination of copper is undesirable because of the formation of a yellowish precipitate of PbI_2 when iodide is added, which obscures the end point of the thiosulfate titration. The fuming with sulfuric acid precipitates most of any Pb(II) present as lead sulfate. Small amounts of $PbSO_4$, however, remain dissolved in the fuming acid; the reason is that $[SO_4^=]$ is relatively small in this very acid solution. Upon dilution, the remaining $PbSO_4$ precipitates quantitatively, provided that the solution is cooled and permitted to stand.

Prolonged fuming with sulfuric acid also dehydrates the blue hydrated cupric ion $Cu(H_2O)_4^{++}$, and a greenish-gray precipitate of anhydrous $CuSO_4$ is likely to separate. When the sulfuric acid solution is diluted later, this precipitate dissolves and the blue color returns.

Before the solution of the alloy is reacted with iodide, the sulfuric acid is neutralized with 15 F NH_3. A small amount of sulfuric acid is then added to provide the $HSO_4^-/SO_4^=$ buffer mentioned in the discussion of the standardization of thiosulfate with copper (page 341).

Other sources of error. As mentioned, the sample is dissolved in nitric acid. The reaction between nitric acid and copper is similar to that between that acid and silver, described on page 145, and produces NO, NO_2, and HNO_2. These reduction products of HNO_3 must be removed, because any one of them initiates air oxidation of iodide,

$$2NO_2 + 3I^- = I_3 + 2NO_2^-$$

$$2NO_2^- + 3I^- + 4H^+ = 2NO + I_3^- + H_2O$$

$$2NO + O_2 = 2NO_2$$

Fuming with sulfuric acid completely removes all HNO_3, but traces of nitrogen oxides are left, probably as nitrosulfuric acid (NO_2SO_3H) and similar compounds. They are expelled by subsequent brief boiling after dilution.

The tendency of cuprous iodide to adsorb tri-iodide is a further possible source of error. The adsorbed tri-iodide gives a buff color to the precipitate, which obscures the end point. Furthermore, it may cause recurring end points, and the results may be as much as 0.3 per cent low. It has been found that the adsorption of tri-iodide may be minimized by adding SCN^- to the solution just before the end point. Since CuSCN is less soluble than CuI, at least the surface layers of the CuI will be changed into CuSCN, which has a smaller tendency to adsorb I_3^-. Furthermore, the small amount of Cu^{++} left after the reaction with the iodide is decreased still further by the addition of SCN^-,

$$2Cu^{++} + 3I^- + 2SCN^- = 2CuSCN(s) + I_3^-$$

because of the lower solubility of CuSCN relative to that of CuI. This makes the production of I_3^- more quantitative and decreases any interference by the formation of Cu(II) complexes. The thiocyanate must not be added before most of the tri-iodide has been reduced by titration with thiosulfate, so as to avoid appreciable reduction of tri-iodide by the thiocyanate.

PROCEDURES

15-1 Preparation and standardization of a thiosulfate solution. Gently boil 1 liter of distilled water for 5 min in a 1500-ml beaker or conical flask. Allow to cool. Weigh out 25 g of $Na_2S_2O_3 \cdot 5H_2O$ and 0.1 g of Na_2CO_3. Dissolve both in the freshly boiled water. Transfer this 0.1 F $Na_2S_2O_3$ solution to a clean, labeled bottle with a ground-glass stopper.

Dry about 1.5 g of pure KIO_3 at 170 to 180°C. After cooling, accurately weigh out a quantity between 1.2 and 1.5 g and transfer it to a 250-ml volumetric flask. Dissolve by adding distilled water, and carefully dilute to the mark. Thoroughly mix the solution, and calculate its concentration. Transfer to a clean, labeled bottle with a ground-glass stopper.

Pipet 25.00 ml of the standard KIO_3 solution into a 200-ml flask. Dissolve 3 g of KI in 25 ml of water. Boil 2 ml of 6 F HCl to remove any Cl_2 and add to the KI solution. No iodine color should appear; such color would indicate the presence of iodate or of other oxidizing agents. Add the acid iodide solution without delay to the iodate solution in the titration vessel. Slowly swirl, and titrate with thiosulfate; vigorous shaking and undue delay must be avoided to minimize loss of iodine vapor. When the iodine color has become indistinct, but not before, add 5 ml of starch-indicator solution and continue the titration with fractions of drops until the starch-iodine color has disappeared. Repeat this titration with two further aliquots of the iodate solution, and compute the formality of the thiosulfate solution. Since this standardization is based on a single weighing, it may be wise to repeat it as a check.

15-2   Preparation of the solution of the copper alloy sample. Compute the approximate sample weight that is equivalent to 30 to 40 ml of the standard thiosulfate solution. Accurately weigh out three samples and transfer them to 200-ml flasks. To each sample add 5 ml of 6 F HNO_3. Cover the flasks with small watch glasses and heat, if necessary, until solution is essentially complete. Avoid loss by spattering. If the dissolving of the brass presents difficulties, add 5 ml of 6 F HCl. If the tin content of the original sample is high, the brass turnings may become covered by a layer of $SnO_2 \cdot xH_2O$; remove any such layer with a glass rod. A final white turbidity or suspension of $SnO_2 \cdot xH_2O$ will be dissolved by the fuming with sulfuric acid.

Remove the watch glass, add 10 ml of 9 F H_2SO_4, and carefully evaporate until copious, dense white fumes of H_2SO_4 begin to appear. This may be done safely by *continuously* swirling the flask and keeping it directly over the burner. The fumes of HNO_3 that appear at first are less dense than those of H_2SO_4 and must not be mistaken for them;

the latter will not appear until the H_2SO_4 is approximately 18 F, which means evaporation to about half the volume of the 9 F H_2SO_4 added. The H_2SO_4 fumes fill the *whole flask* and may also be recognized by a choking sensation produced by even a very small amount. Fuming of the sulfuric acid should not be prolonged unnecessarily.

Permit the mixture to cool for a few minutes, and continue the cooling by letting tap water run over the outside of the flask (use of tap water prior to an initial cooling period may cause the flask to crack). Slowly add 5 ml of distilled water, 1 ml at a time, to the cool solution; if necessary, cool the flask from the outside. (This is the reverse of the order recommended on page 5 for adding sulfuric acid to water; the present sequence is used to avoid transferring the solution to another vessel.) A precipitate of $PbSO_4$ may appear at this point and should be disregarded.

Add another 15 ml of water and boil for 1 to 2 min to make certain that the last traces of nitrous oxides have been removed. Cool again to room temperature, and slowly neutralize the solution by adding 15 F NH_3 from a dropper; neutralization is recognized by the first perceptible violet-blue color of the $Cu(NH_3)_4^{++}$ complex [or the formation of a precipitate of $Cu(OH)_2$]. The solution must be kept cool to avoid spattering. Add 3 F H_2SO_4 in drops until the $Cu(NH_3)_4^{++}$ color just disappears, and add 1 ml in excess to achieve buffering by the conjugate acid-base pair HSO_4^- and $SO_4^=$. Cool to room temperature. The solution volume should not exceed 40 ml at this point.

15-3 Iodometric determination of copper. Prepare a solution of 4 g KI in 10 ml of water, and add it to the solution of the alloy. Gently and continuously swirl the solution, and rapidly titrate it with standard 0.1 F thiosulfate solution. The thiosulfate should be added rapidly until the iodine color becomes indistinct. In the very first titration of this kind the presence of the buff-colored precipitate may be confusing. Thus it may be helpful to let the mixture in the flask come to rest, to hold the flask so that the buret tip is close to the surface of the liquid, and to observe whether or not one drop of thiosulfate causes local bleaching of the *solution*. Starch indicator should not be added before this occurs. For later runs the required volume of titrant should, as always, be calculated with the slide rule.

Add 3 ml of starch-indicator solution, and titrate until the blue starch-iodine color of the *solution* has almost disappeared. Add 2 g of KSCN, swirl the solution, and titrate until the blue color has entirely disappeared. If in doubt about having passed the end point, add 1 ml of starch-indicator solution and observe whether or not this causes darkening of the solution.

15-4 Computation of results. Compute the percentage of copper for each of the samples titrated. Calculate the mean of these values and the absolute and relative unbiased standard deviations (see page 83).

PROBLEMS

15-1 Equilibrium constant and standard potentials. From the standard potentials of the half-reactions (15-3) and (15-4) compute the equilibrium constant for reaction (15-5).

15-2 Vapor pressure of iodine above a tri-iodide solution. From the data given at the beginning of Chapter 15 compute the vapor pressure of iodine at 25°C above a solution that is 0.20 F in KI and 0.05 F in I_2.

15-3 Formal solubility of iodine in an iodide solution. From the data given at the beginning of Chapter 15 calculate the formal solubility of iodine at 25°C in a 0.10 F solution of KI.

15-4 Determination of copper in brass. A brass sample weighing 0.2413 g was treated as described in the procedures of Laboratory Assignment 15. In the titration with 0.1037 F thiosulfate solution 31.25 ml was used. What was the weight percentage of copper in the brass?

15-5 Standardization of thiosulfate. In standardizing thiosulfate against KIO_3 it was found that 28.37 ml of thiosulfate solution was equivalent to 25.02 ml of a KIO_3 solution prepared by dissolving 1.684 g of KIO_3 in water and carefully diluting to 250.1 ml. What was the concentration of the thiosulfate solution?

15-6 Determination of barium. A sample containing $BaCO_3$ and weighing 0.512 g was dissolved in HNO_3, the solution was neutralized and buffered at a pH of 5, and $BaCrO_4$ was precipitated quantitatively by the addition of K_2CrO_4 solution. The $BaCrO_4$ precipitate was filtered, washed, and dissolved in HCl. Two grams of solid KI was added and the mixture gently swirled and titrated with 0.1013 F thiosulfate solution. The titration required 38.68 ml. What was the percentage of Ba in the sample?

15-7 Concentration of a strong acid. To 25.00 ml of a solution of HCl were added excess quantities of KIO_3 and of KI. The tri-iodide produced was titrated with 0.1083 F thiosulfate solution, requiring 32.49 ml. What was the formality of the original HCl solution?

15-8 Complex-formation constant and electrode potentials. The table overleaf shows the potentials assumed by a silver electrode in solutions containing Ag^+ and $S_2O_3^=$ ions. To explain these potentials, assume that the formation of only one complex between Ag^+ and $S_2O_3^=$ is involved (Ag^+ forms no complex with ClO_4^-). Find the correct formula of this complex and the complex formation constant.

concentration of solution, F		
AgClO$_4$	Na$_2$S$_2$O$_3$	*potential, volts*
1.00×10^{-3}	0.100	-0.013
1.00×10^{-3}	1.00	-0.129
1.00	None	$+0.792$

15-9 Electrode potentials in liquid ammonia.   There are many analogies between aqueous solutions and solutions in liquid ammonia (bp,-33°C). Answer the following questions by using the standard potentials given below, which have been corrected to a somewhat hypothetical 25°C.

$$E°, \text{ volt}$$

$$Ca(NH_2)_2(s) + 2e^- = Ca(s) + 2NH_2^- \qquad -2.83$$
$$Ca^{++} + 2e^- = Ca(s) \qquad -2.17$$
$$K^+ + e^- = K(s) \qquad -2.04$$
$$NaNH_2(s) + e^- = Na(s) + NH_2^- \qquad -2.02$$
$$Na^+ + e^- = Na(s) \qquad -1.89$$
$$NH_3 + e^- = \tfrac{1}{2}H_2(g) + NH_2^- \qquad -1.59$$
$$NH_4^+ + e^- = \tfrac{1}{2}H_2(g) + NH_3 \qquad 0$$

(*a*) Arrange the amides of Ca, K, and Na in order of increasing solubility.
(*b*) Find K_{SP} for calcium amide.
(*c*) Find the autosolvolysis product $[NH_2^-][NH_4^+]$ (at 25°C).

REVIEW QUESTIONS

15-1.   Formulate equations for the reactions that take place when the sample (assumed to be a pure Cu-Zn alloy) is dissolved, when the iodide is added, and when the mixture is titrated with thiosulfate.

15-2.   Under what conditions is thiosulfate solution unstable?

15-3.   Why are oxides of nitrogen removed from the solution before potassium iodide is added?

15-4.   Briefly list possible sources of error associated with the use of tri-iodide solutions and of thiosulfate solutions.

15-5.   What is the purpose of fuming the brass solution with sulfuric acid?

15-6.   What is the reason for adding potassium thiocyanate to the titration mixture?

15-7.   How can the presence of iron in amounts larger than traces be kept from interfering with the determination of copper?

15-8.   What are the pH limits in the iodometric determination of copper and what are the reasons for these limits?

15-9.   Briefly discuss the effects of the following supposed deviations from the recommended procedures in the iodometric determination of copper. (*a*) Some of the thiosulfate had decomposed to sulfur and sulfite; (*b*) the addition of KSCN just before the observation of the final end point was deleted; (*c*) after the KI had been added and prior to the titration with thiosulfate solution a period of 15 min elapsed; (*d*) oxides of nitrogen were still present in the solution when the KI was added; (*e*) the brass sample contained substantial amounts of Pb and Sn; (*f*) the brass sample contained substantial quantities of Fe.

REFERENCES

I. M. Kolthoff and E. B. Sandell, *Textbook of Quantitative Inorganic Analysis*, 3rd ed., Chap. 39, Macmillan, New York, 1952.

H. A. Laitinen, *Chemical Analysis*, Chap. 21, McGraw-Hill, New York, 1960.

E. H. Swift, *Introductory Quantitative Analysis*, Chap. 9, Prentice-Hall, Englewood Cliffs, N.J., 1950.

*In favorable cases the method
of continuous variation permits
the determination of the integer n
in the equilibrium A + nB = AB_n.
Separate solutions of A and of B,
but of the same formality, are prepared
and mixed in different proportions.
For each mixture a quantity characteristic
of the complex AB_n is measured. This
quantity reaches a maximum when
the ratio of original solutions of A and B
is 1: n, so that n may be determined
by finding the location of this maximum.
In the examples chosen to demonstrate the method,
AB_n is highly colored and A and B are colorless
or almost so; absorbances of the
different mixtures are measured
at a wavelength where AB_n absorbs strongly.
The method is often called Job's method,
after one of its originators.*

sixteen

THE METHOD OF CONTINUOUS VARIATION

GENERAL PRINCIPLES

Consider two molecular or ionic species A and B, both colorless, which combine to form AB_n, a colored compound or a complex ion, by the reaction

$$A + nB = AB_n$$

not colored   colored

The equilibrium expression for this reaction is

$$[AB_n]/[A][B]^n = K_f \qquad (16\text{-}1)$$

where K_f is the formation constant of the compound.

351

Suppose that the concentrations of A and B are varied in such a way that the sum of their formal concentrations is kept at the constant value c. Let x be the formal concentration of A, $c - x$ that of B, and y that of AB_n, so that

$$[A] = x - y \qquad [B] = c - x - ny \qquad [AB_n] = y$$

and

$$y/[(x - y)(c - x - ny)^n] = K_f \tag{16-2}$$

The internal transmittance of the solution is given [Eq. (11-10), page 227] by

$$T_i = I/I_0 = 10^{-\varepsilon by}$$

so that the negative logarithm of T_i, or the absorbance A_i, is proportional to y,

$$A_i = -\log T_i = \varepsilon by \tag{16-3}$$

where ε is the molar absorptivity of AB_n.

When K_f is very large, the amount of complex formed is limited by the total supply of A or that of B, whichever is depleted first. In the limit of an infinite K_f the concentration of AB_n is given by two slanted straight lines that intersect when

$$(c - x) : x = n : 1 \tag{16-4}$$

where the concentration of AB_n reaches its maximum value (see Fig. 16-1 for the case $n = 4$, as well as Prob. 16-1). It can be seen by suitable differentiation (see Prob. 16-2) that the location of the maximum of $y = [AB_n]$ as a function of x remains unchanged for finite values of K_f and is thus always given by (16-4) (Fig. 16-1). This maximum is the less pronounced the smaller K_f; it is possible to obtain a good estimate of K_f from a detailed analysis of the experimental curve, but this will not be pursued here. For the compound AB_4 illustrated by Figure 16-1, the curve for a finite K_f is approximately a straight line near $x = 0$ and a fourth-power parabola near $x = 4$ (see Prob. 16-5).

Since the absorbance of the solution is, by Equation (16-2), proportional to y, it shows a maximum also when the condition (16-4) is satisfied. Thus, to obtain n, the absorbance is determined as a function of x, the maximum is located, and n is evaluated from Equation (16-4). In the ideal situation the absorbances of uncombined A and B are negligible at the wavelength chosen to measure the absorbance of AB_n. A small contribution to the total absorbance by A or B can be corrected for by using the additivity property (11-12) (page 230) of the

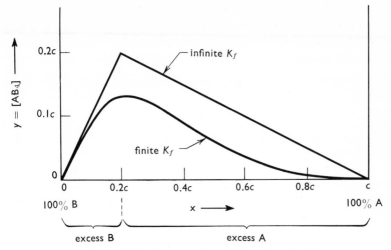

Figure 16-1   Concentration of AB_4 as function of x.

absorbance. This contribution depends, of course, on the precise amounts of unreacted A or B, which can be computed only if n and K_f are known. It is, however, usually adequate to subtract the absorbances that would be caused by A and B if there had been no formation of AB_n. This represents overcorrection, but as long as the correction is small, the position of the maximum will not be significantly affected by it.

The method works only if AB_n is the only complex formed or if the concentrations and absorbances of any other complexes are small compared with those of AB_n under the conditions of the experiment. To check on this point, the entire absorption spectrum of each mixture must be determined and plotted against the wavelengths as abscissa. If only one species AB_n is responsible for the absorption, these spectra are identical provided that the changed concentrations of AB_n in the different mixtures are taken into account. If several complexes are formed, their absorption spectra usually differ considerably and there is a systematic change in the absorption spectrum of the mixture as the ratio of A to B is changed.

Often A, B, or both have acidic or basic properties, so that the effective complex-formation constant may depend on the pH. There exist, in fact, situations in which *different* complexes predominate at different pH values. It is therefore important to carry out the measurements at a constant pH. This may be accomplished by adding buffering components in equal concentrations to the original solutions of A and of B so that the concentration of buffer is not changed upon mixing.

The components of the buffering system or other constituents of the solution (here collectively called C and D) may form additional compounds (e.g., complexes) with both A and B, so that further equilibria may have to be considered. However, the essential aspects of the situation remain unchanged, provided (1) the compounds formed involve only one A or one B and are thus of the form AC_p, BD_q, etc.; (2) the constituents C and D are present in large enough concentrations that formation of compounds with A and B does not change [C] and [D] significantly. Under these circumstances the concentration of A is proportional to the sum S_A of the concentrations of A and all compounds of A with C and D, $[A] = k_A S_A$ (see Prob. 16-4). Similarly, [B] is proportional to an analogous quantity S_B, $[B] = k_B S_B$. Equation (16-1) thus leads to the related equation

$$[AB_n]/S_A S_B = k_A k_B{}^n K_f = K_f' \qquad (16\text{-}5)$$

The salient features of the method remain unaffected, and the absorbance as a function of x has a maximum when Equation (16-4) is satisfied, provided the absorbances of all constituents of the solution other than AB_n are negligible or can be corrected for. The equilibrium constant K_f' that may be estimated from a more detailed analysis of the graph of the absorbance against x is, of course, a "formal" constant only, valid for the particular concentrations of C and D for which it was obtained. To evaluate K_f itself, the mass-action constants of the other equilibria involved would have to be known. An example of this situation is the case of hydration equilibria in aqueous solutions discussed earlier (page 205).

A requirement of the method of continuous variation is that the physical quantity measured to determine the amount of AB_n has additive properties, so that contributions by A and B can be corrected for; preferably, such contributions are negligibly small. The method may, for example, be used to determine the composition of a slightly soluble compound AB_n by estimating the amounts of precipitate formed in different mixtures. In practice, the method has mainly been used to find the compositions and measure the formation constants of colored complex ions. Several other methods of exploring complex formation by optical measurements also exist. All these are restricted, of course, to colored compounds. Of more general applicability are the following two methods: The first is based on the fact that all complexing agents are also acids or bases. Complex formation thus may significantly affect the pH of an unbuffered solution. Conversely, measurement of the pH as a function of the concentrations of A and B may provide information on equilibria between different complexes and A and B. In the second method the concentration of the metal ions is determined potentiometrically. In spite of the existence of several methods the interpretation of the data obtained is often difficult.

The formula of the complex of Fe(III)
with a complexing agent
is determined by
the method of continuous variation.

Laboratory assignment 16
(1 to 2 periods)

THE FORMULA OF A COMPLEX ION

DISCUSSION

In the procedures to follow, the formulas of complexes of tripositive iron with several complexing agents are determined. All solutions are acid, buffered by the system $HSO_4^-/SO_4^=$. Since the acid constant of HSO_4^- is about 10^{-2}, the pH of the solution is in the neighborhood of 2. The first of the two solutions to be mixed (solution I) is c F in Fe(III) aside from the excess of buffer it contains. The second solution (solution II) is c F in the complexing agent and contains HSO_4^- and $SO_4^=$ in the same concentrations as solution I. In the mixture of solutions I and II the pH thus remains constant, and so does the sulfate concentration.

355

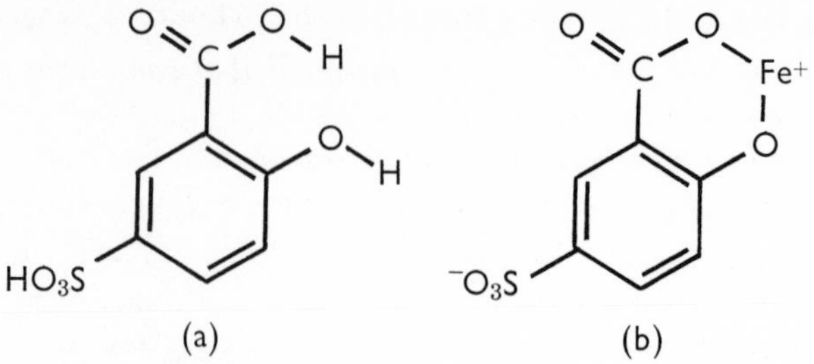

Figure 16-2   (a) Structure of sulfosalicylic acid; (b) a possible structure of the iron complex.

The latter is important, since Fe(III) is known to form sulfate complexes. The different complexing agents are the following:

1 Thiocyanate (SCN$^-$).   Thiocyanate forms several intensely red complexes with Fe(III), which are the basis of a test for iron and which are used in the Volhard titration (Chap. 7). HNCS is a strong acid, and the buffering is thus not particularly important. Under the conditions of this experiment one of the thiocyanate complexes predominates, and the others are formed at higher concentrations (see Prob. 16-3).

2 Sulfosalicylic acid.   This compound consists of a benzene ring to which are attached a carboxyl group, a hydroxyl group, and a sulfonic acid group (Fig. 16-2). (The two resonating forms of the benzene ring are not shown in the figure.) The sulfonic acid group accounts for the solubility of the compound. It is strongly acidic and does not carry a proton in an aqueous solution. A hydroxyl group attached to a benzene ring is usually weakly acidic, so that sulfosalicylic acid is a triprotic acid (abbreviated H_3SS). The complex-forming particle is known to be SS^{3-}, and the six-membered ring containing the Fe atom, shown in Figure 16-2b, is presumably formed upon chelation.

Again, one Fe^{3+} may complex with one or more sulfosalicylic acid ions, and the method of continuous variation permits making a decision. Buffering is important, since the concentration of SS^{3-} depends on the pH.

3 Tiron, or disodium dihydroxybenzene disulfonate.   The anion of this salt consists of a benzene ring to which are attached two sulfonic acid and two hydroxyl groups (Fig. 16-3). The two hydroxyl groups are acidic, so that the anion may be abbreviated as $H_2Tir^=$. The chelation involves the two oxygen atoms of the ion Tir^{4-}, a five-ring being formed. By the method of continuous variation it is possible to find the ratio of

356

Tir^{4-} to Fe(III) in the complex formed at the pH and at the concentrations prevailing.

It will be noted in passing that polydentate complexes are usually most stable if five-membered rings or six-membered rings are involved. Examples other than those discussed here are the metal chelates of EDTA (Fig. 12-5, page 257) and of Erio T (Fig. 12-7, page 260; the two O atoms of the hydroxyl groups and one of the N atoms are used in the chelate formation).

PROCEDURES

Instructions are given (1) for the general operation of the method of continuous variation and (2) for the preparation of the solutions for the different systems, one of which is to be investigated.

16-1   Preparation of the mixtures.   Obtain from the laboratory instructor solutions I and II for the system you are to investigate. Solution I contains Fe(III), and solution II contains the complexing agent, both at the same formality; both solutions also contain the same concentrations of $HSO_4^-/SO_4^=$ buffer. Prepare in the following manner nine mixtures containing solutions I and II in the respective ratios: 1:9, 2:8, 3:7, 4:6, 5:5, 6:4, 7:3, 8:2, 9:1. If available, use separate burets for delivering measured volumes of solutions I and II. Any ordinary buret can be used for the second buret; it does not need to be calibrated. Before filling the burets, follow the usual practice of rinsing with 1- to 2-ml portions of the solution to be delivered. Deliver into dry test tubes q ml of solution I and $(10.0 - q)$ ml of solution II, where q is a multiple of 1.0. Mix by stirring and label the test tubes.

16-2. Measurements of absorbances.   Determine the absorbances of the nine mixtures and those of solutions I and II ($A = -\log T$).

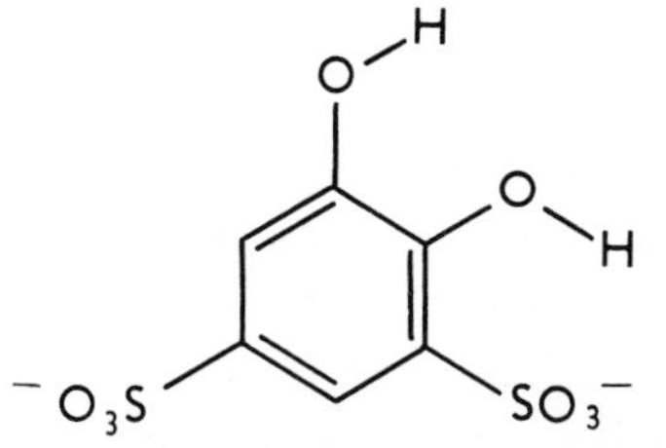

Figure 16-3   Structure of $H_2Tir^=$, the anion of tiron.

The colorimeter should be permitted to warm up for at least 10 min. Use the same instrument and the same colorimeter tube for all measurements. Adjust to the wavelength appropriate to the system being investigated (see Procedure 16-4). Rinse the tube several times and fill it either with distilled water or with one of the eleven solutions to be examined. Before inserting the tube in the colorimeter, check for suspended particles, air bubbles, scratches, and the like. Alternate absorbance measurements on the solutions with checks of zero absorbance settings for distilled water.

16-3 Evaluation of data. Correct the absorbances of the mixtures by subtracting $q/10$ times the absorbance of the Fe(III) solution (solution I). As stated earlier, this amounts to an overcorrection; if desired, a better correction may be applied once n is known. Plot the absorbances against the milliliters of Fe(III) solution, and find the position of the maximum. The abscissa of this maximum does not always coincide with that of the intersection of the tangents through the first and last points of the curve. Report the value of n.

16-4 Description of the solutions and recommended wavelengths for transmittance measurements. All solutions are buffered by the system $HSO_4^-/SO_4^=$ in the following concentrations: 0.050 F $(NH_4)_2SO_4$ and 0.025 F H_2SO_4. In addition, solutions I and II have the following composition:

I	II
(a) 4×10^{-3} F $FeNH_4(SO_4)_2$	(a) 4×10^{-3} F NH_4SCN
(b) 2×10^{-3} F $FeNH_4(SO_4)$	(b) 2×10^{-3} F sulfosalicylic acid
(c) 2×10^{-3} F $FeNH_4(SO_4)$	(c) 2×10^{-3} F tiron

Solution I(a) is to be used with solution II(a) etc. Solutions I(b) and I(c) are identical.

Wavelengths recommended:

Thiocyanate	447 mμ
Sulfosalicylic acid	502 mμ
Tiron	660 mμ*

PROBLEMS

16-1 Continuous-variation curve for infinitely large complex-formation constant. Plot y as a function of x for the limiting case of an infinitely large constant K_f and for the parameter values $n = 1, 2, 3$. The symbols are explained at the beginning of the chapter.

* If the colorimeter used is not sufficiently sensitive in the red, the small absorbance maximum at 412 mμ can be used instead.

16-2   Position of the maximum of $y(x)$.   Show that at the maximum of $y(x)$, as defined by Equation (16-2), the relation $n = (c - x)/x$ holds, irrespective of the value of K_f.

16-3   The complexes between Fe(III) and thiocyanate.   The complex-formation constants for the reaction

$$Fe(SCN)_{n-1}^{+4-n} + SCN^- = Fe(SCN)_n^{+3-n}$$

have been reported to have the following values: $K_1 = 140$, $K_2 = 16$, $K_3 = 1$.

   a. Compute the concentrations of the species $Fe(SCN)_n^{+3-n}$ with $n = 1, 2$, and 3 when the formal concentrations of Fe^{3+} and SCN^- are both 10^{-3}.

   b. The molar absorptivity ε of the complex $FeSCN^{++}$ is 4700 (mole/liter)$^{-1}$ cm^{-1} at 447 mμ, the maximum of the absorption band; the molar absorptivities of $Fe(SCN)_2^+$ and $Fe(SCN)_3$ equal approximately two and three times this value. Compute the transmittance of the solution just described at a path length of 1.3 cm.

   c. In the presence of $SO_4^=$ ions equilibria such as

$$Fe^{3+} + SO_4^= = FeSO_4^+$$

$$FeSCN^+ + SO_4^= = Fe(SCN)(SO_4)$$

exist. Use the constants given in Tables V-5 and V-6 (pages 400, 401) to compute the concentrations of the different species containing Fe(III) in a solution that is 10^{-3} F in $FeNH_4(SO_4)_2$, 10^{-3} F in NH_4SCN, 0.050 F in $SO_4^=$, and 0.025 F in H_2SO_4.

16-4   Compound formation between species at greatly different concentrations. Consider a solution containing the species A, C, and D that are at equilibrium with the species AC and AD_2. Assume that the formal concentration of A, $c_A = [A] + [AC] + [AD_2]$, is small compared to the formal concentrations of C and D. By considering the equilibria involved, show that when the formal concentration of A is changed by one means or another, the molar concentration [A] remains approximately proportional to c_A.

16-5   Shape of continuous-variation curve.   Show that for the compound A_nB_m the continuous-variation curve $y(x)$ [Eq. 16-2] has the forms near $x = 0$ and $x = 1$ that are indicated by the following expressions:

$$y \approx const \cdot x^n \qquad \text{when } x \ll 1$$

$$y \approx const \cdot (1 - x)^m \qquad \text{when } (1 - x) \ll 1$$

REVIEW QUESTIONS

16-1.   Briefly describe the salient features of the continuous-variation method.

16-2.   Briefly discuss the conditions under which the method of continuous variations can be applied to find the formula of a complex. Include tests that may be used to ensure that these conditions are satisfied.

appendix I

ERRORS AND
SIGNIFICANT FIGURES

A major part of this appendix consists of a first introduction to mathematical statistics to serve as a guide in the treatment of errors in experimental work. The aim has been accuracy rather than avoidance of complexities, and difficult concepts have not been ignored. It is unlikely that this material will be mastered in one reading. Rather than worry unduly about points that are unclear on first study, let the matter rest, and try at a later time. This is good practice whenever one is dealing with difficult ideas.

A text in statistics may be helpful in answering some of the questions that may arise. Several such texts are listed on page 381. As a beginning,

Appendix I

your objective should be to understand significant figures and to have some grasp of the concepts of accuracy, precision, standard deviation, systematic and random errors, and error propagation. In addition, the last section, on computational aids, should be studied for its generally useful suggestions.

ERRORS, ACCURACY, AND PRECISION

These three concepts may be defined as follows. The *error* of an observation is the difference between it and the actual, or true, value of the quantity observed. The *accuracy* of a set of observations is the difference between the average of the values observed and the true value of the observed quantity. The *precision* of a set of measurements is a measure of the range through which they run. It indicates the degree of their reproducibility.

The meanings of accuracy and of precision are thus quite different. A set of observations may have high precision and low accuracy at the same time. In general, both these terms are used, not in a strict quantitative sense, but rather in a qualitative, descriptive way.

Since the true value of an observable can rarely if ever be divined by insight, the error of an observation remains, in principle, always unknown. There are ways, however, in which the accuracy of a set of observations can be estimated. Some are discussed later.

Errors are often classified as either systematic or random.

Systematic errors may be caused by fundamental flaws in the experimental equipment (e.g., unequal lengths of the arms of an analytical balance, unknown to the observer) or by inadequate understanding of the theory underlying the measurement (e.g., unwarranted neglect of air buoyancy of weights and of object being weighed) or may have their source in the observer. He may, for example, be prejudiced by prior information, as when he is repeating thermometer readings, when it would be very hard to forget estimates of fractional degrees made just a moment earlier. Systematic errors do not average out even if the observations are repeated many times.

Random errors are accidental errors that vary in a completely unreproducible way from measurement to measurement. The concept of randomness can best be explained by the use of examples, such as the sequence of heads and tails in tossing a perfect coin, which is said to be random. Random errors find their origin, at least in part, in the limited precision of instrument readings (e.g., the reading of a vernier

362

with engraved scale marks of finite widths) and in the degree to which external conditions (e.g., the temperature of a ruler) are controlled.

Errors are sometimes classified as either determinate or indeterminate, depending on whether or not their cause is known. Determinate systematic errors can be eliminated by suitable corrections. Although the causes of indeterminate systematic errors may be sought by appropriate experiments, it may be a very difficult matter to discover their existence.

An important approach is to measure the quantity to be investigated in several fundamentally different ways. Close agreement of the result makes the existence of systematic errors less likely, but there never is certainty of their complete absence.

Another way to find possible systematic errors is as follows: In most experiments the results depend on parameters that can be changed, such as the sample size in a chemical analysis. These parameters are varied in separate experiments through as wide a range as possible, and the results are plotted as a function of the parameters. A theoretical curve that describes the dependence of the measurements on the parameters and gives a best fit to the points is drawn. Depending on the importance of the experiments and the nature of the curve, this best fit may be accomplished by eye or by more refined techniques such as the method of least squares, which is beyond the range of this appendix. The scattering of the measured points about the curve may show a *trend*: they would be fitted better by a curve that differs from any of the ones expected on theoretical grounds. This means that an external influence has been overlooked, that a systematic error is present. If the curve appears to fit the measured points, the absence of certain types of systematic errors may be inferred; others may still go undiscovered. If

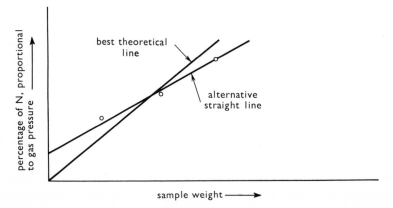

Figure I-1   Results of nitrogen determinations.

there is significant scatter of the points from the curve, it may be a matter of statistical tests whether this scatter is random or not.

A simple example is provided by the results of determinations of nitrogen in an unknown. The method consists of liberating the nitrogen as N_2 gas by chemical means and measuring the gas pressure at constant volume. Figure I-1 shows the points obtained in three determinations with widely different sample weights. Since the amount of N_2 evolved is expected to be proportional to the sample weight, possible theoretical curves must be straight lines through the origin, the best of which is shown.

Obviously, an alternative straight line of lesser slope but nonzero intercept fits the points better. The hidden systematic influence in this example proved to be the presence of water vapor, which was inadvertently not corrected for. It increases the pressure of the gas by a constant value in each determination, since its amount is proportional to the constant total volume of the gas. The slope of the alternative straight line in Figure I-1 indicates the correct percentage of N, and its intercept is a measure of the water vapor present. There may be other systematic errors still present whose size is proportional to the sample size. Examples are incorrect volume calibration, solubility of N_2 in water, and inadequacies of the chemical reaction involved: a fixed percentage of the total nitrogen might be liberated as NH_3 rather than as N_2.

Random errors can be treated statistically as discussed in a later section and can thus provide ways of estimating the accuracy of a set of measurements, always excluding the undetected presence of a systematic error.

.A good example of situations that may arise concerns Avogadro's number N, the number of atoms in exactly 12 g of C^{12} atoms. The value that was accepted for many years corresponds on the new atomic weight scale to

$$N = (0.6064 \pm 0.0006) \times 10^{24}$$

and a recent value on the same scale is (DuMond and Cohen, 1961)

$$N = (0.602237 \pm 0.000090) \times 10^{24}$$

The plus or minus quantities are the standard deviations of the mean, which will be discussed in a later section and which are computed by statistical analysis of the data. The second value lies shockingly outside the plus or minus range given for the older value, and for the following reason: One important method of determining Avogadro's number involves Millikan's oil-drop method of measuring the electron charge. He and his successors used a value of the viscosity of air that later proved to be wrong by almost 1 per cent. The old value of N became suspect when other means of determining it became more and more reliable and suggested a lower value.

SIGNIFICANT FIGURES

In general, results of observations should be reported in such a way that the last digit given is the only one whose value may be in doubt. These digits, excluding leading zeros, are termed *significant figures*. Note that there is uncertainty about the number of significant figures in a weight reported to be 2350 kg, where the zero may be significant or not. The matter is clarified by reporting the weight either as 2.35×10^3 kg or as 2.350×10^3 kg, whichever applies.

No general agreement exists about the degree of uncertainty associated with the last figure. Many authors feel that an accuracy of one unit of the decimal position of the last figure given is implied. For example, an object reported as weighing 27.3 g might actually weigh 27.2 g, but a lesser weight or one above 27.4 g is improbable. Again, if the weight is reported to be 27.300 g, its true value presumably would lie between 27.299 and 27.301 g. Suppose, however, that the laboratory balance used to find the result of 27.3 g is known to have an accuracy of about 0.2 g. To report the weight as 27.3 g would imply higher accuracy than had actually been obtained. It has been suggested that the last figure should be written as a subscript if the accuracy is less than one unit in the appropriate decimal position; thus $27._3$ g.

The situation might more accurately be expressed by reporting the weight as 27.3 ± 0.2 g, with a meaning just as vague, or just as precise, as the statement: "The balance has an accuracy of about 0.2 g." This is not good practice, however, since this notation is very ambiguous. It has been indiscriminately used to state the standard deviation, the average deviation, the probable error, all to be discussed in the next section, or just to express the feelings of the experimenter for his measurements. When writing plus or minus a quantity, indicate precisely what you mean.

Unless a statistical analysis of a number of measurements has been made, the system of significant figures is usually adequate and useful and its shortcomings are unimportant. Note that the number of significant figures with which a quantity is given roughly expresses its *relative accuracy*.

STATISTICAL ANALYSIS

In this section are indicated some results of mathematical statistics, as applied to measurements afflicted with random errors.*

* For details and proofs, which are omitted here, see any introductory text on mathematical statistics. Two such texts are listed at the end of this appendix.

Some definitions will be given first. Suppose that a quantity denoted by x has been measured n times and that the individual observations, all made with the same precision, are x_1, x_2, x_3, ...; x_i, ..., x_n. The *average*, or *mean*, m of these n measurements is defined by the expression

$$m = (x_1 + x_2 + \cdots + x_i + \cdots + x_n)/n = \sum x_i/n \qquad \text{(I-1)}$$

The deviation of an individual measurement x_i from m is $x_i - m$, but it should be noted that the mean of all deviations is zero by (I-1):

$$\sum (m - x_i)/n = nm/n - \sum x_i/n = 0$$

The mean of the values x_i has thus been so chosen that the positive and negative deviations from it just cancel each other. To find a measure of the spread of the observed values, the sign of the deviations has to be eliminated in some way before averaging. One possibility is to average the absolute values of the deviations. The result is called the *average deviation a*,

$$a = \sum |x_i - m|/n \qquad \text{(I-2)}$$

However, this quantity is not amenable to simple statistical treatment and is therefore not recommended. This is partly due to the fact that, although it is easy to take absolute values in computations, algebraic manipulations of absolute values are troublesome.

Another way to remove the $\pm$ signs is to square all deviations. This leads to the *variance s^2*, defined here by

$$s^2 = \sum (m - x_i)^2/(n - 1) \qquad \text{(I-3)}$$

The square root s of the variance is called the *standard deviation*. Frequently the denominator n rather than $n - 1$ is used in the definitions of variance and standard deviation. The denominator $n - 1$ is preferred here, since the n quantities $m - x_i$ are not independent but, rather, satisfy the equation $\Sigma(m - x_i) = 0$. More sophisticated analysis shows that s^2, as defined by (I-3), is free of what is called *bias*, a term that cannot be elaborated without a good deal of background. If there is danger of confusion, s, as defined by (I-3), should be called the *unbiased standard deviation*.

It can be shown by statistical analysis that the average of a set of observations is the "best estimate" of the quantity being measured, where the words in quotation marks have a carefully defined technical meaning that will not be discussed further here. Correspondingly, the so-called *residuals r_i*,

$$r_i = m - x_i \tag{I-4}$$

are best estimates of the errors of the individual measurements x_i. Often the *relative standard deviation* and *other relative quantities* are instructive. They are obtained by dividing the corresponding absolute quantity by the average m. When the need arises to distinguish between a quantity and its relative value, the term *absolute* is sometimes used as the opposite of "relative." Note that in this connection "absolute" does not have the connotation of *without sign*.

Much theoretical work has been done on the important question of the probability that a certain error may occur. The function describing the relative frequency of occurrence of a certain measurement x, when the number of measurements tends to infinity, is termed the frequency function $f(x)$, where x is considered to be a continuous variable. An important example of such a frequency function is

$$f(x) = [1/\sigma\sqrt{2\pi}]e^{-(x-\mu)^2/2\sigma^2} \tag{I-5}$$

which describes the distribution to which many types of measurements approximate. A graph of this function is shown in Figure I-2. The area $f(x)\ dx$ is the probability with which the measured value x is expected to lie in the interval bounded by x and $x + dx$. The factor in front of the exponential function in (I-5) has been so chosen that the total area under the curve is equal to unity. The constant e is the base

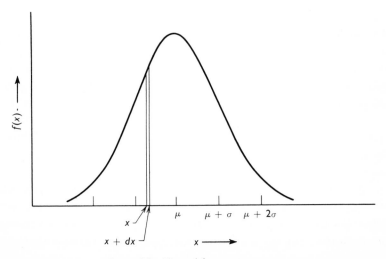

Figure I-2 Normal-frequency curve.

TABLE I-1 *Some Areas Defined by the Normal-Frequency Curve*

ordinates	per cent total area
-0.674σ and $+0.674\sigma$	50.0
$-\sigma$ and $+\sigma$	68.3
-2σ and $+2\sigma$	95.4

of the natural logarithm, and the parameter μ is the true value of the quantity being measured, which, of course, can never be known. The parameter σ describes the spread of the measurements, and if a large number of observations is made, their standard deviation s approaches the limit σ, as their number increases beyond limit. The above function (I-5) has the name *Gaussian frequency function*. If measurements tend to occur with a frequency described by this function when their number increases beyond limits, they are said to be *normally distributed*.

Note the symmetrical nature of the normal-frequency curve of Figure I-2, indicating that normally distributed positive and negative errors are equally probable. Small errors occur relatively much more frequently than do large ones. The larger the parameter σ, the wider is the peak of the curve and the lower the precision of the measurements.

Table I-1 shows some areas enclosed by abscissa, ordinates, and the normal-frequency curve. A random measurement of a normally distributed variable would thus lie, respectively, with about 50, 68, or 95 per cent probability in the ranges $\pm 0.67\sigma$, $\pm\sigma$, or $\pm 2\sigma$.

Statistical theory provides answers to the following questions: Consider the set of all possible measurements of a certain quantity, and *assume* that this so-called *population* of observations is normally distributed with parameters μ and σ. What is the expected distribution of the means of finite sets of n observations, each taken from this population at random, forming so-called *random samples of size n* of the population? The result is that these means are again normally distributed, with the mean again μ and the variance σ^2/n. The square root of this variance $\sigma/\sqrt{n}$ is called the *standard deviation of the mean*, or the *standard error of the mean*. It is a quantity often computed for a set of measurements.

Suppose, next, that the population is *not* distributed normally. Its mean μ and variance σ^2 are then defined by equations analogous to (I-1) and (I-3) with the sums extended over the entire (infinite) population and not just over a sample (or being replaced by suitable integrals).

For this case, the *central-limit theorem* states that the distribution of the means of random samples of size *n approaches* the normal distribution with mean μ and variance σ^2/n, as *n* goes to infinity. This fact is at the root of the great importance of the normal distribution.

Note that the values *m* and *s* characterizing a set of measurements by Equations (I-1) and (I-3) are not to be confused with the parameters μ and σ representative of the population; rather, they represent the "best unbiased estimates" for μ and σ. If the sample size is small, its average *m* and its standard deviation *s* are quite likely to deviate accidentally from the parameters μ and σ that characterize the population and that in general are not known. For example, if a sample of size 3 is taken from a normally distributed population, the best estimate of σ is *s* but the probability that the ratio s^2/σ^2 lies within the rather large limits 0.105 and 2.30 is only 80 per cent. This illustration is particularly pertinent, since many determinations in the laboratory assignments of this text are to be carried out in triplicate.

It is possible to derive a frequency function in terms of the sample parameters *m* and *s* rather than the unknown population parameters μ and σ. For the case of a normally distributed population this leads to *Students' t distribution* of the means *m* of random samples, which depends on the sample size *n*. (The name Student was the pseudonym used by W. S. Gosset, a brewery statistician who derived this important function. The letter *t* is ordinarily used to designate the independent variable in the mathematical expression of this function.)

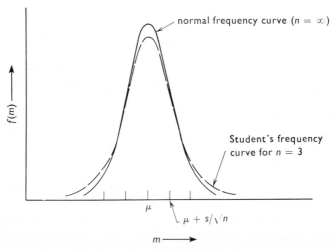

Figure I-3   Normal and Student's frequency curves.

TABLE I-2   *Some Confidence Limits*

sample size n	confidence levels	
	95%	*99%*
2	$\pm 12.71s/\sqrt{n}$	$\pm 63.66s/\sqrt{n}$
3	$\pm\ 4.30s/\sqrt{n}$	$\pm\ 9.93s/\sqrt{n}$
4	$\pm\ 3.18s/\sqrt{n}$	$\pm\ 5.84s/\sqrt{n}$
10	$\pm\ 2.26s/\sqrt{n}$	$\pm\ 3.25s/\sqrt{n}$
∞	$\pm\ 1.96s/\sqrt{n}$	$\pm\ 2.58s/\sqrt{n}$

The case $n = 3$ is illustrated in Figure I-3, which also shows a normal-frequency curve for comparison. The peak of the normal curve is steeper, and the tails are lower. If, therefore, the normal-frequency function is used in cases to which the t distribution actually applies, too high probabilities are computed for measurements to fall within a specified range around the mean. The discrepancy becomes worse the smaller the sample, and Student's t function thus should be used even for a sample size as large as 10.

Table I-2 lists the values of certain interval limits so chosen that the probability of finding m inside a given interval of center μ is respectively 95 and 99 per cent. For example, if four observations have been made, with a mean m and a standard deviation s, the chance is 95 per cent that m lies between $\mu - 3.18s/2$ and $\mu + 3.18s/2$; it is 99 per cent for m to lie in the interval $\mu \pm 5.84s/2$. This interval is called the *confidence interval*; the plus or minus quantities are the *confidence*, or *fiducial*, *limits*; and the corresponding probability is the *confidence level*. The size of a confidence interval depends, of course, on the sample size n. The case $n = \infty$ coincides with the normal distribution. More complete tables are available in texts on statistics.

A confidence level of 95 per cent or even 99 per cent must not be allowed to impart a false sense of security. It is not equal to a level of 100 per cent, which corresponds, in general, to infinitely large confidence limits, nor does any confidence level have a bearing on the question whether or not systematic errors are absent.

Among other important questions being dealt with in mathematical statistics are the following: In general, the means of two sets of observations of the same quantity are different. How different need they be so that the difference can be considered as significant? If one or several measurements deviate considerably from the mean, can they properly be rejected? Concerning this last question, it is controversial whether or not a single observation can be rejected on statistical grounds alone. The only really good criterion is whether some unsatisfactory behavior or procedure involving the result in question can be found through study of the notebook. If so, the result should be rejected no matter how close to the mean it is. The problem has also been discussed on page 83. For further details see the two references given at the end of this appendix.

In concluding this section, several quantities that are sometimes encountered in discussions of experimental results are defined.

The *median* is obtained by arranging all measurements according to their sizes. If the number of values is odd, the median equals the value in the center of this sequence; if not, it is the average of the two most centrally located values. If the population of observations is distributed in a strongly asymmetrical fashion, the median is sometimes preferred to the mean, because it may be more representative.

The *range* of measurements is the difference between the largest and the smallest observed values. It is useful when the number of observations is small, of the order of two or three.

The *probable error p* is defined by the requirement that the probability of a measurement's falling within the range $m - p$ to $m + p$ is $\frac{1}{2}$. The relationship

$$p = 0.674s \tag{I-6}$$

which is allegedly valid for normal distribution, can be found in many textbooks. It is based on the figures in the first line of Table I-1. It contains, however, the further assumption that $\sigma = s$, which has less chance of being correct the smaller the sample on which s is based, as has previously been discussed. The relationship between p and s should therefore be based on the Student t distribution appropriate to the sample size. Because of this complication, and because s has the more direct statistical significance, it is preferable to p.

The relationship between average deviation a (I-2) and standard deviation s (I-3)

$$a \approx 0.8s \tag{I-7}$$

is sometimes stated, but actually it holds only for normal distributions.

The standard deviation of a single observation or that of the mean is usually reported to one or two figures, and the mean is given to the same decimal position. Examples of this are the values of Avogadro's number N shown in the first section of this appendix.

PROPAGATION OF ERRORS

Often a quantity is not measured directly but has to be computed from the values of one or several observed variables, which may be afflicted with errors. It then becomes important to understand how the error of the result can be estimated from the errors of the observations —of how the error propagates through the functional relationship between observations and result.

To understand the principles involved, the question will first be treated in an elementary way. An account of the results of statistical analysis will follow. Consider first the addition or substraction of two numbers A and B, afflicted, respectively, with errors a and b. These errors are not known, but it is instructive to find out how the error of the result depends on them. Addition or subtraction yields

$$(A + a) \pm (B + b) = (A \pm B) + (a \pm b) \tag{I-8}$$

The quantities a and b may be independently positive or negative. For both addition and subtraction, the error will thus lie between the limits $|a + b|$ and $|a - b|$.

To examine the error inherent in the product of $A + a$ and $B + b$, we multiply,

$$(A + a)(B + b) \approx AB + aB + bA$$

where ab has been neglected on the grounds that both a and b are presumed to be small compared with A and B, respectively.

Remember to ask, whenever neglecting a "small" quantity: "Small compared with what? What effect does the neglecting have on the final answer?"

The result is better appreciated by considering the *relative error*, the error divided by AB,

$$(A + a)(B + b)/AB \approx 1 + a/A + b/B \tag{I-9}$$

It is seen that the relative error of the result is the sum of the relative errors of A and B, which are a/A and b/B, respectively.

To deal with division, it is useful to employ the following approximation for the quantity $1/(1 \pm d)$, which is valid when d is sufficiently small, so that d^2 can be neglected when compared with 1.

$$1/(1 \pm d) = 1 \mp d + d^2 \mp d^3 + \cdots \approx 1 \mp d \tag{I-10}$$

Either all the lower or all the upper signs must be used. The correctness of the equals sign in (I-10) can best be seen by multiplying both sides by $1 \pm d$, whence $1 = 1 \mp d + d^2 \mp d^3 + \cdots \pm d - d^2 \pm d^3 - d^4 + \cdots$ On the right side everything except 1 cancels.

The above expression (I-10) is a special case of the more general approximation

$$(1 \pm d)^n = 1 \pm (n/1)d + [n(n-1)/1 \times 2]d^2 + \cdots$$

$$(1 \pm d)^n \approx 1 \pm nd \qquad \text{when } (nd)^2 \ll 1 \tag{I-11}$$

which is a consequence of what is known as the binomial theorem. For example,

$$\sqrt{1 \pm d} \approx 1 \pm d/2 \tag{I-12}$$

as long as $d^2/8$ may be neglected when compared with 1.

Considering now division, use of (I-10) yields the approximation

$$(A + a)/(B + b) = (A + a)/B(1 + b/B) \approx [(A + a)/B](1 - b/B)$$

$$= A/B + a/B - Ab/B^2 - ab/B^2$$

Again the result involving relative errors is the one of most interest. Dividing by A/B and neglecting ab/AB as small compared with 1 results in

$$[(A + a)/(B + b)]/[A/B] \approx 1 + a/A - b/B \tag{I-13}$$

Hence in multiplication as well as in division the magnitude of the relative error of the result lies between the limits $|a/A + b/B|$ and $|a/A - b/B|$.

A final example concerns the square root of $A + a$,

$$\sqrt{A + a} = \sqrt{A}(1 + a/2A + \cdots) \approx \sqrt{A} + a/2\sqrt{A} \tag{I-14}$$

where (I-12) has been used. The relative error of $\sqrt{A}$ is seen to be half the relative error of A.

In general, the errors are not known, and the quantities a and b are to be thought of as estimates of errors. The foregoing discussion makes plausible the results of statistical theory, which are given below. They are based on normal distributions for all variables, and standard deviations are used to serve as estimates of the errors.

Let capital letters like A denote the means of sets of observations and lower-case letters like a their standard deviations. For addition or subtraction it is found that the variance of the result is the sum of the variances of the individual terms. Since the standard deviation is the square root of the variance, a representative formula is

$$\text{standard deviation of } A + B - C = \sqrt{a^2 + b^2 + c^2} \tag{I-15}$$

For multiplication and division it is the relative standard deviations, like a/A, that count. A representative case follows:

$$\text{relative standard deviation of } AB/C = \sqrt{(a/A)^2 + (b/B)^2 + (c/C)^2}$$

$$\tag{I-16}$$

Appendix I

The relative standard deviation of the square root of A is $a/2A$, as may be presumed from (I-14).

As a representative example of a more complicated case, the relative standard deviation of

$$\sqrt{(A + B)/C}$$

is considered. Let the standard deviation of

$$A + B = D \text{ be } d = \sqrt{a^2 + b^2}$$

The relative standard deviation of

$$(A + B)/C = D/C \text{ is } \sqrt{(d/D)^2 + (c/C)^2}$$

Thus, relative standard deviation of $\sqrt{[(A + B)/C]}$ is

$$\tfrac{1}{2}\sqrt{(a^2 + b^2)/(A + B)^2 + (c/C)^2} \qquad (I\text{-}17)$$

In additions and subtractions the situation is simplest when one standard deviation is much larger than the others; they simply can be neglected. For multiplication and division the situation is similar, except that it is the relative standard deviations that must be considered. In more general cases, formulas like (I-15) to (I-17) must be used.

To give a numerical example, assume that the volume of a gas is 47.50 ± 0.05 ml at a pressure of 740.3 ± 0.2 mm and a temperature of $26.3 \pm 0.2\,°C$, where the quantities after the $\pm$ are standard deviations. The amount of gas and its standard deviation are to be found. The amount of gas is given by $n = pV/RT = 1.8828$ mmole. The relative variance of the result is the sum of the relative variances of the volume, pressure, and absolute temperature, as follows:

$$[s^2(V)]/V^2 = (0.05/47.5)^2 = 1.19 \times 10^{-6}$$
$$[s^2(p)]/p^2 = (0.2/740)^2 = 7.24 \times 10^{-8}$$
$$[s^2(T)/T^2 = (0.2/299)^2 = 44.6 \times 10^{-8}$$
$$[s^2(n)]/n^2 = (1.19 + 0.07 + 0.45) \times 10^{-6}$$
$$= 1.71 \times 10^{-6}$$

$$[s(n)]/n = 1.31 \times 10^{-3} \qquad s(n) = 2.48 \pm 10^{-3} \text{ mmole}$$

The result thus may be expressed as 1.8828 ± 0.0025 mmole of gas, where the $\pm$ quantity must be explicitly referred to as the standard deviation.

It is desirable to adjust the accuracies of the different measuring operations that eventually combine in a final answer. For example, if a percentage composition is to be determined, the relative accuracy of the sample weight should match that of all other operations. Many methods of chemical analysis can be performed with an accuracy of about 1 part in 1000. If so, it would be a waste of time to weigh a 12-g ore sample to 0.1 mg, corresponding to 1 part in 120,000; it will be satisfactory to weigh it to the nearest 0.01 g. On the other hand, when sums or differences are involved, the absolute accuracy must be considered. For example, the weight of a precipitate is often determined by weighing it with the crucible containing it and subtracting the weight of the empty crucible. If the precipitate weighs on the order of 0.1 g, all weighings must be to the nearest tenth of a milligram, even though the crucible may weigh 20 g.

It may be useful to state the general law of propagation of errors, although it involves partial derivatives. If the quantity desired is the function $F(A, B, C)$ then the variance f^2 of F is

$$f^2 = (\partial F/\partial A)^2 a^2 + (\partial F/\partial B)^2 b^2 + (\partial F/\partial C)^2 c^2$$

provided that there are no correlations between the variances a^2, b^2, and c^2.

COMPUTATIONAL AIDS AND PROCEDURES

Rounding off. This is governed by the following rules: Discard the unwanted digits. Increase the last retained digit by one unit (*round up*) if the highest discarded digit is larger than 5 or if it is equal to 5 but followed by other digits some of which are different from zero. Leave the last retained digit unchanged (*round down*) if the highest digit discarded is less than 5. If the digits discarded are a 5 followed by zeros only or else by nothing, round to the nearest even figure. This last convention has the consequence that, in the long run, the total number of possible values that are rounded up to a certain quantity is equal to the number that are rounded down to it. For example, if the original values happen to be given to two decimal places and both these are to be dropped, all numbers from 4.51 to 5.49 will be rounded to 5, all numbers from 5.50 to 6.50 to 6, etc.

Addition and subtraction. First, look for the term of lowest absolute accuracy. This determines the accuracy warranted for the result, and it is meaningless and even misleading to give the result with more significant figures than correspond to this accuracy. However, rounding all other terms to this accuracy is not desirable, because rounding errors may accumulate in the subsequent computations and affect the figures finally retained. Instead, before adding or subtracting, round the terms given with higher accuracy in a preliminary fashion

TABLE I-3 *Addition and Subtraction*

$$
\begin{array}{r}
+24.35 \\
-\ 9.575 \\
+11.2 \\
+\ 0.46 \\
\hline
\end{array}
$$

premature rounding
to accuracy of result
not recommended

rounding to one or
two places beyond
accuracy of result

$$
\begin{array}{r}
+24.4 \\
-\ 9.6 \\
+11.2 \\
+\ 0.5 \\
\hline
26.5
\end{array}
$$

$$
\begin{array}{r}
+24.35 \\
-\ 9.58 \\
+11.2 \\
+\ 0.46 \\
\hline
26.43
\end{array}
$$

answer is too large by
one unit in last place

final rounding

26.4

only, retaining one or two places beyond the accuracy warranted for the result. Perform the additions or substractions, and finally round the result. An example is given in Table I-3.

Multiplication and division.   The situation is like that discussed for addition and subtraction, except that relative rather than absolute accuracies are involved. The result must not be given with a relative accuracy that is higher than that of the term with lowest relative accuracy. However, to prevent the accumulation of rounding errors, terms given with higher relative accuracy must be rounded in a preliminary way only; that is, one or two figures beyond the relative accuracy of the result must be retained. Final rounding is performed at the end.

When numbers close to unity are involved, proceed as in the following example, which makes use of Equations (I-10) and (I-12) of the preceding section on Propagation of Errors.

$$
\sqrt{0.9974/1.0012} = \sqrt{(1 - 0.0026)/(1 + 0.0012)}
$$

$$
= \sqrt{(1 - 0.0026)(1 - 0.0012 + \underset{\text{neglect}}{(0.0012)^2} - \cdots)}
$$

$$
= \sqrt{1 - 0.0026 - 0.0012 + \underset{\text{neglect}}{0.0026 \cdot 0.0012} + \cdots}
$$

$$
\approx 1 - 0.0038/2 = 0.9981
$$

Similarly, when dividing two numbers of almost equal magnitude, follow the example given next:

$$0.3542/0.3473 = (0.3473 + 0.0069)/0.3473$$
$$= 1.0000 + (0.0069/0.3473) = 1.0000 + 0.0199$$
$$= 1.0199$$

The last fraction was evaluated by using a slide rule.

General intermediate computations. In computations that are more involved than those just given, calculate intermediate results to one or two places beyond the accuracy warranted by the data, and round off the final results only. This prevents computational rounding-off errors from affecting the final answer. The accuracy of the result is to be established separately by an analysis of the propagation of the errors of the measurements.

The following example illustrates the danger of paying too much attention to significant figures in intermediary steps and of neglecting small terms on that basis. The problem is to find the H^+ concentration of a 0.1 F NaOH solution by a method that is elaborate but has been chosen particularly for this example.

Since the sum of the concentrations of positive charges must equal that of negative charges

$$[H^+] + [Na^+] = [OH^-]$$

Inserting $[Na^+] = 0.1$ and $[OH^-] = 10^{-14}/[H^+]$ and rearranging results in a quadratic equation,

$$[H^+]^2 + 0.1[H^+] - 10^{-14} = 0$$

which is solved by

$$[H^+] = [-0.1 + \sqrt{(0.1)^2 + 4 \times 10^{-14}}]/2 \qquad \text{(I-18)}$$

(The solution with the negative square root has no physical meaning because it leads to a negative $[H^+]$.) It may now be argued that the significant figures of $(0.1)^2$ in the radicand suggest that the term 4×10^{-12} is of no concern and that to keep it would give the proceedings an undesirable aura of false precision. Deletion of this term leads, however, to $[H^+] = 0$, which is wrong. The term must therefore be retained. The square root may be evaluated approximately by use of Equation (I-12):

$$\sqrt{(0.1)^2(1 + 4 \times 10^{-12})} = 0.1(1 + 2 \times 10^{-12} + \cdots) \approx 0.1 + 2 \times 10^{-13}$$

(Note that to find this square root in a table would have required a

377

table of much higher accuracy than is usually available.) The 0.1 from the square root precisely cancels the 0.1 preceding it in (I-18), and the final answer is

$$[H^+] = 10^{-13}$$

Although this answer can be obtained more quickly by other means (page 159), the elaborate treatment chosen demonstrates what may happen in more complicated situations when simple considerations no longer can be used. In essence the 0.1 and the 10^{-14} in Equation (I-18) were treated as if they were algebraic symbols.

If extensive algebraic developments are required, they should be carried through to the final result symbolically and computations should be performed only in the end. Computation of intermediate results may cause errors, because terms that should be identical may become slightly different through rounding off and may no longer cancel in the end as they should. Note, however, that it is often simpler in intermediate algebraic manipulations to treat a given numerical value *as if it were the symbol* for the quantity it represents, rather than to invent a letter symbol just for the one occasion.

Significant figures for logarithms. In this text the decadic logarithm of a quantity x is denoted by log x and its natural logarithm by ln x. By application of calculus it can be shown that the absolute error $\Delta(\log x)$ of the decadic logarithm of x is proportional to the relative error of x, or to $\Delta x/x$,

$$\Delta(\log x) \approx \Delta x/(x \ln 10) = 0.43(\Delta x/x)$$

This relationship is illustrated in Table I-4.

If a quantity is known to a certain number of significant figures, the question that arises is how many significant figures are appropriate

TABLE I-4 *Logarithms of Numbers Differing by 0.01 Per Cent*

x	log x
9999	3.99996
10000	4.00000
10001	4.00004

$$\Delta x/x = 10^{-4}$$
$$\Delta(\log x) = 4 \times 10^{-5}$$

for its decadic logarithm. Consideration of the preceding discussion and of a table of logarithms indicates that the mantissa should have either the same number of significant figures or else one more than the original quantity, depending on whether the original quantity is closer to the next power of 10 just below it or to that just above it.

Note also that the relative accuracy of a slide rule is constant over its entire range.

Computation of the mean. In computing the mean m of a series of values x_i it simplifies numerical work to assume first a convenient preliminary value h for this mean, to which is added the average of the differences $x_i - h$. This leads to the correct result,

$$m = \sum x_i/n = \sum [h + (x_i - h)]/n = h + \sum (x_i - h)/n$$

If you are not thoroughly familiar with operations involving the sum operator Σ, you should prove this formula and the one given further below by explicitly writing out all the sums.
Example:

$$x_i = 3.62, 3.69, 3.59, 3.65$$

$$h = 3.60$$

$$\sum (x_i - h)/4 = 10^{-2}(2 + 9 - 1 + 5)/4 = 0.15/4 = 0.0375$$

$$m = 3.6375$$

Computation of the standard deviation. Again, the starting point is a preliminary value h, as above. With its aid the following transformation involving the variance s^2 can be made:

$$(n - 1)s^2 = \sum (m - x_i)^2 = \sum [m - h - (x_i - h)]^2$$
$$= n(m - h)^2 + \sum (x_i - h)^2 - 2(m - h) \sum (x_i - h)$$

However, by definition of m, $\sum (x_i - h) = n(m - h)$, so that

$$s^2 = [\sum (x_i - h)^2/(n - 1)] - n(m - h)^2/(n - 1)$$

This is applied to the example given earlier.

$$\sum (x_i - h)^2 = (4 + 81 + 1 + 25)10^{-4} = 111 \times 10^{-4}$$

$$n(m - h)^2 = 4 \times 14.06 \times 10^{-4} = 56.25 \times 10^{-4}$$

$$s^2 = (111 - 56.25) \times 10^{-4}/3 = 18.3 \times 10^{-4}$$

$$s = 0.043$$

The special case of $h = 0$ results in the expressions

$$s^2 = [\sum x_i^2 - nm^2]/(n - 1) = [\sum x_i^2 - (\sum x_i)^2/n]/(n - 1)$$

where again the definition of m (I-1) has been used. In both expressions only one

379

subtraction is needed, which is of advantage when no intermediate value h has been assumed in computing the mean so that the differences $x_i - h$ are not available from the earlier calculations. Both formulas are well suited to the use of a desk computer. The second expression does not require prior knowledge of the mean m.

In the example considered,

$$\sum x_i^2 = 52.9311 \qquad (\sum x_i)^2/4 = 52.9256$$

$$s^2 = 18.3 \times 10^{-4} \qquad s = 0.043$$

The final results may be reported as

$$m = 3.638 \qquad s = 0.043 \qquad s/\sqrt{n} = 0.022$$

or if the standard deviation is not reported, as

$$m = 3.6_4$$

PROBLEMS

I-1 Chloride analysis.   In an analysis of a soluble chloride, 2.3472 g of the unknown was dissolved in distilled water and diluted to exactly 100.00 ml. Three aliquot portions of 25.00 ml each were reacted with silver nitrate solution. The resulting AgCl precipitates were filtered, washed, and dried. Their weights were found to be 0.8417, 0.8424, and 0.8399 g, respectively. (*a*) Compute the mean, the range, the mean deviation, and the standard deviation of these values. (*b*) Compute the standard deviation of the mean and the fiducial limits for confidence levels of 95 and 99 per cent. (*c*) Experience in the use of the analytical balance and of volumetric equipment indicates the following approximate standard deviations for single observations: balance, 0.2 mg; 100-ml volumetric flask, 0.02 ml; 25-ml pipet, 0.03 ml. What is the relative standard deviation of a determination of the weight per cent of chloride estimated from these data? Compare this with the relative value of the standard deviation computed from the experimental data. (*d*) Is the precision of any of the above measurements excessive? Discuss.

I-2 Coulometric analysis.   In a coulometric analysis that was carried out like that in Laboratory Assignment 13 the voltage drop across the standard resistor of 100.00 ± 0.01 ohm was 1.344 ± 0.002 volt, the titration time was 389.2 ± 0.5 sec, and the sample weight was 782.3 ± 0.1 mg. The volumetric flask used to dilute the sample solution contained 500.00 ± 0.15 ml, and the pipet used to obtain the sample aliquot delivered 25.00 ± 0.02 ml. All $\pm$ quantities are standard deviations. How many weight per cent As_2O_3 did the sample contain and what was the standard deviation?

I-3 Interplanar spacings in crystals.   The spacings d of sets of net planes in a crystal can be measured by determining the angle 2ϑ at which X rays of wavelength λ are diffracted. The spacings then follow from the Bragg equation, $d = \lambda/(2 \sin \vartheta)$. Suppose that the standard deviation of a measurement of ϑ is

1.0 min and that the wavelength is known with a relative standard deviation of 40 ppm. What is the relative standard deviation of $\sin \vartheta$ and of d when the angle ϑ is respectively about 40°, 75°, 85°, and 88°? What is the best range of ϑ for measuring accurate spacings?

REVIEW QUESTIONS

I-1. Briefly define the following terms and quantities: error, accuracy, precision, random error, systematic error, significant figures, average, unbiased standard deviation, variance, average deviation, median, range, residual.

I-2. Briefly recapitulate the rules for rounding off numbers.

I-3. How do the variances of different terms combine when these terms are to be multiplied, divided, added, or subtracted?

I-4. Does the statistical evaluation of confidence limits take into account the possibility of systematic errors?

REFERENCES

Mathematical statistics

P. G. Hoel, *Introduction to Mathematical Statistics*, Wiley, New York, 1954.

D. A. S. Fraser, *Statistics: An Introduction*, Wiley, New York, 1958.

Statistics in quantitative analysis

H. A. Laitinen, *Chemical Analysis*, Chap. 26, McGraw-Hill, New York, 1960.

Rejection of a questionable observation

R. B. Dean and W. J. Dixon, "Simplified statistics for small numbers of observations," *Anal. Chem.*, **23**, 636–638 (1951).

W. J. Blaedel, V. W. Meloche, and J. A. Ramsay, "A comparison of criteria for the rejection of measurements," *J. Chem. Educ.*, **28**, 643–647 (1951).

General text on research

E. B. Wilson, Jr., *An Introduction to Scientific Research*, McGraw-Hill, New York, 1952. This book not only contains a thorough discussion of statistics and errors but covers many other important aspects of research. It should be studied by all embarking on a career in research.

appendix II

THE SINGLE-PAN
BALANCE

In recent years a new type of balance has been developed (mainly by E. Mettler) that is based on the substitution method of weighing and has only one pan. Weights ranging from 0.1 g to a total of 200 g are suspended on the same side of the beam as the pan and are counterpoised by a constant weight on the opposite side of the beam [see Figure II-1(a)]. An object is weighed by placing it on the pan and removing weights on the pan side of the beam until the sum of the weights removed is within 0.1 g but still on the low side of the weight of the object [see Figure II-1(b)]. This is done automatically by turning knobs, and a dial shows the sum of the weights thus removed. Once the weight difference between object and weights removed is less than 0.1 g, the beam is permitted to find its equilibrium position. The motions of the beam are strongly damped by an air dashpot that prevents any swinging motion. The beam deflection is shown greatly magnified by the optical projection of a scale and a vernier on a small screen. The scale reads directly in milligram (up to 100 mg or 0.1 g); tenths of milligrams are established by the vernier position. The total weight of the object in grams may be read off the dial (to one place after the decimal point), the illuminated scale (two further decimal places), and the vernier (the fourth decimal place).

The load on the balance is *constant* within 0.1 g. This type of balance has therefore also been called a *constant-load balance*. From the discussion of the balance principles in Chapter 3 (pages 38 to 43), it follows that the sensitivity of such a balance is constant, which makes it possible to indicate the equilibrium position of the beam directly in terms of weight.

Although equal arm lengths is an essential feature of the two-pan balance, the main knife edge in the single-pan balance is placed much closer to the pan end of the beam so as to reduce the weight needed as counterpoise. This reduces the total load on the beam and also the wear on the main knife edge. Single-pan balances have also been called *unequal-arm balances* because of this construction detail.

A spring-loaded pan brake may be released by pushing a button in the center of the beam-arrest knob. This permits the pan to swing

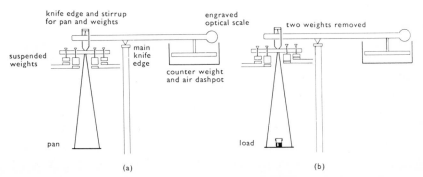

Figure II.I Schematic diagram of the operation of single-pan balance (a) without load, and (b) with load, and with some weights removed.

freely and is used before releasing the beam to allow the center of mass of pan, weights, and load to assume a position directly under the pan support.

There is a zero-adjust knob that is used to adjust the zero line of the vernier when the balance is not loaded and all weights are in place to coincide with the zero line of the scale. This adjustment of the zero point must be checked frequently.

The beam-arrest knob has three positions in which the beam is, respectively, arrested, partially released, and released; the three positions of the knob are suitably marked. This knob must always be rotated *slowly and gently*. It is *important that the beam be arrested* when the load is added to the pan, when the 100-g weight is added to or removed from the beam, and when the balance is not in use. When turning the knobs that manipulate weights less than 100 g it is permissible to have the beam-arrest knob at the "partially released" position.

The knob operating the heaviest likely weight for the object is always rotated first, and the effect observed by watching the projected scale. When too much weight has been taken away the words "remove weight" appear on the projection screen, indicating that the knob should be turned back one notch. The knobs controlling the lower weights are successively turned until the "remove weight" appears and are then turned back one position.

Single-pan balances are convenient and rapid in operation. Weighing is reduced to the turning of a few knobs, and the reading of a dial and a projected scale. Beam equilibrium is established rapidly because beam swings are suppressed by air damping. The accuracy of a well-adjusted single-pan balance is comparable to that of a two-pan analytical balance. The carefully calibrated weights are well protected since they remain enclosed in the balance case and are not handled manually. Single-pan balances are, however, very expensive, and the deceptive simplicity of their operation easily leads to rough treatment of the delicate mechanism. In particular, careless operation of the beam arrest causes excessive wear of the crucial knife edges and knife edge supports. *Like any analytical balance, the single-pan balance is a delicate instrument and requires careful operation and exacting cleanliness.*

If a single-pan balance is to be used rather than a two-pan balance, Chapter 3 should nevertheless be studied carefully, except for the section *Details of operation*, page 45. A procedure for the operation of a single-pan balance follows.

PROCEDURE FOR WEIGHING WITH A SINGLE-PAN BALANCE

Remove all objects from the pan, turn all weight knobs to zero, and close the doors of the balance case. Push the pan-brake button several times, until the pan remains at rest when the button is pushed. Slowly turn the beam-arrest knob to the "partially released" position and let the beam assume its equilibrium position. Turn the zero-adjust knob until the zero lines of projected scale and vernier coincide. Slowly arrest the beam. The zero adjustment must be checked frequently.

Place the object on the pan with the beam arrested. Close the doors and operate the pan-brake button until the pan is in its equilibrium position. To adjust the weight knobs start with the knob controlling the largest weight likely for the object. If this is the 100 g knob keep the beam arrested while rotating the knob. Release the beam partially by slow rotation of the beam-arrest knob and observe whether the "remove weight" sign appears or not. If it does, slowly arrest the beam again and turn the 100-g knob back to its original position. The beam arrest knob may now be turned slowly to the "partially released" position and the knobs controlling successively lower weights rotated until the "remove weight" sign appears, whence the knob just operated is turned back one notch. When the 0.1-g knob has been adjusted the beam-arrest knob is slowly rotated to the "released" position. After the projected scale stops moving, its position relative to the vernier is read. The dial shows the weight of the object to the 0.1-g digit, and the scale and vernier reading provides three further digits. Enter the weight of the object in your notebook, slowly arrest the beam, remove the object, close the doors of the balance case, and turn the weight knobs to the zero positions.

Always treat the balance carefully and observe the utmost cleanliness. For rules of balance care see pages 53 to 55. If the balance appears to be out of adjustment call the instructor. Never attempt adjustments yourself.

appendix III

HOW TO STUDY AND HOW
TO SOLVE PROBLEMS

STUDY HABITS

To study efficiently, observe the following points.

1. *Do it now.* Keep up with lectures and homework. Subsequent developments are based upon understanding of current material. If you fall behind, make an *immediate* effort to catch up again.

2. *Principles should be understood, not memorized.* When studying an assignment, skim rapidly through it first, then reread it slowly with pencil and paper handy. Jot down key words, retrace mathematical developments, and rework examples given. Frequently close the book and recapitulate in your own words. Remain critical, and do not accept

without question. Make notes on points that remain unclear, and have them explained to you.

3. *Study regularly*, but not too long at a time. If you make no progress, go on to some other work and come back to chemistry later. Your approach may have changed.

4. *Explain what you have learned to someone else.* You yourself will notice aspects that you have not understood, and frequently points that previously were obscure will clear up. Teaching a subject is the best way to learn it.

5. *Get a good night's sleep before an examination.* If you study your notes and text regularly, as suggested above, and if you do your homework, there will be no need to cram for examinations. Information that you try to get into your head on the eve of an examination is likely to be unavailable when the need for it is urgent.

ADVICE FOR SOLVING PROBLEMS

The purpose of problems is to provide situations that permit the student to learn how well he has understood the principles involved and to help him to broaden his understanding. This purpose is defeated if problems are solved by rote, a procedure that teaches the student little beyond the ability to deal with further problems of the same sort. Each problem should therefore be reasoned out anew.

The following advice is offered as help in finding the solution of a difficult problem of a kind that the student has not seen before.

1. *Read the problem carefully*, look at the data given, think of pertinent principles and facts, ask yourself what it is that needs to be found, and generally *concentrate* until you have assembled in your mind all factors bearing on the problem. If the situation is complicated, draw a diagram such as an organization chart or a flow diagram.

2. If no solution occurs to you, change the problem by simplifying it, by placing constraints on it, by considering special cases, or in other ways that may come to mind.

3. It is not advisable to try to remember how a similar previous problem was worked. Half the time you will remember wrong. It is safer and certainly more beneficial to make a fresh start with every problem. Do not try to learn "schemes" for working problems, because they do not provide insight into principles.

4. If you cannot work a given problem, go to the next one, and come back to the first problem later. If you still are unable to make

headway, get someone to help you. Rework problems you missed after they have been explained in class.

5. Make every effort to have numerical answers correct. This is the only way to combat the tendency to slipshod arithmetical errors natural to most of us, and it provides valuable training in the *accurate* use of the slide rule. Unless indicated otherwise, good slide-rule accuracy is satisfactory. Examine answers to be sure they make physical sense. Check orders of magnitude of numerical answers; check and show appropriate dimensions. If the answer requested is an equation or general formula, test whether it is satisfactory in all the limiting cases you can think of.

appendix IV

FREE ENERGY, EQUILIBRIUM CONSTANTS, AND CELL POTENTIALS

The brief exposition of thermodynamic relationships given in this appendix is largely descriptive because a knowledge of thermodynamics would be needed to prove many of the statements given.

The free energy. The thermodynamic link between the standard potential of an electrochemical cell and the equilibrium constant of the cell reaction involves an important thermodynamic quantity, the *free energy F*, more precisely called the Gibbs free energy. In most reactions or processes only part of the energy available may be converted into work and the remainder shows up as heat. In addition, in constant-pressure processes work performed against or done by the external pressure is generally not useful. Work other than that connected with expansion or contraction is called *net work*. Examples are electrical work and chemical work used to drive a second reaction. The *free energy* of a system is the *maximum portion of the energy that may be converted into net work* in a *constant temperature and pressure process*. (If work related to volume changes is to be included, another free energy, called the Helmholtz free energy, must be used.)

A given quantity of a substance has a free energy associated with it, just as it has a volume or a temperature. The free energy of a substance depends on the temperature and the pressure and is an *extensive* quantity, i.e., it is proportional to the amount of substance, as are the volume and the mass. Its value as a function of temperature and pressure can be determined experimentally. For gases that are nearly ideal, and in some other cases, the free energy can also be calculated theoretically.

Consider now a reaction in which as many formula weights of reactants as are indicated by the coefficients in the balanced reaction equation are transformed into the corresponding number of formula weights of products. Let F (reactants) be the sum of the free energies of the reactants and let F (products) be the sum of the free energies of the products. The difference between the two is ΔF, defined by*

$$F \text{ (products)} = F \text{ (reactants)} + \Delta F \qquad \text{(IV-1)}$$

It may be shown by thermodynamics that for reactions proceeding at constant temperature and pressure the free-energy loss of the system represents the *maximum net work* that may be gained from the reaction. This maximum net work is thus $-\Delta F$. If the reaction is accompanied by irreversible phenomena such as friction, the work obtained will be smaller than $-\Delta F$.

The laws of thermodynamics show that a chemical reaction can proceed at constant temperature and pressure only if the free energy of the reacting system is thereby decreased. In other words, if the free energy of the reactants is *greater* than that of the products, the reaction is thermodynamically allowed; the reaction converts reactants of higher free energy into products of lower free energy and thus decreases the free energy of the system. The ΔF for a thermodynamically allowed reaction is therefore negative; and the more negative it is, the greater is the tendency for the reaction to proceed. If the free energy of the

---

* A Δ quantity always signifies the *change* in the quantity considered, so that its addition to the old value produces the new value. It is thus equal to the new value diminished by the old one. For example, if the length l_1 of a rod changes to l_2 because of a change in temperature, $\Delta l = l_2 - l_1$.

reactants is *smaller* than that of the products, ΔF is positive and the reaction is forbidden by thermodynamics. Such a reaction has a tendency to go to the left rather than to the right; and the larger ΔF, the greater this tendency. When ΔF for a reaction is zero or the free energy of the reactants is equal to the free energy of the products, the reacting system is at equilibrium and the reaction has no tendency to go either to the right or to the left.

Equilibrium constants.   The free-energy difference between reactants and products in their *standard states* (unit concentrations or activities for dissolved species, 1 atm pressures for gases, etc.) is designated by $\Delta F°$. This is called the *standard free-energy difference*, and it depends on the temperature only. When reactants and products are not in their standard states, ΔF is related to $\Delta F°$ by

$$\Delta F = \Delta F° + RT \ln Q \qquad \text{(IV-2)}$$

where Q is the mass-action expression of the reaction equation containing the concentrations (or activities), partial pressures, etc., of the products and reactants, which are, of course, not equilibrium values in general. This Q is similar to the Q of the Nernst equation (14-10), except that there Q refers to a half-reaction.

When equilibrium between reactants and products exists, ΔF is zero and $RT \ln Q$ must equal $-\Delta F°$, which is a constant at constant temperature. It follows that at equilibrium and for constant temperature, Q must be equal to a constant K, which is none other than the *mass-action constant*: The condition $Q = K$ expresses the mass-action law, and the mass-action law is a thermodynamic consequence of Equation (IV-2) that relates ΔF to the concentrations, etc., of the reactants and products. It is further seen that the standard free-energy difference $\Delta F°$ and the equilibrium constant K are connected by the important equation

$$\Delta F° = -RT \ln K \qquad \text{(IV-3)}$$

Note that positive, zero, and negative values of $\Delta F°$ correspond to equilibrium constants that are respectively smaller than, equal to, and larger than 1. When the reaction equation is written in the reverse direction, $\Delta F°$ changes its sign, so that K is replaced by $1/K$. All of this is consistent with previous considerations of the behavior and meaning of K.

Electrode potentials.   Consider a redox reaction, in which there is reduction of one species and oxidation of another. It is always possible, at least in theory, to construct an electrochemical cell that utilizes this reaction as cell reaction, the oxidation taking place at the anode and the reduction at the cathode. Let

$$E_{total} = E_{cathode} - E_{anode} \tag{IV-4}$$

be the potential difference between the cathode and anode of the cell, and let n be the number of electrons that are involved in the reaction as written, so that by the passage of n moles of electrons through the cell as many formula weights of reactants are changed into products as are indicated by the coefficients of the reaction equation. The electrical work produced by this passage of n faradays of electricity, at constant temperature and pressure, is $n\mathscr{F}E_{total}$, where $\mathscr{F}$ is the faraday. This work may be obtained in calories by expressing the potential in volts and the faraday in cal/volt, as follows: 1 coulomb = 1 volt amp sec/volt = 1 joule/volt = (1/4.184) cal/volt; $\mathscr{F} = 96,500/4.184 = 23,060$ cal/volt mole. If E_{total} is positive, the electrical work is performed by the cell on its surroundings; if E_{total} is negative, it is work that must be expended to force the n faradays through the cell against the potential $|E_{total}|$. This work corresponds to a loss or a gain in the free energy of the cell, and thus

$$\Delta F = -n\mathscr{F}E_{total} \tag{IV-5}$$

or

$$E_{total} = -\Delta F/n\mathscr{F} \tag{IV-6}$$

Note that E_{total} is independent of the amounts of substances taking part in the reaction. It is an *intensive* quantity, like the temperature and the pressure. This is verified by considering that the extensive quantity ΔF is divided by n in Equation (IV-6). When reactants and products in the electrochemical cell are in their standard states, E_{total} becomes E_{total}°, the difference between the *standard* potentials of cathode and anode, and ΔF becomes ΔF°, so that

$$\Delta F^\circ = -n\mathscr{F}E_{total}^\circ \tag{IV-7}$$

Combining (IV-7) with (IV-3) and (IV-4) and rearranging the result, the desired relationships between the cell potential and the equilibrium potential are obtained,

$$E_{total}^\circ = E_{cathode}^\circ - E_{anode}^\circ = (RT/n\mathscr{F}) \ln K = (2.303RT/n\mathscr{F}) \log K \tag{IV-8}$$

and

$$K = 10^{2.303RT(E_{cathode}^\circ - E_{anode}^\circ)/n\mathscr{F}} \tag{IV-9}$$

At 25°C the quantity $2.303RT/n\mathscr{F}$ has the value 0.0592 volt,* which provides the connection with Equation (14-27), page 312.

More generally, using (IV-2), (IV-6), and (IV-7),

$$E_{total} = -\Delta F/n\mathscr{F} = -\Delta F°/n\mathscr{F} - (RT/n\mathscr{F})\ln Q$$

$$E_{total} = E°_{total} - 2.303(RT/n\mathscr{F})\log Q \qquad \text{(IV-10)}$$

which is the Nernst equation for the electrochemical cell considered. When the anode of this cell is chosen to be the standard hydrogen electrode, E_{anode} becomes zero by definition, E_{total} equals $E_{cathode}$, and (IV-10) becomes the Nernst equation for the electrode potential of the cathode. At a temperature of 25°C this is identical with Equation (14-10), page 305.

Half-cell emf values and electrode potentials. It is customary to assign free-energy changes to half-reactions by assigning the arbitrary value of zero to the free-energy change of the hydrogen half-reaction at standard conditions. This is consistent with the convention that the electrode potential of the standard hydrogen electrode is zero. The half-cell emf of any half-cell is defined by the equation

$$E_{half\text{-}cell} = (-\Delta F_{half\text{-}cell})/n\mathscr{F} \qquad \text{(IV-11)}$$

and is thus the free-energy decrease that results from the reaction of one electron. Its sign depends on the way the half-reaction is written, because the sign of the free-energy decrease depends on that. It is a sign-bivariant quantity. In contrast, the electrode potential is the potential an electrode physically assumes when the given half-cell is combined with the standard hydrogen electrode. The sign of the electrode potential therefore does not depend on the way the half-reaction is written. It is a sign-invariant quantity.

Thermodynamic relationships. It is one of the results of thermodynamics that the standard free-energy difference $\Delta F°$ between reactants and products of a chemical reaction may be obtained experimentally by thermal measurements on the individual pure substances involved. As is seen from Equation (IV-3), $\Delta F°$ may also be determined by measuring the equilibrium constant of the reaction, and if the reaction is electrochemical, by measuring the cell potential [Eqs. (IV-7) and (IV-10)]. It is therefore possible to obtain values for all three quantities, the standard free-energy change, the equilibrium constant, and the electrode potential of an electrochemical reaction by measuring just one of the three. Two of these or all three have been measured for many reactions, with results

* $\mathscr{F} = 23{,}060$ cal/volt mole, $R = 1.986$ cal/mole deg, $T = 298°$K, $RT/\mathscr{F} = (2.303 \times 1.986 \times 298)/23{,}060 = 0.0592$ volt.

that have always been consistent with each other within the accuracy of the experiments.

For many other reactions it is, however, impractical or impossible to measure the three quantities separately. The equilibrium may, for example, be very one-sided, and the concentrations of the products may completely dominate those of the reactants, or inversely, so that it is hard to obtain accurate measurements of the equilibrium constant. For example, in the reaction

$$2Ag^+ + Zn(s) = Zn^{++} + 2Ag(s)$$

the equilibrium is overwhelmingly in favor of the right side, with a concentration of Ag^+ of the order of 10^{-26} when that of Zn^{++} is about 1. It would therefore be impossible to determine the equilibrium constant from concentration measurements. However, the potential established between a Zn and an Ag electrode dipping into connected half-cells that contain, respectively, Zn^{++} and Ag^+ ions at standard concentrations can easily be measured, and the equilibrium constant can be computed from that value.

An equilibrium of interest may be reached at a very slow rate, or side reactions may prevent its establishment entirely, so that neither the equilibrium constant nor the cell potential may be measured. For example, the potential of the couple MnO_4^-/Mn^{++} cannot be measured in an alkaline or neutral solution, because in such a solution MnO_4^- is reduced to $MnO_2(s)$ rather than to Mn^{++}. Nevertheless, this potential and the corresponding equilibrium constant may be calculated from free-energy considerations—in this particular case by using the standard potential of the MnO_4^-/Mn^{++} couple measured at zero pH, and calculating the desired quantities from Equations (IV-10) and (IV-9).

Whenever an equilibrium constant or a cell potential is not accessible to direct measurement, it may be determined from the free energies of all substances involved, provided these are known from thermal measurements or from measurements of equilibrium constants or cell potentials of other reactions that relate the substances considered to still others with known free-energy values. This is of great practical use; and it is one of the important results of chemical thermodynamics that it is possible to establish from free-energy considerations alone whether a reaction is possible in principle, without experimental study of the reaction. Of course, only the position of the equilibrium can be determined, and not whether the equilibrium is actually established. That a given reaction is possible thermodynamically is a necessary but not a sufficient condition for its occurrence, and it takes examination of the rates to establish whether a possible equilibrium is also attained with reasonable speed. If it is not, increase of temperature often increases the rates sufficiently to make the reaction practicable, or the addition of catalysts may speed the reaction sufficiently. Although a change of temperature in general affects the equilibrium *position*, this position is *not changed by the addition of catalysts*. The reason is that the value of the equilibrium constant depends only on the standard free-energy difference of products and reactants, and free energies are properties of substances alone and are not affected by the presence of catalysts. Free-energy considerations thus save time and effort by ruling out the impossible, whereas examination of rates is still required to establish whether the possible is actually feasible.

Thermodynamic relationships, such as the mass-action law, the Nernst equation, and the relationship between electrode potentials, equilibrium constants, and standard free energies, all pertain to *macroscopic* quantities such as temperature, pressure, potential, and concentrations. Thermodynamics does not provide explanations of these relationships in terms of atoms and molecules. Such *microscopic* explanations require the elaborate apparatus of quantum mechanics and statistical mechanics. The value of thermodynamics lies in establishing macroscopic relationships without the need for microscopic details, and often long before such details are available or understood.

REFERENCES

L. K. Nash, *Elements of Chemical Thermodynamics*, Addison-Wesley, Reading, Mass., 1962.
B. H. Mahan, *Elementary Chemical Thermodynamics*, Benjamin, New York, 1963.

appendix V

TABLES

TABLE V-1   *Atomic and Formula Weights*
(Based on $C^{12} = 12$)

Acetic acid ($HC_2H_3O_2$)	60.03	Hg_2Cl_2	472.08
Ag	107.87	I	126.90
AgBr	187.78	K	39.10
AgCl	143.25	KBr	119.01
Ag_2CrO_4	331.74	KCl	74.55
AgI	234.77	$K_2Cr_2O_7$	294.20
$AgNO_3$	169.88	KH phthalate ($KHC_8H_4O_4$)	204.24
Al	26.98	KI	166.00
As	74.92	KIO_3	214.00
As_2O_3	197.84	$KMnO_4$	158.04
Ba	137.34	KNO_3	101.11
$BaCl_2$	208.24	KOH	56.11
$BaCrO_4$	253.34	KSCN	97.17
$BaSO_4$	233.40	K_2SO_4	174.26
Br	79.91	Mg	24.31
C	12.00	Mn	54.94
CO_2	44.00	N	14.01
Ca	40.08	NH_3	17.03
$CaSO_4$	136.14	NH_4Cl	53.49
Cl	35.45	NH_4SCN	76.11
Co	58.93	Na	22.99
Cr	52.00	Na acetate ($NaC_2H_3O_2$)	82.01
Cu	63.54	NaBr	102.90
CuI	190.44	Na_2CO_3	105.98
$CuSO_4 \cdot 5H_2O$	249.68	NaCl	58.44
F	19.00	$NaHCO_3$	84.00
Fe	55.85	$NaNO_2$	69.00
$FeNH_4(SO_4)_2 \cdot 12H_2O$	482.20	$NaNO_3$	85.00
H	1.008	NaOH	40.00
HBr	80.92	Na_2SO_3	126.04
HCl	36.46	Na_2SO_4	142.04
HF	20.01	$Na_2S_2O_3$	158.10
HI	127.91	Ni	58.71
H_3NSO_3 (sulfamic acid)	97.09	O	16.00
HNO_2	47.02	P	30.97
HNO_3	63.02	Pb	207.19
H_2O	18.02	$PbSO_4$	303.25
H_2O_2	34.02	S	32.06
H_3PO_4	97.99	Sn	118.69
H_2S	34.08	$SnCl_2$	189.59
H_2SO_4	98.08	SnO_2	150.69
Hg	200.59	Sulfamic acid (H_3NSO_3)	97.09
$HgCl_2$	271.49	Zn	65.37

TABLE V-2 *Relative Density of Water at Various Temperatures*

The relative densities are grams per milliliter; these values can be converted to absolute densities, grams per cubic centimeter, by multiplication by the factor 0.999973.

temp, °C	relative density	temp, °C	relative density	temp, °C	relative density
15	0.99913	21	0.99802	27	0.99654
16	.99897	22	.99780	28	.99626
17	.99880	23	.99756	29	.99597
18	.99862	24	.99732	30	.99567
19	.99843	25	.99707	31	.99537
20	0.99823	26	0.99681	32	0.99505

TABLE V-3 *Partial Pressures of Water at Various Temperatures*

t, °C	pH_2O, mm	t, °C	pH_2O, mm
15	12.8	27	26.6
16	13.6	28	28.2
17	14.5	29	29.9
18	15.5	30	31.7
19	16.5	31	33.6
20	17.5	32	35.5
21	18.6	33	37.6
22	19.8	34	39.8
23	21.0	35	42.0
24	22.3	36	44.4
25	23.7	37	46.9
26	25.1	38	49.5

TABLE V-4   *Solubility Products*

Ag·Ag(CN)$_2$	5×10^{-12}	CuSCN	2×10^{-11}
AgBr	4×10^{-13}	Fe(OH)$_3$	10^{-36}
AgCl	1.8×10^{-10}	FeS	10^{-22}
Ag$_2$CrO$_4$	2×10^{-12}	Hg$_2$Br$_2$*	1×10^{-21}
AgI	1×10^{-16}	Hg$_2$Cl$_2$*	2×10^{-18}
AgOH	2×10^{-8}	Hg$_2$I$_2$*	7×10^{-29}
AgSCN	1×10^{-12}	MgCO$_3$	3×10^{-5}
Al(OH)$_3$	2.0×10^{-33}	MgF$_2$	8×10^{-8}
BaCO$_3$	2×10^{-9}	Mg(OH)$_2$	9×10^{-12}
BaCrO$_4$	3×10^{-10}	Mn(OH)$_2$	10^{-14}
BaF$_2$	3×10^{-6}	Ni(OH)$_2$	10^{-14}
Ba(OH)$_2$	10^{-3}	NiS	10^{-27}
BaSO$_4$	1.1×10^{-10}	PbCO$_3$	3×10^{-14}
CaCO$_3$	5×10^{-9}	PbCl$_2$	1.7×10^{-5}
CaC$_2$O$_4$ (oxalate)	2.6×10^{-4}	PbCrO$_4$	2×10^{-14}
CaF$_2$	3.4×10^{-11}	PbSO$_4$	2×10^{-8}
Ca(IO$_3$)$_2$	3.3×10^{-7}	SrCO$_3$	7×10^{-10}
CaSO$_4$	2×10^{-5}	SrF$_2$	8×10^{-10}
Cr(OH)$_3$	10^{-30}	SrSO$_4$	5×10^{-7}
CuBr	4×10^{-8}	ZnCO$_3$	3×10^{-8}
CuCl	1×10^{-6}	Zn(OH)$_2$	4.5×10^{-17}
CuI	4×10^{-12}	ZnS(α)	10^{-24}
Cu(OH)$_2$	10^{-19}	ZnS(β)	10^{-25}
CuS	10^{-42}		

* Solutions contain predominantly the species Hg_2^{++}.

TABLE V-5   *Acid Constants* K_a

(See also Table 9-3, page 208)

Acetic	$HAc \equiv CH_3COOH$	1.8×10^{-5}
Ammonium ion	NH_4^+	5.5×10^{-10}
		$(K_b = 1.8 \times 10^{-5})$
Arsenic	H_3AsO_4	$K_1 = 5.6 \times 10^{-3}$
		$K_2 = 1.7 \times 10^{-7}$
		$K_3 = 3 \times 10^{-12}$
Arsenious	H_3AsO_3	$K_1 = 6 \times 10^{-10}$
		$K_2 = 3 \times 10^{-14}$
Boric	H_3BO_3	$K_1 = 6.4 \times 10^{-10}$
Carbonic	H_2CO_3	$K_1 = 4.4 \times 10^{-7}$
		$K_2 = 4.8 \times 10^{-11}$
Chlorous	$HClO_2$	1.0×10^{-2}
Chromic	H_2CrO_4	$K_1 = 1.2$
		$K_2 = 3.2 \times 10^{-7}$
Formic	$HCOOH$	1.7×10^{-4}
Dichromic	$H_2Cr_2O_7$	K_1 large
		$K_2 = 8.5 \times 10^{-1}$
$2HCrO_4^- = Cr_2O_7^= + H_2O$		$K = 40$
Hydrazinium ion	$^+H_3NNH_2$	1.0×10^{-8}
		$(K_b = 1.0 \times 10^{-6})$
Hydrazoic acid	HN_3	1.2×10^{-5}
Hydrocyanic	HCN	2×10^{-9}
Hydrofluoric	HF	6.7×10^{-4}
Hydrogen sulfide	H_2S	$K_1 = 9.1 \times 10^{-8}$
		$K_2 = 1.2 \times 10^{-15}$
Hydroxylaminium ion	^+H_3NOH	8.2×10^{-7}
		$(K_b = 1.2 \times 10^{-8})$
Hypobromous	$HBrO$	2.0×10^{-9}
Hypochlorous	$HClO$	1.1×10^{-8}
Hypoiodous	HIO	3×10^{-11}
Iodic	HIO_3	2×10^{-1}
Nitrous	HNO_2	4.5×10^{-4}
Oxalic	$HOOCCOOH$	$K_1 = 5.6 \times 10^{-2}$
		$K_2 = 7.2 \times 10^{-5}$
Phosphoric	H_3PO_4	$K_1 = 7.1 \times 10^{-3}$
		$K_2 = 6.2 \times 10^{-8}$
		$K_3 = 4.4 \times 10^{-13}$
Phosphorous	H_3PO_3	$K_1 = 1.0 \times 10^{-2}$
		$K_2 = 2.6 \times 10^{-7}$
Phthalic	$C_6H_4(COOH)_2$	$K_1 = 1.2 \times 10^{-3}$
		$K_2 = 3.1 \times 10^{-6}$
Sulfuric	H_2SO_4	K_1 large
		$K_2 = 1.2 \times 10^{-2}$
Sulfurous	H_2SO_3	$K_1 = 1.2 \times 10^{-2}$
		$K_2 = 5 \times 10^{-6}$
Thiocyanic	$HNCS$	1.4×10^{-1}

TABLE V-6 *Complex-formation Constants*

$AgCl_{i-1}^{(2-i)+} + Cl^- = AgCl_i^{(1-i)+}$	$K_1 = 2.0 \times 10^3$
	$K_2 = 90$
	$K_3 = 1.6$
$Ag^+ + 2CN^- = Ag(CN)_2^-$	10^{21}
$Ag(NH_3)_{i-1}^+ + NH_3 = Ag(NH_3)_i^+$	$K_1 = 2.1 \times 10^3$
	$K_2 = 8.2 \times 10^3$
$Al(OH)_3(s) + OH^- = Al(OH)_4^-$	40
$Ba^{++} + OH^- = BaOH^+$	4.4
$Ca^{++} + OH^- = CaOH^+$	20
$Cr(OH)_3(s) + OH^- = Cr(OH)_4^-$	10^{-2}
$Cu^{++} + OH^- = CuOH^+$	2×10^6
$Cu(OH)_2(s) + 2OH^- = Cu(OH)_4^=$	5×10^2
$Cu(NH_3)_{i-1}^{++} + NH_3 = Cu(NH_3)_i^{++}$	$K_1 = 2.0 \times 10^4$
	$K_2 = 4.1 \times 10^3$
	$K_3 = 9.6 \times 10^2$
	$K_4 = 1.7 \times 10^2$
$FeCl_{i-1}^{(4-i)} + Cl^- = FeCl_i^{(3-i)+}$	$K_1 = 33$
	$K_2 = 4.5$
	$K_3 = 10^{-1}$
	$K_4 = 10^{-2}$
$Fe^{3+} + NO_3^- = FeNO_3^{++}$	10
$Fe(SCN)_{i-1}^{(4-i)+} + SCN^- = Fe(SCN)_i^{(3-i)+}$	$K_1 = 1.4 \times 10^2$
	$K_2 = 16$
	$K_3 = 1$
$Fe(SO_4)_{i-1}^{(1-2i)+} + SO_4^= = Fe(SO_4)_i^{(3-2i)+}$	$K_1 = 1.7 \times 10^2$
	$K_2 = 1 \times 10^2$
$Fe^{3+} + HSO_4^- = FeHSO_4^{++}$	6
$FeSO_4^+ + HSO_4^- = Fe(SO_4)(HSO_4)$	2.3
$FeSCN(SO_4)_{i-1}^{(4-2i)+} + SO_4^= = FeSCN(SO_4)_i^{(2-2i)+}$	$K_1 = 90$
	$K_2 = 41$
$Mg^{++} + OH^- = MgOH^+$	3.8×10^2
$Pb(OH)_2(s) + OH^- = Pb(OH)_3^-$	50
$Sn(OH)_4(s) + 2OH^- = Sn(OH)_6^=$	5×10^3
$Sr^{++} + OH^- = SrOH^+$	7
$Zn(NH_3)_{i-1}^{++} + NH_3 = Zn(NH_3)_i^{++}$	$K_1 = 1.8 \times 10^2$
	$K_2 = 2.2 \times 10^2$
	$K_3 = 2.5 \times 10^2$
	$K_4 = 1.1 \times 10^2$
$Zn(OH)_2(s) + 2OH^- = Zn(OH)_4^=$	10

TABLE V-7 *Standard Electrode Potentials*
(See also Table 14-1, page 306)

For an extensive collection of standard electrode potentials, see W. M. Latimer, "Oxidation Potentials," 2nd ed., Prentice-Hall, Englewood Cliffs, N.J., 1952, and G. Charlot, "Selected Constants Oxydo-Reduction Potentials," Pergamon Press, New York, 1958. Values accompanied by special conditions in parentheses are formal potentials, as explained on page 314; the values given have been measured by E. H. Swift and collaborators.

$Ag^+ + e^- = Ag(s)$	0.7994
$Ag_2O(s) + H_2O + 2e^- = 2Ag(s) + OH^-$	0.342
$AgCl(s) + e^- = Ag(s) + Cl^-$	0.2224
$AgBr(s) + e^- = Ag(s) + Br^-$	0.071
$AgI(s) + e^- = Ag(s) + I^-$	-0.152
$Ag_2S(s) + 2e^- = 2Ag(s) + S^=$	-0.71
$Ag_2CrO_4(s) + 2e^- = 2Ag(s) + CrO_4^=$	0.447
$Al^{3+} + 3e^- = Al(s)$	-1.66
$H_2AlO_3^- + H_2O + 3e^- = Al(s) + 4OH^-$	-2.35
$As_2O_3(s) + 6H^+ + 6e^- = 2As(s) + 3H_2O$	0.234
$H_3AsO_4 + 2H^+ + 2e^- = H_3AsO_3 + 2H_2O$	0.56
$As(V) + 2e^- = As(III)$	0.577 (in 1 F HCl or 1 F HClO$_4$)
$Ba^{++} + 2e^- = Ba(s)$	-2.90
$Be^{++} + 2e^- = Be(s)$	-1.85
$BiO^+ + 2H^+ + 3e^- = Bi(s) + H_2O$	0.28
$Br_2(l) + 2e^- = 2Br^-$	1.0652
$Ca^{++} + 2e^- = Ca(s)$	-2.87
$Cd^{++} + 2e^- = Cd(s)$	-0.402
$Ce(IV) + e^- = Ce(III)$	1.7 (in 1 F HClO$_4$) 1.61 (in 1 F HNO$_3$) 1.44 (in 1 F H$_2$SO$_4$) 1.23 (in 1 F HCl)
$Cl_2(g) + 2e^- = 2Cl^-$	1.359
$2HClO + 2H^+ + 2e^- = Cl_2(g) + 2H_2O$	1.63
$HClO_2 + 2H^+ + 2e^- = HClO + H_2O$	1.64
$ClO_2(g) + H^+ + e^- = HClO_2$	1.27
$ClO_3^- + 2H^+ + e^- = ClO_2(g) + H_2O$	1.15
$ClO_4^- + 2H^+ + 2e^- = ClO_3^- + H_2O$	1.19
$Co(II) + 2e^- = Co(s)$	-0.28
$Co(III) + e^- = Co(II)$	1.82 (in 1 F H$_2$SO$_4$) 1.83 (in 1 F HNO$_3$)
$Cr^{3+} + 3e^- = Cr(s)$	-0.74
$Cr(III) + e^- = Cr(II)$	-0.38 (in 1 F HCl) -0.51 (in 0.1 F HF)
$Cr_2O_7^= + 14H^+ + 6e^- = 2Cr^{3+} + 7H_2O$	1.33
$Cs^+ + e^- = Cs(s)$	-2.952

$Cu^+ + e^- = Cu(s)$	0.521
$Cu_2O(s) + H_2O + e^- = Cu(s) + 2OH^-$	−0.358
$CuCl(s) + e^- = Cu(s) + Cl^-$	0.137
$Cu^{++} + 2e^- = Cu(s)$	0.337
$Cu^{++} + e^- = Cu^+$	0.153
$Cu^{++} + I^- + e^- = CuI(s)$	0.85
$F_2(g) + 2e^- = 2F^-$	2.87
$Fe^{++} + 2e^- = Fe(s)$	−0.440
$Fe^{3+} + e^- = Fe^{++}$	0.771
	0.732 (in 1 F HClO$_4$)
	0.700 (in 1 F HCl)
	0.68 (in 1 F H$_2$SO$_4$)
	0.61 (in 1 F H$_2$SO$_4$ and
	0.5 F H$_3$PO$_4$)
$2H^+ + 2e^- = H_2(g)$	0.0000
$Hg_2^{++} + 2e^- = 2Hg(l)$	0.792
$Hg_2Cl_2(s) + 2e^- = 2Hg(l) + 2Cl^-$	0.2680
$Hg_2Br_2(s) + 2e^- = 2Hg(l) + 2Br^-$	0.1392
$2Hg^{++} + 2e^- = Hg_2^{++}$	0.907
$I_2(s) + 2e^- = 2I^-$	0.534
$I_3^- + 2e^- = 3I^-$	0.535
$HIO + H^+ + 2e^- = I^- + H_2O$	0.99
$Ra^{++} + 2e^- = Ra(s)$	−2.92
$Rb^+ + e^- = Rb(s)$	−2.93
$2IO_3^- + 12H^+ + 10e^- = I_2(s) + 6H_2O$	1.19
$H_5IO_6 + H^+ + 2e^- = IO_3^- + 3H_2O$	1.6
$K^+ + e^- = K(s)$	−2.925
$Li^+ + e^- = Li(s)$	−3.03
$Mg^{++} + 2e^- = Mg(s)$	−2.37
$Mn^{++} + 2e^- = Mn(s)$	−1.190
$MnO_2(s) + 4H^+ + 2e^- = Mn^{++} + 2H_2O$	1.23
$MnO_4^- + 8H^+ + 5e^- = Mn^{++} + 4H_2O$	1.51
$HNO_2 + H^+ + e^- = NO(g) + H_2O$	0.99
$NO_3^- + 3H^+ + 2e^- = HNO_2 + H_2O$	0.94
$Na^+ + e^- = Na(s)$	−2.698
$Ni^{++} + 2e^- = Ni(s)$	−0.23
$H_2O_2 + 2H^+ + 2e^- = 2H_2O$	1.77
$O_2(g) + 4H^+ + 4e^- = 2H_2O$	1.229
$O_2(g) + 2H^+ + 2e^- = H_2O_2$	0.69
$H_3PO_3 + 2H^+ + 2e^- = H_3PO_2 + H_2O$	−0.50
$H_3PO_4 + 2H^+ + 2e^- = H_3PO_3 + H_2O$	−0.276
$Pb^{++} + 2e^- = Pb(s)$	−0.126
$PbSO_4(s) + 2e^- = Pb(s) + SO_4^=$	−0.356
$PbO_2(s) + 4H^+ + 2e^- = Pb^{++} + 2H_2O$	1.47
$S(s) + 2H^+ + 2e^- = H_2S(g)$	0.141

$HSO_4^- + 9H^+ + 8e^- = H_2S(g) + 4H_2O$	$+0.316$
$2H_2SO_3 + 2H^+ + 4e^- = S_2O_3^= + 3H_2O$	0.40
$HSO_4^- + 3H^+ + 2e^- = SO_2(g) + 2H_2O$	0.14
$S_4O_6^= + 2e^- = 2S_2O_3^=$	0.09
$SbO^+ + 2H^+ + 3e^- = Sb(s) + H_2O$	-0.212
$Sn^{++} + 2e^- = Sn(s)$	-0.140
$Sn(OH)_6^= + 2e^- = HSnO_2^- + H_2O + 3OH^-$	-0.90
$Sn(IV) + 2e^- = Sn(II)$	0.14 (in 1 F HCl)
$Sr^{++} + 2e^- = Sr(s)$	-2.89
$TiO^{++} + 2H^+ + e^- = Ti^{3+} + H_2O$	0.1
$Tl^+ + e^- = Tl(s)$	-0.336
$Tl^{3+} + 2e^- = Tl^+$	1.28
$V^{3+} + e^- = V^{++}$	-0.255
$VO^{++} + 2H^+ + e^- = V^{3+} + H_2O$	0.361
$V(OH)_4^+ + 2H^+ + e^- = VO^{++} + 3H_2O$	1.00
$Zn^{++} + 2e^- = Zn(s)$	-0.7628

appendix VI

EQUIPMENT
AND REAGENTS

Returnable items

1	Asbestos pad
3	Beakers, 150 ml
2	Beakers, 250 ml
3	Beakers, 400 ml
1	Beaker, 800 ml
1	Bottle, narrow mouth, glass stopper 500 ml
1	Bottle, n.m.g.s., 1000 ml
1	Bottle, polyethylene, 250 ml (for squeeze bottle)
1	Bottle, polyethylene, 1000 ml, with screw cap

3	Bottles, weighing, 25 mm by 40 mm
1	Bulb, rubber, 60 ml, for pipets
1 or 2	Burets, 50 ml, with glass or Teflon valve
1	Buret without valve (Mohr buret)
2	Burners, Bunsen or Tirrill, with 1 flame spreader to fit
1	Clamp, buret, double
2	Clamps, buret, single
1	Clamp, test tube
4	Crucibles, sintered glass, medium
1	Cylinder, graduated, 10 ml
1	Cylinder, graduated, 25 ml
1	Cylinder, graduated, 100 ml
1	Desiccator
2	Flasks, conical, 50 ml
2	Flasks, conical, 125 ml
6	Flasks, conical, 200 ml
3	Flasks, conical, 500 ml
1	Flask, flat bottom, round neck, also called Florence flask, 1000 ml (for wash bottle)
1	Flask, suction
1	Flask, volumetric, 100 ml
1	Flask, volumetric, 250 ml
1	Flask, volumetric, 500 ml
1	Funnel, crucible, with rubber tubing
1	Funnel, short stem, 65 mm
1	Funnel, long stem, 65 mm
2	Funnels, short stem, 45 mm
	Gas tubing, 6 ft, Koroseal
1	Magnet, coated, $\frac{3}{8}$ in. diameter, 1 in. long (stirring bar)
1	Magnet, uncoated, $\frac{1}{8}$ in. by $\frac{5}{16}$ in. by $\frac{7}{8}$ in.
1	Pipet, transfer, 10 ml
1	Pipet, transfer, 25 ml
2	Rings, iron
1 or 2	Ringstands
1	Scoopula, stainless steel
1	Spatula, porcelain
1	Spatula, stainless steel
	Stoppers, rubber, one two-hole each for each set of conical flasks and for 1000-ml flask; one one-hole stopper for filter flask; one one-hole stopper for 250-ml polyethylene bottle

1	Test-tube rack
1	Test tube, 22 mm by 175 mm
2	Test tubes, 13 mm by 100 mm
12	Test tubes, 15 mm by 125 mm
2	Test tubes, 18 mm by 150 mm
1	Thermometer, 110°C
1 or 2	Tripods
6	Watch glasses, 40 mm
3	Watch glasses, 75 mm
3	Watch glasses, 100 mm

Nonreturnable items

4	Bulbs, rubber, 2 ml, for droppers
1	Brush, test tube, large
1	Brush, test tube, small
1	File, triangular
	Filter paper, 1 box, 9 cm
	Glass rod, 2 ft, 4 mm
	Glass tubing, 1 ft, 5 mm
	Glass tubing, 8 ft, 6 mm
	Labels, 1 box
	Matches, 1 box
	pH paper, universal, 1 vial
2	Policemen, rubber
	Rubber tubing, 6 in., $\frac{3}{16}$ in. by $\frac{1}{16}$ in., for wash bottle
1	Sponge
2	Towels
1	Vial, 1 dram
4	Vials, $\frac{1}{2}$ dram
2	Wire gauze

General equipment

Balance, analytical, chainomatic, with weights
Balance, pulp, 1-kg capacity, 10-mg sensitivity
Balance, triple beam
Beaker, or conical flask, 1500 ml (for preparation of large volumes of solutions)
Colorimeter
Control panel for coulometric experiment (p. 286)
Coulometric cell with electrodes (p. 287; for electrode construction details see below)

Drying oven, electrical
Glass wool
Hot plate
Magnetic stirrer
Power supply, voltage-stabilized (like Heathkit PS 3)
Student potentiometer
Timer, electric, $\frac{1}{10}$-sec intervals, with 1000-sec total

Electrode construction details. The Pt anode is made by welding a 4-cm piece of 0.020-in. Pt wire to a 2- by 2-cm piece of 0.005-in. Pt foil. For the welding place the wire on the foil and both on a block of steel. Heat the Pt pieces with a gas-air torch to a red heat and hit the wire sharply with a hammer. The cathode consists of a 4-cm piece of 0.020-in. Pt wire. Both anode and cathode are sealed into 15-cm lengths of 4-mm soft-glass tubing. To attach the Cu leads to the Pt wires inside the tubes, place a 1.5 cm length of 18 gauge 50-50 rosin-core solder in the tube, insert the Cu wire, and carefully heat in a Bunsen flame until the solder melts. Cool slowly.

REAGENTS

Reagents and equipment for each assignment are listed in the last section of this appendix.

Acids

Hydrochloric, 6 *F*. Dilute 500 ml of 36 per cent HCl of specific gravity 1.19 to 1 liter.

Nitric, 6 *F*. Dilute 375 ml of 69 per cent HNO_3 of specific gravity 1.42 to 1 liter.

Phosphoric, 14.6 *F*. Use 85 per cent H_3PO_4 of specific gravity 1.69.

Sulfuric, 9 *F*. Dilute 500 ml of 95 per cent H_2SO_4 of specific gravity 1.84 to 1 liter.

Sulfuric, 3 *F*. Dilute 165 ml of 95 per cent H_2SO_4 to 1 liter.

Bases

Ammonia, 15 *F*. Use 29 per cent solution of NH_3 of specific gravity 0.90.

Sodium hydroxide, 6 *F*. Dissolve 255 g of 95 per cent NaOH in water, cool, and dilute to 1 liter.

Sodium hydroxide, 1 *F*. Dissolve 42.5 g of 95 per cent NaOH in water, and dilute to 1 liter.

Solutions of salts

Ferric nitrate, 0.5 *F*.

$$175 \text{ g Fe(NO}_3)_3 \cdot 6H_2O$$
or
$$202 \text{ g Fe(NO}_3)_3 \cdot 9H_2O$$

per liter.

Mercuric chloride, saturated. 75 g $HgCl_2$ per liter.

Potassium permanganate, 0.1 F. 16 g $KMnO_4$ per liter.

Silver nitrate, 0.2 F. 34 g $AgNO_3$ per liter.

Sodium bicarbonate, 0.2 F. 17 g $NaHCO_3$ per liter.

Sodium sulfite, 0.5 F. 63 g Na_2SO_3 per liter.

Stannous chloride, 0.5 F. Dissolve 113 g of iron-free $SnCl_2$ in 500 ml of 6 F HCl, and dilute to 1 liter. Add 10 to 20 g of "mossy" tin to the container.

Indicator solutions

Acid-base indicators

Bromcresol green	1 g of Na salt in 1 liter water
Bromthymol blue	1 g in 1 liter ethanol
Methyl orange	1 g in 1 liter water
Methyl red	2 g in 1 liter ethanol
Phenolphthalein	2 g in 1 liter ethanol
Phenol red	1 g in 1 liter ethanol
Thymolphthalein	1 g in 1 liter ethanol

Metal indicator

Erio T	5 g in 500 ml of either diethanolamine or triethanolamine

Potential indicator

Sodium diphenylamine sulfonate	2 g in 1 liter water

Starch-indicator

Grind 2 g of starch (potato, rice, or arrowroot) in a mortar with 20 ml of cold water. Pour the resulting thin paste slowly into 500 ml of boiling water while stirring the paste continuously. Add 2.5 g of formamide or 0.02 g of mercuric iodide as preservative. Gently boil for 15 to 20 min, and let it stand overnight. Decant the clear supernatant liquid.

Commercially available "soluble starch" may also be used. The procedure is the same, except that decantation is not necessary.

SPECIAL EQUIPMENT AND REAGENTS, LISTED BY LABORATORY ASSIGNMENTS

The quantities are about what will be used by 200 students. The preparation of reagents is as indicated in the preceding general list of reagents.

Assignment 3 (page 56).　Unknown weights (such as numbered brass slugs weighing between 2 and 10 g).

Assignment 4 (page 88).   Forty liters of 0.2 *F* AgNO$_3$, 6 *F* HNO$_3$, 6 *F* HCl, and 15 *F* NH$_3$. Chloride unknown samples (available commercially). Bottle for discarding AgCl should be available.

Assignment 5 (page 108).   A pulp balance of 1 kg capacity and sensitivity of 10 mg should be available if calibration of the volumetric flasks is desired.

Assignment 6 (page 122).   Two pounds sulfamic acid, reagent grade. Nitrite samples are prepared by mixing sodium nitrite and sodium chloride. They must be well dried and kept dry to remain stable. Small coated and uncoated magnets.

Assignment 7 (page 144).   Six grams of AgNO$_3$ per student, preferably dispensed in screw-cap vials to prevent waste and contamination of the silver nitrate in the stock bottles. Five pounds of KSCN and 12 liters of 0.5 *F* Fe(NO$_3$)$_3$ solution. Unknowns are alloy-wire samples cut so that one piece corresponds to 3 to 4 milliequivalents of silver. Alloy should contain no Sn and less than 30 per cent Cu. Bottle for discarded AgSCN should be available.

Assignment 8 (page 178).   Prepare ahead of time 2 liters of 50 per cent NaOH solution in polyethylene container provided with siphon and soda-lime tube to prevent absorption of air CO$_2$. Let stand until carbonate residue has settled. Dispense 6 ml of clear supernatant to each student. Also needed, 3 lb of KH phthalate as primary standard, 3 lb of K$_2$ phthalate, Na$_2$ phthalate, or Na$_2$ succinate for blank titrations, pH meter, and magnetic stirrer.

Indicator solutions.   Dispense in 30-ml bottles, provided with droppers: $\frac{1}{2}$ to 1 liter of solutions of bromcresol green, bromthymol blue, methyl red, phenol red, and 1 liter of phenolphthalein solution.

Unknown solutions.   Solutions of the following acids (about 0.1 to 0.2 *N*) have been found suitable: acetic acid, formic acid, KH oxalate, KH phthalate, NaH diglycolate, and NaH tartrate. Prepare solutions with distilled water that has been boiled for 10 min and let cool, and sterilize the bottles to contain the solutions by boiling. Under these conditions a few drops of toluene added as preservative is usually satisfactory.

Assignment 9 (page 210).   One hundred milliliters $\frac{1}{15}$ *F* H$_3$PO$_4$ per student desiring to perform this optional experiment; 85 per cent H$_3$PO$_4$ is 14.6 *F*, and thus about 5 ml should be diluted to 1 liter; pH meter and magnetic stirrer; $\frac{1}{2}$ to 1 liter of thymolphthalein solution.

Assignment 10 (page 221).   Phenolphthalein indicator solution and glass wool. Exchange resin: Amberlite 120 H or Dowex 50 (analytical grade, 20 to 50 mesh); dispense wet in 500-ml wide-mouth screw-cap bottles filled to capacity. Total quantity needed about 5 lb. Labeled wide-mouth liter bottles should be provided for discarded resin. Old resin should be regenerated with 6 F HCl before being issued to students.

Unknowns: Approximately 0.1 to 0.15 N solutions of mixtures of $Cu(NO_3)_2$, $Ni(NO_3)_2$, and $Co(NO_3)_2$.

Assignment 11 (page 243).   One liter of 85 per cent H_3PO_4, 2 lb $(NH_4)_2S_2O_8$, 2 lb KIO_4, 8 liters 0.5 F Na_2SO_3, and 6 F HNO_3. Unknown and known steel samples must be low in V and Cr, Ni, Co, Cu. Colorimeter.

Assignment 12 (page 265).   Two pounds of disodium salt of EDTA, 8 liters of 6 F NaOH (in polyethylene bottles), 4 lb NH_4Cl, 8 liters of concentrated NH_3. Primary standard-grade Zn, 1 g per student, should be dispensed in individual screw-cap vials. Dispense, in 30-ml bottles provided with droppers, $\frac{1}{2}$ liter Erio T solution. $MgSO_4$ unknowns are available commercially. No commercial source for ZnO has been found.

Assignment 13 (page 291).   Twenty liters of 1 F NaOH, 36 liters generating solution (see below), 12 liters 0.2 F $NaHCO_3$ solution, and 5 liters of starch-indicator solution. Coulometric cell, control panel, power supply, magnetic stirrer, timer, and student potentiometer. Unknowns containing As_2O_3 are available commercially.

Generating solution.   Dissolve 0.2 g As_2O_3 in a small amount of 1 F NaOH. Dissolve 2.0 kg of KI and 1.0 kg of $NaHCO_3$ in water. Mix, dilute to 12 liters, and place in bottle with siphon. Two such preparations are needed for 200 students.

Assignment 14 (page 324).   Primary-standard $K_2Cr_2O_7$ should be dispensed in screw-cap vials, 2.5 to 3 g per student. Further required are 8 liters of 0.1 F $KMnO_4$ solution, 15 liters of saturated $HgCl_2$ solution, 18 liters of 0.5 F $SnCl_2$ solution, 30 liters 9 F H_2SO_4, 16 liters of 85 per cent H_3PO_4, 2 liters of 0.2 per cent Na diphenylamine sulfonate indicator (dispensed in 30-ml dropper bottles), and 6 F HCl. Iron ore samples (available commercially) should not contain much carbonaceous material. For potentiometric titration (optional): pH meter, Pt electrode, calomel electrode, magnetic stirrer. Pure iron wire for optional standardization and for optional potentiometric titration.

Assignment 15 (page 343).   Primary standard KIO_3 should be dispensed in screw-cap vials, 1.2 to 1.5 g per student. Further needed are 12 lb $Na_2S_2O_3 \cdot 2H_2O$, 30 g Na_2CO_3, 12 lb KI, 4 lb KSCN, 8 liters of 9 F H_2SO_4, 6 F HCl, 6 F HNO_3, 3 F H_2SO_4, 15 F NH_3. Five liters of starch-indicator solution. Brass samples, available commercially.

Assignment 16 (page 355).   Prepare 24 liters of solution that is 0.025 F in H_2SO_4 [33.3 ml conc. (18 F) H_2SO_4 in 24 liter] and 0.050 F in $(NH_4)_2SO_4$ [156 g $(NH_4)_2SO_4$ in 24 liter]. For solutions Ia, b, c and IIa, b, c, dissolve in 4 liters each of this buffer the following quantities of substances:

Ia 7.715 g $FeNH_4(SO_4)_2 \cdot 12H_2O$
Ib 3.858 g $FeNH_4(SO_4)_2 \cdot 12H_2O$
Ic 3.858 g $FeNH_4(SO_4)_2 \cdot 12H_2O$
IIa 1.218 g NH_4SCN or 1.555 g KSCN
IIb 1.745 g sulfosalicylic acid or 2.033 g sulfosalicylic acid dihydrate
IIc 2.657 g Tiron (disodium salt, monohydrate).
Colorimeter.

The concentrations of these solutions must be accurate to 1 per cent.

appendix VII

ANSWERS
TO PROBLEMS

3-2   23.5903 g
3-3   NaCl vacuum wt, 1.00043 g; 0.043%
          H_2O wt in air 1.06 g less; 0.11%
3-4 $\overline{OD} = 0.1_7$ mm; 0.5 μ
3-5 $W(1) = W(1^*) + 0.0001_2$ g
          $a_R/a_L = 1.00006_7$ if $W(1)$ equals 1 g within 1%
3-6   0.2%; 2 mg
3-7 $d > 3.5$; $4.9 < d < 28(!)$
4-1   10 milliformula weights (mfw) NaCl, 2 mfw $NaHCO_3$

4-2   (*a*) 187.56; (*b*) 51.18%, (*c*) 1.954 g, (*d*) 6.422 × 10^{21}

4-3   89.9%

4-4   6

4-5   (*a*) Al_4C_3, (*b*) $Sn_2Fe(CN)_6$, (*c*) K_2PtCl_6, (*d*) Na_2HPO_4, (*e*) HF_2ClSi

4-6   1.2%

4-7 $60._3$%

4-8 0.7_7

4-9   (*a*) $c_n = c_0 [vn/(V + nv)]^n$

(*b*) $n = 1, 61; n = 3, 9261$

4-10   (*a*) 35 ml, (*b*) 48.68% Cl, (*c*) 8.3%
NaCl; 91.7% KCl;
precision about 45 ppt for NaCl, 4 ppt for KCl

5-1   Volume concentrations: 1.78 *F*; $[Mg^{++}] = 1.78$; $[Cl^-] = 3.56$.
Weight concentrations: $MgCl_2$, 1.85 gfw/kg H_2O; Mg^{++},
1.85 mole/kg H_2O; Cl^-, 3.70 mole/kg H_2O

5-2   18.3 *F* H_2SO_4

5-3 $n = 1, 0.99969c; n = 2, (1 - 1.7 \times 10^{-5})c;$
$n = 3, (1 - 9.8 \times 10^{-7})c$

5-4 $V_{20} = (1.004_1)W_{26}{}^{air}$

5-5   (*a*) 0.1428 *F*, (*b*) 0.99884

5-6   5.17 g/liter

5-7   55.4

5-8   493 g; 4.03 gfw

5-9   (*a*) 1000.28_5 ml, (*b*) −0.06 cm, (*c*) −0.11 cm

5-10   0.10000 *F*

6-1   110 mg $NaNO_2$

6-2   0.45 g/liter

6-3   77.9 g/mole

6-4 $V_2/V_1 = 1.139$

6-5   20 ml CO, 80 ml C_2H_6

6-6   563 ml

6-7   947 g

6-8   (*a*) 21.7 moles, (*b*) 4.42 atm, (*c*) 13.5 g/liter

6-9   (*a*) 0.577, (*b*) 0.577 atm, (*c*) 0.258 mole

6-10   10.75

6-11   (*a*) 512 ml, (*b*) 0.244 liter

7-1 2×10^{-12} *F*

7-2 $[Pb^{++}] = 1.6 \times 10^{-2}$; $[Cl^-] = 3.2 \times 10^{-2}$;
$[SO_4^=] = 1.2 \times 10^{-6}$

7-3 $1.3 \times 10^{-5} \, M$

7-4 $0.19 \, M$

7-6   (*a*) 1.6×10^{-16}, (*b*) 1.6×10^{-14} gfw/liter

7-8 $1.3 \, M$

7-9   (*a*) 1.0×10^{-4}, (*b*) 1.3×10^{-5}, (*c*) 1.8×10^{-6}

8-1   (*a*)   Equiv.wt = 8.99 g/equiv.;   at.wt = i(8.99) g/mole;   Al = 26.98; (*b*) 0.444 equiv.

8-2   (*a*) 0.30, (*b*) 7.02

8-3 $K = 2.0 \times 10^{-4}$

8-4   0.12

8-5 $c_1 = 0.014 \, F$; $c_2 = 0.086 \, F$

8-6   (*a*) 2.3_5, (*b*) 4.0_7, (*c*) 8.2_0

8-7   1.98 ml; phenolphthalein or thymol blue

8-8 7.0_2

8-9   (*a*) $d(\text{pH})/dx \approx (Vc_1 - x)^{-1} + (Vc_2 + x)^{-1}$
      (*b*) Concentrations are equal

8-10   99.45 ml acid; 99.95 ml base

8-12   (*a*) 2×10^{-11}, (*b*) 3×10^{-13} (*c*) 2×10^{-9}, (*d*) 0.033

8-13 6.4_8

8-15   98% complete; $K_i \approx 10^{-9}$

8-16   0.105 gfw HAc; 0.105 gfw NaAc

9-1   (*a*) 12.5_7, (*b*) 12.1_8, (*c*) 9.7_8, (*d*) 7.3_8, (*e*) 4.6_8

9-2 $[\text{H}_2\text{PO}_4^-] = 0.20$; $[\text{HPO}_4^=] = 0.25$; $[\text{H}_3\text{PO}_4] = 1.4 \times 10^{-6}$;
      $[\text{PO}_4^{3-}] = 2.2 \times 10^{-6}$; pH = 7.30

9-3   (*a*) p ml NaOH, q ml NaOH; HCl, $0.1000(2q - p)/25.00 \, F$
      H_3PO_4, $0.004(p - q) \, F$; $p/2 \le q \le p$

9-4 $0.0657 \, F \, \text{Na}_2\text{CO}_3$; $0.0116 \, F \, \text{NaOH}$

9-5 $[\text{PO}_4^{3-}] = 1.7 \times 10^{-6}$
      $[\text{HPO}_4^=] = 0.38$
      $[\text{H}_2\text{PO}_4^-] = 0.62$
      $[\text{H}_3\text{PO}_4] = 8.7 \times 10^{-6}$

9-6   (*a*) 0.023, (*b*) 4.7×10^{-3}, (*c*) 3.1×10^{-5}

9-7   6.1

11-1   0.277

11-2   24 $(\text{mole/liter})^{-1} \, \text{cm}^{-1}$

11-3   15.4 $\text{mole}^{-1}/\text{cm}^{-1}$

11-4   13.5 mm

11-5   (*a*) 0.412, (*b*) $4.36 \times 10^{-4} \, M$

11-6   (*a*) A prop. $[A]^2$ when $[B] \gg [A]$
      (*b*) A prop. $[B]$ when $[A] \gg [B]$

11-7 $T = e^{-1} = 0.368$

11-8   (a) 42%, (b) same

11-9 $1.3_7 \times 10^4$

11-10 $\mp 0.087;\ \mp 0.0055;\ \mp 0.011$

12-1 $3.6 \times 10^{-6}\ F$

12-2   (a) $10\ M$, (b) no change

12-3   (a) 3.3_3, (b) 11.7_0

12-4   (a) $0.05\ F$, (b) $[CN^-] = 2.5 \times 10^{-6}$
        $[OH^-] = [HCN] = 3.5 \times 10^{-6}$

12-5 $5 \times 10^{-4}\ F$

12-6 1.3×10^{-3}

12-7 $1.8\ M$

12-8 4×10^{-7} gfw/liter

12-9   0.12

12-10 1.1×10^{-13}

13-1 $K_2Cr_2O_7$, 1.200 N, 0.800 N; $BaCl_2$, 0.400 N; H_2O_2, 0.400 N; KIO_3, 0.800 N; KI, 0.400 N; $CuSO_4$, 0.200 N; $Na_2S_2O_3$, 0.400 N; $KMnO_4$, 1.000 N

13-2   3.85 mg

13-3   Anode, positive pole

13-4   720 mg

13-5   5.22 ml O_2; 9.3 ml HCl

13-6   45 ml

13-7   8.55 g

13-8   1.297 amp

14-1   0.611 volt for $Zn + Pb^{++} = Zn^{++} + Pb$ (spontaneous), Zn negative, Pb cathode

14-2 $K = 6$

14-3 $K = 2 \times 10^7$

14-4   (a) $K_{titr} = 3 \times 10^{12}$, (b) 1.7×10^6

14-5   (a) Unstable, (b) stable, (c) pH = 1.2_7

14-6 $[Cu^{++}] = 0.05$; $[Ag^+] = 5 \times 10^{-9}$; $([Cu^+] = 2 \times 10^{-4})$

14-7   99.90 ml, 0.79 volt; 100.00 ml, 1.24 volts; 100.10 ml, 1.32 volts

14-8   (a) 6.5, (b) 5×10^3

14-9   (a) 1.7×10^{-8}, (b) 1.70

14-10 3×10^{34} atm

14-12   11.36%

15-1 2×10^{12}

15-2 0.11_5 mm

15-3 $0.050\ F$

15-4 85.33%

15-5 0.1665 F

15-6 35.0%

15-7 0.1407 F

15-8 $Ag(S_2O_3)_2{}^{3-}$; 4×10^{12}

15-9 (a) $Ca(NH_2)_2$, KNH_2, $NaNH_2$, (b) 5×10^{-23}, (c) 2×10^{-27}

16-3 (a) $[FeSCN^{++}] = 1.1 \times 10^{-4}$; $[Fe(SCN)_2{}^+] = 1.6 \times 10^{-6}$; $[Fe(SCN)_3] = 1.4 \times 10^{-9}$;

(b) 0.20_4

(c) $[SO_4{}^=] = 0.025$; $[HSO_4{}^-] = 0.050$; $[SCN^-] = 10^{-3}$; $[H^+] = 2.4 \times 10^{-2}$ $(Fe^{3+}) = 6 \times 10^{-5}$; $[FeSO_4{}^+] = 2 \times 10^{-4}$; $[Fe(SO_4)_2{}^-] = 6 \times 10^{-4}$; $[FeHSO_4{}^{++}] = 2 \times 10^{-5}$; $[Fe(SO_4)(HSO_4)] = 3 \times 10^{-5}$; $[Fe(SO_4)(SCN)] = 2 \times 10^{-5}$ $[Fe(SO_4)_2(SCN)^-] = 2 \times 10^{-5}$; $[FeSCN^{++}] = 8 \times 10^{-6}$; $[Fe(SCN)_2{}^+] = 10^{-7}$; $[Fe(SCN)_3] = 10^{-10}$; $[NH_4{}^+] = 0.1$

I-1 (a) $m = 0.8413$ g, $r = 2.5$ mg, $a = 1.0$ mg, $s = 1.3$ mg

(b) $s_m = 0.75$ mg, confidence limits: 95%, ± 3.2 mg; 99%, ± 7.4 mg

(c) $(\sigma/m)_{est} = 0.12\%$, $(\sigma/m)_{obs} = 0.15\%$

(d) Precision of sample weight excessive

I-2 6.472%; $p = 0.014$

I-3 3.5×10^{-4}; 8.6×10^{-5}; 4.7×10^{-5}; 4.1×10^{-5}; close to 90°.

INDEX

THE PERIODIC SYSTEM OF THE ELEMENTS

	O	I	II	III	IV	V	VI	VII
		H 1						
	He 2	Li 3	Be 4	B 5	C 6	N 7	O 8	F 9
	Ne 10	Na 11	Mg 12	Al 13	Si 14	P 15	S 16	Cl 17

O	I	II	III	IVa	Va	VIa	VIIa	VIII			Ib	IIb	IIIb	IV	V	VI	VII	O
Ar 18	K 19	Ca 20	Sc 21	Ti 22	V 23	Cr 24	Mn 25	Fe 26	Co 27	Ni 28	Cu 29	Zn 30	Ga 31	Ge 32	As 33	Se 34	Br 35	Kr 36
Kr 36	Rb 37	Sr 38	Y 39	Zr 40	Nb 41	Mo 42	Tc 43	Ru 44	Rh 45	Pd 46	Ag 47	Cd 48	In 49	Sn 50	Sb 51	Te 52	I 53	Xe 54
Xe 54	Cs 55	Ba 56	La 57 *	Hf 72	Ta 73	W 74	Re 75	Os 76	Ir 77	Pt 78	Au 79	Hg 80	Tl 81	Pb 82	Bi 83	Po 84	At 85	Rn 86
Rn 86	Fr 87	Ra 88	Ac 89 †															

*Lanthanides

Ce 58	Pr 59	Nd 60	Pm 61	Sm 62	Eu 63	Gd 64	Tb 65	Dy 66	Ho 67	Er 68	Tm 69	Yb 70	Lu 71

†Actinides

Th 90	Pa 91	U 92	Np 93	Pu 94	Am 95	Cm 96	Bk 97	Cf 98	Es 99	Fm 100	Md 101	(No)? 102	Lw 103

ATOMIC WEIGHTS 1961

Based on $C^{12}=12$

Aluminum	Al	26.9815
Antimony	Sb	121.75
Argon	Ar	39.948
Arsenic	As	74.9216
Barium	Ba	137.34
Beryllium	Be	9.0122
Bismuth	Bi	208.980
Boron	B	10.811
Bromine	Br	79.909
Cadmium	Cd	112.40
Calcium	Ca	40.08
Carbon	C	12.01115
Cerium	Ce	140.12
Cesium	Cs	132.905
Chlorine	Cl	35.453
Chromium	Cr	51.996
Cobalt	Co	58.9332
Copper	Cu	63.54
Dysprosium	Dy	162.50
Erbium	Er	167.26
Europium	Eu	151.96
Fluorine	F	18.9984
Gadolinium	Gd	157.25
Gallium	Ga	69.72
Germanium	Ge	72.59
Gold	Au	196.967
Hafnium	Hf	178.49
Helium	He	4.0026
Holmium	Ho	164.930
Hydrogen	H	1.00797
Indium	In	114.82
Iodine	I	126.9044
Iridium	Ir	192.2
Iron	Fe	55.847
Krypton	Kr	83.80
Lanthanum	La	138.91
Lead	Pb	207.19
Lithium	Li	6.939
Lutetium	Lu	174.97
Magnesium	Mg	24.312
Manganese	Mn	54.9380
Mercury	Hg	200.59

Molybdenum	Mo	95.94
Neodymium	Nd	144.24
Neon	Ne	20.183
Nickel	Ni	58.71
Niobium	Nb	92.906
Nitrogen	N	14.0067
Osmium	Os	190.2
Oxygen	O	15.9994
Palladium	Pd	106.4
Phosphorus	P	30.9738
Platinum	Pt	195.09
Potassium	K	39.102
Praseodymium	Pr	140.907
Rhenium	Re	186.2
Rhodium	Rh	102.905
Rubidium	Rb	85.47
Ruthenium	Ru	101.07
Samarium	Sm	150.35
Scandium	Sc	44.956
Selenium	Se	78.96
Silicon	Si	28.086
Silver	Ag	107.870
Sodium	Na	22.9898
Strontium	Sr	87.62
Sulfur	S	32.064
Tantalum	Ta	180.948
Tellurium	Te	127.60
Terbium	Tb	158.924
Thallium	Tl	204.37
Thorium	Th	232.038
Thulium	Tm	168.934
Tin	Sn	118.69
Titanium	Ti	47.90
Tungsten	W	183.85
Uranium	U	238.03
Vanadium	V	50.942
Xenon	Xe	131.30
Ytterbium	Yb	173.04
Yttrium	Y	88.905
Zinc	Zn	65.37
Zirconium	Zr	91.22

Date

P.S.U. MAY 1 3 71

P.S.U. OCT 2 1 71

P.S.U. OCT 15 73

JUN 20 77

SEP 6

Demco 38-297